Section 8 — Ecology and the Environment

Section 9 — Use of Biological Resources

Describing Experiments

Practice Papers

Edexcel Certificate Exam Information

1) You have to do two exams for the Edexcel Certificate in Biology — Paper 1 and Paper 2.

2) Paper 1 is 2 hours long and worth <u>120 marks</u>.   *If you're doing the International GCSE in Biology, it works*

3) Paper 2 is just <u>1 hour</u> long, and it's worth <u>60 marks</u>. *in exactly the same way — so you'll do two papers too.*

4) Some material in the specification will only be tested in Paper 2. The Paper 2 material in this book is marked with a <u>burgundy 'Paper 2' border</u>. The 'Warm-Up Questions' that cover Paper 2 material are <u>printed in burgundy</u> and the 'Exam Questions' are marked with this <u>stamp</u>: PAPER 2

Remember, if you're doing the Edexcel Certificate/International GCSE in
Science (Double Award) you don't need to learn the Paper 2 material.

Published by CGP

From original material by Paddy Gannon.

Editors:
Katie Braid, Gordon Henderson, Rachel Kordan, Sarah Pattison, Camilla Simson, Hayley Thompson.

Contributors:
James Foster, Adrian Schmit.

ISBN: 978 1 78294 182 8

With thanks to Mary Falkner, Rachael Marshall, Glenn Rogers and Sophie Scott for the proofreading.
With thanks to Laura Jakubowski for the copyright research.

With thanks to Getty Images for permission to use the image on page 103.

Data used to construct the graph on page 184 from R. Doll, R. Peto, J. Boreham, I Sutherland.
Mortality in relation to smoking: 50 years' observations on male British doctors.
BMJ 2004; 328: 1519.

Printed by Elanders Ltd, Newcastle upon Tyne.
Clipart from Corel®

Based on the Classic CGP style created by Richard Parsons.

Characteristics of Living Organisms

Welcome to the wonderful world of Biology. It's all about <u>living organisms</u> — which includes you. You may not think you have much in common with a slug or a mushroom, but you'd be wrong. You see, <u>all living organisms</u> share the same <u>eight basic characteristics</u>...

1) They Need **Nutrition**

Living organisms need nutrients to provide them with <u>energy</u> and the <u>raw materials</u> for growth and repair. Nutrients include things like <u>proteins</u>, <u>fats</u> and <u>carbohydrates</u>, as well as <u>vitamins</u> and <u>minerals</u>. See pages 22 to 23.

2) They **Respire**

Organisms <u>release energy</u> from their <u>food</u> by a process called respiration. See pages 49 to 50.

3) They **Excrete** Their **Waste**

Waste products such as <u>carbon dioxide</u> and <u>urine</u> have to be <u>removed</u>. The removal of waste is called excretion. See pages 72 to 73.

4) They **Respond** to Their Surroundings

Living organisms can <u>react</u> to <u>changes</u> in their <u>surroundings</u>. See page 78.

5) They **Move**

Organisms <u>move towards</u> things like <u>water</u> and <u>food</u>, and <u>away</u> from things like <u>predators</u> and <u>poisons</u>. Even plants can move a bit.

6) They Can **Control** Their **Internal Conditions**

Internal conditions include <u>temperature</u> and <u>water content</u>. See page 86.

7) They **Reproduce**

Organisms have to produce <u>offspring</u> (children) in order for their <u>species</u> to <u>survive</u>. See p.95-97.

8) They **Grow** and **Develop**

Yup, even the smallest organisms have to <u>grow</u> and <u>develop</u> into their <u>adult form</u>.

Levels of Organisation

Living organisms are made up of <u>cells</u> — these are like <u>tiny building blocks</u>.

Cells Contain *Organelles*

<u>Organelles</u> are tiny structures <u>within</u> cells. You can only see them using a powerful <u>microscope</u>.

A Typical *Animal Cell* Looks Like This...

Here are some of the organelles found in a <u>typical animal cell</u>:

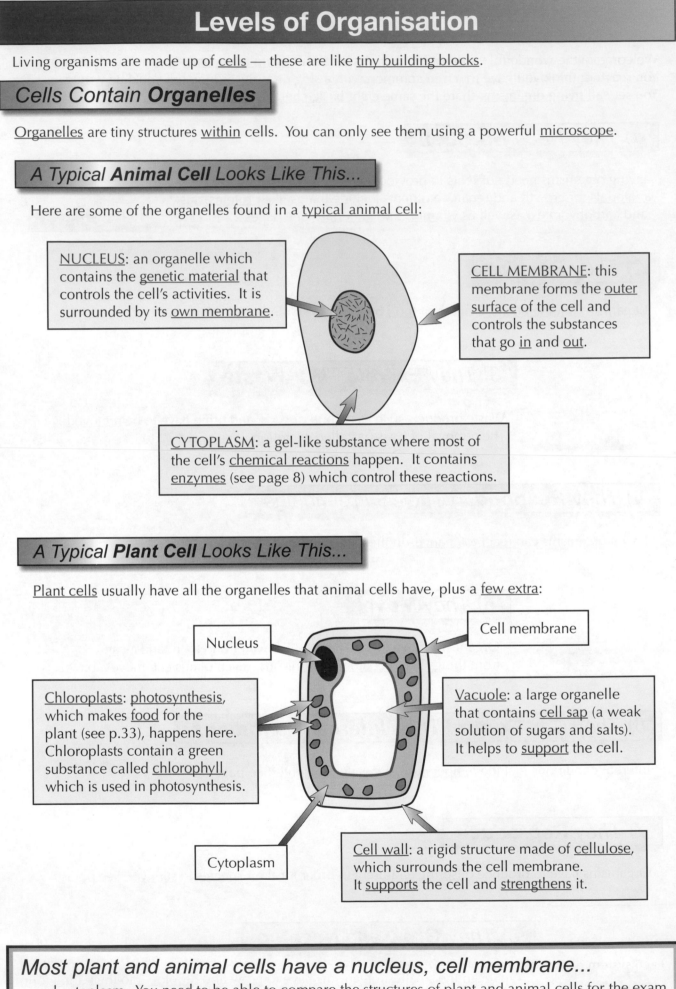

<u>NUCLEUS</u>: an organelle which contains the <u>genetic material</u> that controls the cell's activities. It is surrounded by its <u>own membrane</u>.

<u>CELL MEMBRANE</u>: this membrane forms the <u>outer surface</u> of the cell and controls the substances that go <u>in</u> and <u>out</u>.

<u>CYTOPLASM</u>: a gel-like substance where most of the cell's <u>chemical reactions</u> happen. It contains <u>enzymes</u> (see page 8) which control these reactions.

A Typical *Plant Cell* Looks Like This...

<u>Plant cells</u> usually have all the organelles that animal cells have, plus a <u>few extra</u>:

Nucleus

Cell membrane

Chloroplasts: <u>photosynthesis</u>, which makes <u>food</u> for the plant (see p.33), happens here. Chloroplasts contain a green substance called <u>chlorophyll</u>, which is used in photosynthesis.

Vacuole: a large organelle that contains <u>cell sap</u> (a weak solution of sugars and salts). It helps to <u>support</u> the cell.

Cytoplasm

Cell wall: a rigid structure made of <u>cellulose</u>, which surrounds the cell membrane. It <u>supports</u> the cell and <u>strengthens</u> it.

Most plant and animal cells have a nucleus, cell membrane...

...and cytoplasm. You need to be able to compare the structures of plant and animal cells for the exam — so make sure you learn the features they have in common as well as the differences between them.

Levels of Organisation

Some organisms consist of a <u>single cell</u>. Some organisms are <u>multicellular</u> —
they contain <u>lots</u> of cells, which need some form of <u>organisation</u>.

Cells are **Specialised**

Most cells don't look exactly like the ones on the previous page.
They're <u>specialised</u> to carry out a <u>particular function</u>, so their structures can vary.

For example, in humans, <u>red blood cells</u> are specialised for carrying oxygen
and <u>white blood cells</u> are specialised for defending the body against disease.

red blood cells

white blood cell

Similar Cells *are Organised into* **Tissues**

1) A <u>tissue</u> is a group of similar cells that <u>work together</u> to carry out a <u>particular function</u>.

For example, plants have <u>xylem tissue</u> (for transporting water and mineral salts)
and <u>phloem tissue</u> (for transporting sucrose and amino acids).

2) A tissue can contain <u>more than one</u> cell type.

Tissues *are Organised into* **Organs**

An <u>organ</u> is a group
of different <u>tissues</u>
that <u>work together</u> to
perform a function.

Lungs in mammals and
<u>leaves</u> on plants are two
examples of <u>organs</u> —
they're both made up of
several <u>different tissue types</u>.

lungs

leaves

Organs *Make Up* **Organ Systems**

Organs work together
to form <u>organ systems</u>.
Each system does a <u>different job</u>.

For example, in mammals, the <u>digestive system</u> is made up of
organs including the stomach, intestines, pancreas and liver.

Plants, Animals and Fungi

Living organisms can be arranged into groups, according to the features they have in common.
Three of these groups are plants, animals and fungi...

Learn the Features of Plants, Animals and Fungi

Organism		Description	Examples
Plants	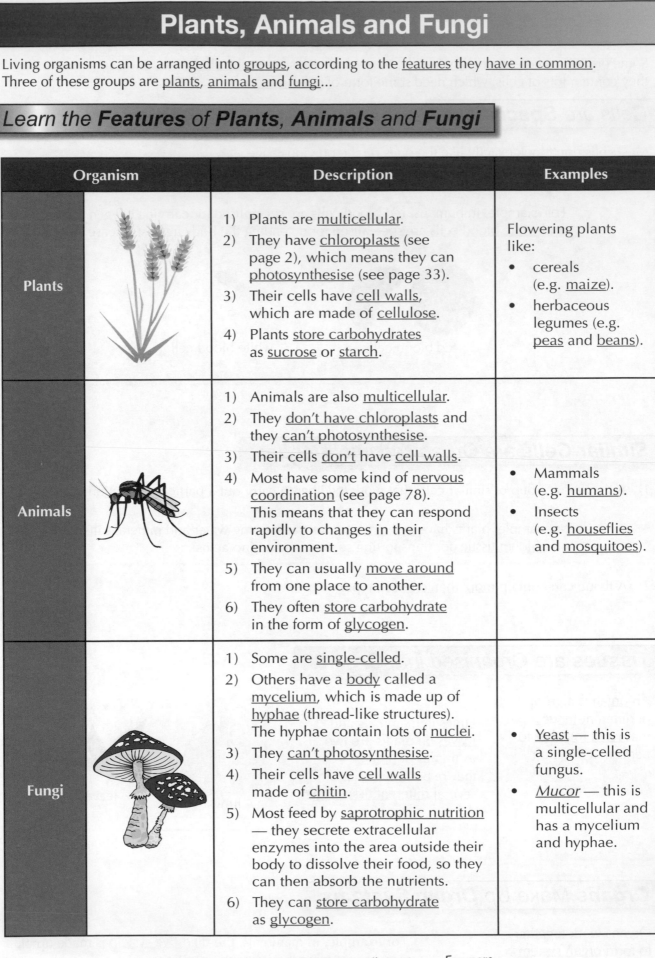	1) Plants are multicellular. 2) They have chloroplasts (see page 2), which means they can photosynthesise (see page 33). 3) Their cells have cell walls, which are made of cellulose. 4) Plants store carbohydrates as sucrose or starch.	Flowering plants like: • cereals (e.g. maize). • herbaceous legumes (e.g. peas and beans).
Animals		1) Animals are also multicellular. 2) They don't have chloroplasts and they can't photosynthesise. 3) Their cells don't have cell walls. 4) Most have some kind of nervous coordination (see page 78). This means that they can respond rapidly to changes in their environment. 5) They can usually move around from one place to another. 6) They often store carbohydrate in the form of glycogen.	• Mammals (e.g. humans). • Insects (e.g. houseflies and mosquitoes).
Fungi		1) Some are single-celled. 2) Others have a body called a mycelium, which is made up of hyphae (thread-like structures). The hyphae contain lots of nuclei. 3) They can't photosynthesise. 4) Their cells have cell walls made of chitin. 5) Most feed by saprotrophic nutrition — they secrete extracellular enzymes into the area outside their body to dissolve their food, so they can then absorb the nutrients. 6) They can store carbohydrate as glycogen.	• Yeast — this is a single-celled fungus. • Mucor — this is multicellular and has a mycelium and hyphae.

Plants, animals and fungi have different cell structures. For more on the structure of plant and animal cells, see page 2.

Protoctists, Bacteria and Viruses

Learn the **Features** of **Protoctists**, **Bacteria** and **Viruses**

Organism	Description	Examples
Protoctists	1) These are <u>single-celled</u> and <u>microscopic</u> (really tiny). 2) Some have <u>chloroplasts</u> and are similar to <u>plant cells</u>. 3) Others are more like <u>animal cells</u>.	• *Chlorella* (plant-cell-like) • *Amoeba* (animal-cell-like) — lives in pond water.
Bacteria	1) These are also <u>single-celled</u> and <u>microscopic</u>. 2) They <u>don't</u> have a <u>nucleus</u>. 3) They have a <u>circular chromosome</u> of <u>DNA</u>. 4) Some can <u>photosynthesise</u>. 5) Most bacteria <u>feed</u> off <u>other organisms</u> — both living and dead.	• *Lactobacillus bulgaricus* — can be used to make milk go sour and turn into yoghurt. It's rod-shaped. • *Pneumococcus* — spherical (round) in shape.
Viruses	1) These are <u>particles</u>, rather than cells, and are <u>smaller</u> than bacteria. 2) They can only <u>reproduce</u> inside <u>living cells</u>. Organisms that depend on other organisms to live are called <u>parasites</u>. 3) They <u>infect all types</u> of living organisms. 4) They come in loads of <u>different shapes</u> and <u>sizes</u>. 5) They don't have a cellular structure — they have a <u>protein coat</u> around some <u>genetic material</u> (either <u>DNA</u> or <u>RNA</u>).	• <u>Influenza virus</u> • <u>Tobacco mosaic virus</u> — this makes the leaves of tobacco plants discoloured by stopping them from producing chloroplasts. • <u>HIV</u>

There's more on DNA on p.93-94. DNA and RNA are both nucleic acids, so they're fairly similar.

Some Organisms Are **Pathogens**

<u>Pathogens</u> are <u>organisms</u> that cause <u>disease</u>. They include some <u>fungi</u>, <u>protoctists</u>, <u>bacteria</u> and <u>viruses</u>.

PROTOCTIST: *Plasmodium*, which causes <u>malaria</u>.
BACTERIUM: *Pneumococcus*, which causes <u>pneumonia</u>.
VIRUSES: <u>Influenza virus</u> (which causes '<u>flu</u>') and <u>HIV</u> (which causes <u>AIDS</u>).

Bacteria is the plural of bacterium.

Warm-Up and Exam Questions

It's easy to think you've learnt everything in the section until you try the questions.
Don't panic if there's a bit you've forgotten, just go back over that bit until it's firmly fixed in your brain.

Warm-Up Questions

1) Give two similarities and two differences between the structure
   of an animal cell and the structure of a plant cell.
2) Describe the structure of a mycelium.
3) Name a protoctist with a structure similar to: a) a plant cell   b) an animal cell.
4) Name the organism that causes malaria. Is it a bacterium, virus, protoctist or fungus?

Exam Questions

1   All living organisms are made up of cells, which contain organelles.

   a)   The cell nucleus is an organelle. Describe the structure of a cell nucleus.

(2 marks)

   b)   Copy and complete the table
         by describing the function of
         each organelle.

Organelle	Function
cell membrane	
cytoplasm	
vacuole	
chloroplast	

(4 marks)

2   The following passage is about different levels of organisation within multicellular organisms.
     Copy and complete the passage using suitable words.

   A cell is made up of different .... A group of similar ....
   which work together to perform a particular .... make up a tissue.
   An .... is formed by several different organs working together.

(4 marks)

3   Read the information below and answer the question that follows.

   The picture on the right shows an adult starfish.
   Starfish are found in oceans around the world.
   On the undersides of their arms they have small
   structures called 'tube feet', which are very
   sensitive to chemicals in the water, helping them
   to detect food. When they detect food, they move
   their arms to travel in the right direction.
   Each of their arms contains two gonads, which
   release eggs or sperm into the water.

   Suggest and explain **three** pieces of evidence from the
   passage that show starfish are living organisms.

(3 marks)

Exam Questions

4 A bean plant produces carbohydrate during photosynthesis.

    a) Name the organelles present in the cells of a bean
       plant which allow it to photosynthesise.

(1 mark)

    b) State **two** substances that a bean plant may store carbohydrate as.

(2 marks)

5 The growth of wheat plants can be slowed down by both fungi and insect pests.

The table on the right shows information about the cells from both a fungus and an insect found on a wheat plant.

Feature	Organism A	Organism B
Chloroplasts present	No	No
Cell wall present	No	Yes
Glycogen store	Yes	Yes

    a) Use information from the table to explain which organism (**A** or **B**) is an insect.

(1 mark)

    b) The fungus secretes enzymes onto the wheat, then absorbs the nutrients.
       State the name of this process.

(1 mark)

    c) Which organism (fungus or insect) can sense when it's on a source of food?
       Give a reason for your answer.

(1 mark)

6 The diagrams show the bacteria *Lactobacillus bulgaricus* and *Pneumococcus*.

                A   B

    a) i) Which diagram (**A** or **B**) shows *Lactobacillus bulgaricus*? Explain your answer.

(1 mark)

       ii) Describe how *Lactobacillus bulgaricus* can be used by the food industry.

(1 mark)

    b) *Pneumococcus* is a pathogen. Explain what is meant by the term pathogen.

(1 mark)

    c) *Lactobacillus bulgaricus* and *Pneumococcus* do not photosynthesise.
       Suggest how these bacteria obtain the nutrients they need.

(1 mark)

    d) Give **three** structural features of a typical bacterial cell.

(3 marks)

7 Viruses can infect every type of living organism.

    a) The leaves of a tobacco plant can become discoloured if it is infected by a particular
       virus. Name the virus that affects tobacco plants in this way and explain its effect.

(2 marks)

    b) Name **two** viruses that may infect humans and
       state the disease that each can cause.

(4 marks)

Enzymes

Chemical reactions are what make you work. And enzymes are what make them work.

Enzymes are Catalysts Produced by Living Things

1) Living things have thousands of different chemical reactions going on inside them all the time. These reactions need to be carefully controlled — to get the right amounts of substances in the cells.

2) You can usually make a reaction happen more quickly by raising the temperature. This would speed up the useful reactions but also the unwanted ones too... not good. There's also a limit to how far you can raise the temperature inside a living creature before its cells start getting damaged.

3) So... living things produce enzymes that act as biological catalysts.

> A **CATALYST** is a substance which **INCREASES** the speed of a reaction, without being **CHANGED** or **USED UP** in the reaction.

4) Enzymes reduce the need for high temperatures and we only have enzymes to speed up the useful chemical reactions in the body. These reactions are called metabolic reactions.

5) Enzymes are all proteins and all proteins are made up of chains of amino acids. These chains are folded into unique shapes, which enzymes need to do their jobs (see below).

Enzymes are Very Specific

1) Chemical reactions usually involve things either being split apart or joined together.

2) A substrate is a molecule that is changed in a reaction.

3) Every enzyme molecule has an active site — the part where a substrate joins onto the enzyme.

4) Enzymes are really picky — they usually only speed up one reaction. This is because, for an enzyme to work, a substrate has to be the correct shape to fit into the active site.

5) This is called the 'lock and key' model, because the substrate fits into the enzyme just like a key fits into a lock.

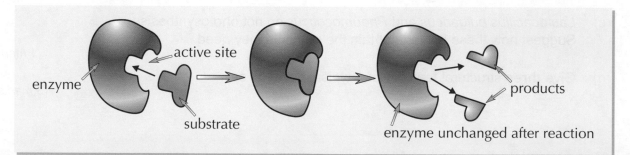

Enzymes speed up chemical reactions

Just like you've got to have the correct key for a lock, you've got to have the right substrate for an enzyme. If the substrate doesn't fit, the enzyme won't catalyse the reaction.

More on Enzymes

Enzymes are clearly very clever, but they're <u>not</u> very versatile.
They need just the right <u>conditions</u> if they're going to work properly.

Enzymes *Like it* **Warm** *but* **Not Too Hot**

1) Changing the <u>temperature</u> changes the <u>rate</u> of an enzyme-catalysed reaction.

2) Like with any reaction, a <u>higher temperature</u> <u>increases the rate</u> at first. This is because more <u>heat</u> means the enzymes and the substrate particles have more <u>energy</u>. This makes the enzymes and the substrate particles <u>move about</u> more, so they're more likely to meet up and react — they have a <u>higher collision rate</u>.

3) <u>Low temperatures</u> have the opposite effect — there's a <u>lower collision rate</u> and so a <u>slower reaction</u>.

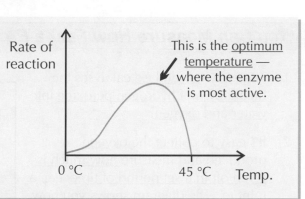

4) If it gets <u>too hot</u>, some of the <u>bonds</u> holding the enzyme together will <u>break</u>.

5) This makes the enzyme <u>lose its shape</u> — its <u>active site</u> doesn't fit the shape of the substrate any more. This means it <u>can't</u> catalyse the reaction and the reaction <u>stops</u> — the enzyme <u>can't function</u>.

6) The enzyme is now said to be <u>denatured</u>. Its change in shape is <u>irreversible</u> (permanent).

7) Each enzyme has its own <u>optimum temperature</u> when the reaction goes <u>fastest</u>. This is the temperature just before it gets too hot and starts to denature. The optimum temperature for the most important <u>human</u> enzymes is about <u>37 °C</u> — the <u>same</u> temperature as our bodies. Lucky for us.

Enzymes *Also Need the* **Right pH**

1) <u>pH</u> also affects enzymes. If it's too high or too low, the pH interferes with the <u>bonds</u> holding the enzyme together. This changes the shape of the active site and <u>denatures</u> the enzyme.

2) All enzymes have an <u>optimum pH</u> that they work best at. It's often <u>neutral pH 7</u>, but <u>not always</u> — e.g. <u>pepsin</u> is an enzyme used to break down <u>proteins</u> in the <u>stomach</u>. It works best at <u>pH 2</u>, which means it's well-suited to the <u>acidic conditions</u> there.

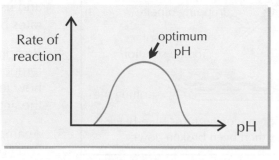

If only enzymes could speed up revision...

Scientists have caught on to the idea that enzymes are <u>really useful</u>. They're used in biological <u>detergents</u> (to break down nasty stains) and in some <u>baby foods</u> (to predigest the food).

Investigating Enzyme Activity

I bet you've been asked countless times how you would <u>investigate</u> the <u>effect of temperature on enzyme activity</u>. Well if you read this page, you'll finally have the answers...

You Can Investigate the Effect of Temperature on Enzyme Activity

There are a couple of different ways to investigate how temperature affects enzyme activity.

You Can Measure How Fast a Product Appears...

1) The enzyme <u>catalase</u> catalyses the <u>breakdown</u> of <u>hydrogen peroxide</u> into <u>water</u> and <u>oxygen</u>.

2) It's easy to <u>collect</u> the <u>oxygen</u> produced and measure <u>how much is given off in a set period of time</u>, e.g. a minute. The diagram shows you how.

3) You can run a <u>series of experiments</u>, each with the <u>water bath</u> at a <u>different temperature</u>, to see how temperature affects the <u>activity</u> of catalase.

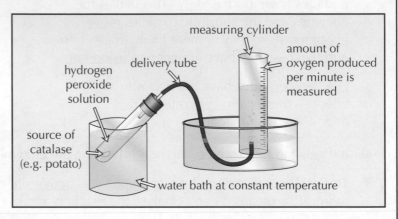

4) Just make sure that you <u>control any variables</u> that might affect the results, e.g. enzyme concentration, pH, volume of solution, etc. This will make it a <u>fair test</u>. See page 159 for more.

...Or How Fast a Substrate Disappears

1) The enzyme <u>amylase</u> catalyses the breakdown of <u>starch</u> to <u>maltose</u>.

2) It's easy to <u>detect starch</u> (the substrate) using <u>iodine solution</u> — if starch is present, the iodine solution will change from <u>browny-orange</u> to <u>blue-black</u>.

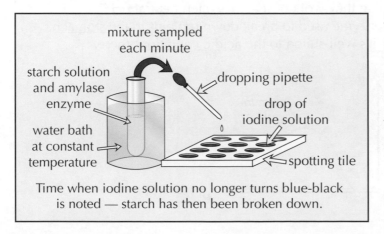

Time when iodine solution no longer turns blue-black is noted — starch has then been broken down.

3) You can <u>time</u> how long it takes for the starch to disappear by <u>regularly sampling</u> the starch solution, and use the times to compare rates between different tests.

4) By <u>adjusting</u> the water bath <u>temperature</u>, you can see how temperature affects the <u>activity</u> of amylase.

5) Again, you need to make sure you <u>control</u> all the <u>variables</u>.

A water bath helps to keep the temperature constant

Everyone loves doing <u>experiments</u> — admittedly there aren't any Bunsen burners involved in the ones above, but they're a good way of seeing science in action. So get learning them.

Diffusion

Diffusion is <u>really important</u> in living organisms — it's how a lot of <u>substances</u> get <u>in</u> and <u>out</u> of cells.

Don't be Put Off by the *Fancy Word*

1) <u>Diffusion</u> is simple. It's just the <u>gradual movement</u> of particles from places where there are <u>lots</u> of them to places where there are <u>fewer</u> of them.

2) That's all it is — just the <u>natural tendency</u> for stuff to <u>spread out</u>.

3) Here's the fancy <u>definition</u>:

> **Diffusion is the <u>net movement</u> of <u>particles</u> from an area of <u>higher concentration</u> to an area of <u>lower concentration</u>.**

4) Diffusion happens in both <u>liquids</u> and <u>gases</u> — that's because the particles in these substances are free to <u>move about</u> randomly.

5) The <u>simplest type</u> is when different <u>gases</u> diffuse through each other. This is what's happening when the smell of perfume diffuses through a room:

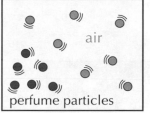 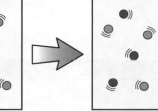

perfume particles diffused in the air

The <u>bigger</u> the <u>difference</u> in concentration, the <u>faster</u> the diffusion rate.

Cell Membranes are Pretty *Clever*...

1) They're clever because they <u>hold</u> the cell together <u>but</u> they let stuff <u>in and out</u> as well.

2) Substances can move in and out of cells by <u>diffusion</u>, <u>osmosis</u> (see the next few pages) and <u>active transport</u> (see page 16).

3) Only very <u>small</u> molecules can <u>diffuse</u> through cell membranes though — things like <u>glucose</u>, <u>amino acids</u>, <u>water</u> and <u>oxygen</u>. <u>Big</u> molecules like <u>starch</u> and <u>proteins</u> can't fit through the membrane.

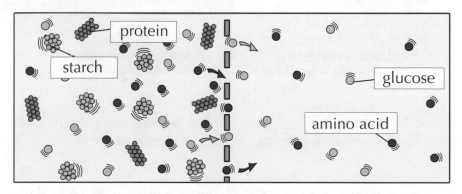

1) Just like with diffusion in air, particles flow through the cell membrane from where there's a <u>higher concentration</u> (more of them) to where there's a <u>lower concentration</u> (not such a lot of them).

2) They're only moving about <u>randomly</u> of course, so they go <u>both</u> ways — but if there are a lot <u>more</u> particles on one side of the membrane, there's a <u>net</u> (overall) movement <u>from</u> that side.

Osmosis

If you've got your head round <u>diffusion</u>, osmosis will be a <u>breeze</u>.
If not, you need to read the previous page...

*Osmosis is a **Special Case** of **Diffusion**, That's All*

Learn this definition of osmosis:

> <u>OSMOSIS</u> is the <u>net movement of water molecules</u> across a <u>partially permeable membrane</u> from a region of <u>higher water concentration</u> to a region of <u>lower water concentration</u>.

1) A <u>partially permeable</u> membrane is just one with very small holes in it. So small, in fact, only tiny <u>molecules</u> (like water) can pass through them, and bigger molecules (e.g. <u>sucrose</u>) can't.

2) A <u>cell membrane</u> is a <u>partially permeable</u> membrane.

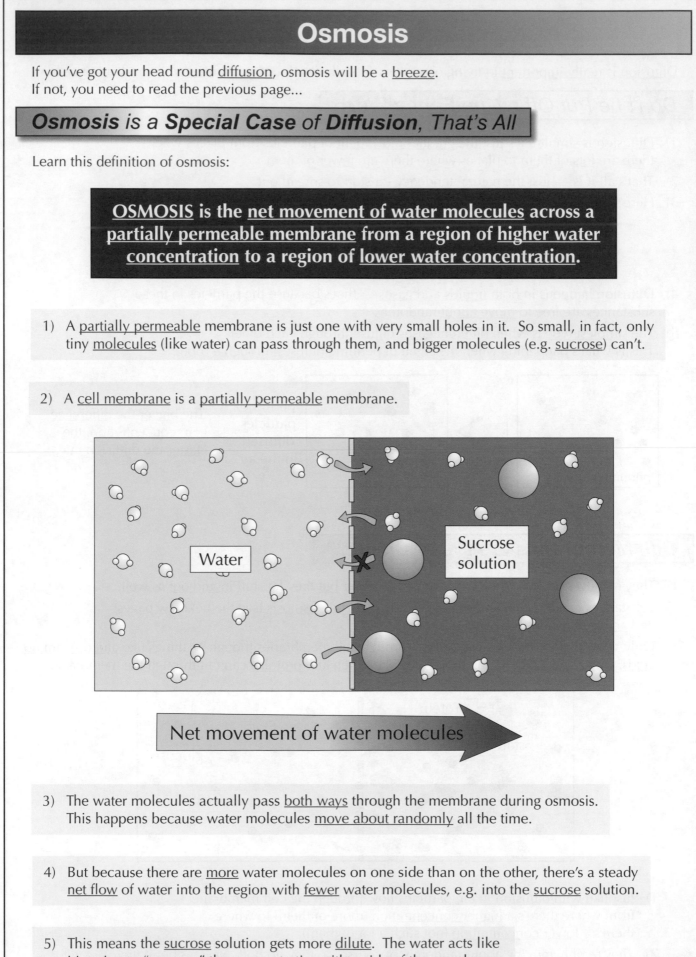

Water

Sucrose solution

Net movement of water molecules

3) The water molecules actually pass <u>both ways</u> through the membrane during osmosis. This happens because water molecules <u>move about randomly</u> all the time.

4) But because there are <u>more</u> water molecules on one side than on the other, there's a steady <u>net flow</u> of water into the region with <u>fewer</u> water molecules, e.g. into the <u>sucrose</u> solution.

5) This means the <u>sucrose</u> solution gets more <u>dilute</u>. The water acts like it's trying to "<u>even up</u>" the concentration either side of the membrane.

Osmosis

You're not learning about osmosis just for fun — it's how water moves into and out of <u>cells</u>, so it's pretty important in biology.

Water Moves Into and Out of Cells by Osmosis

1) <u>Tissue fluid</u> surrounds the cells in the body — it's basically just <u>water</u> with <u>oxygen</u>, <u>glucose</u> and stuff dissolved in it. It's squeezed out of the <u>blood capillaries</u> to supply the cells with everything they need.

2) The tissue fluid will usually have a <u>different concentration</u> to the fluid <u>inside</u> a cell. This means that water will either move <u>into the cell</u> from the tissue fluid, or <u>out of the cell</u>, by <u>osmosis</u>.

3) If a cell is <u>short of water</u>, the solution inside it will become quite <u>concentrated</u>. This usually means the solution <u>outside</u> is more <u>dilute</u>, and so water will move <u>into</u> the cell by osmosis.

4) If a cell has <u>lots of water</u>, the solution inside it will be <u>more dilute</u>, and water will be <u>drawn out</u> of the cell and into the fluid outside by osmosis.

Plants are Supported by Turgid Cells

1) When a plant is well watered, all its cells will draw water in by <u>osmosis</u> and become plump and swollen. When the cells are like this, they're said to be <u>turgid</u>.

2) The contents of the cell push against the cell wall — this is called <u>turgor pressure</u>. Turgor pressure helps <u>support</u> the plant tissues.

3) If there's no water in the soil, a plant starts to <u>wilt</u> (droop). This is because the cells start to lose water and so <u>lose</u> their turgor pressure. The cells are then said to be <u>flaccid</u>.

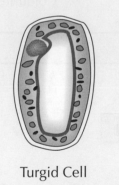 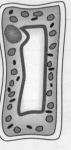

Turgid Cell   Flaccid Cell

4) The plant doesn't totally lose its shape though, because the <u>inelastic cell wall</u> keeps things in position. It just droops a bit.

Water always moves into the more concentrated solution

That's why it's bad to drink seawater. The high <u>salt</u> content means you end up with a much <u>lower water concentration</u> in your blood and tissue fluid than in your cells. All the water is sucked out of your cells by osmosis and they <u>shrivel and die</u>. So next time you're stranded at sea, remember this...

Paper 2

Diffusion Experiments

For all you non-believers — here's an experiment you can do to see diffusion in action.

You Can **Investigate Diffusion** in a **Non-Living System**

Phenolphthalein is a pH indicator — it's pink in alkaline solutions and colourless in acidic solutions. You can use it to investigate diffusion in agar jelly:

1) First, make up some agar jelly with phenolphthalein and dilute sodium hydroxide. This will make the jelly a lovely shade of pink.

2) Then fill a beaker with some dilute hydrochloric acid.

3) Using a scalpel, cut out a few cubes from the jelly and put them in the beaker of acid.

4) If you leave the cubes for a while they'll eventually turn colourless as the acid diffuses into the agar jelly and neutralises the sodium hydroxide.

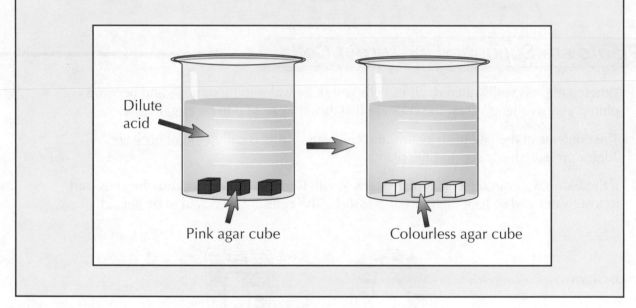

Dilute acid

Pink agar cube

Colourless agar cube

Investigating the **Rate** of Diffusion

1) You can investigate the rate of diffusion by using different sized cubes of agar jelly and timing how long it takes for each cube to go colourless.

2) The cube with the largest surface area to volume ratio (see page 17) will lose its colour quickest.

You could get asked to describe a diffusion experiment in the exam

OK, so not the most exciting experiment in the world, but make sure you know how to do it. You could use different pH indicators to stain the jelly.

Osmosis Experiments

Well what do you know — there are experiments that show <u>osmosis</u> in action too.

You Can **Investigate Osmosis** in **Living** and **Non-Living Systems**

Living system — *potato cylinders*

1) Cut up an innocent <u>potato</u> into identical cylinders, and get some beakers with <u>different sugar solutions</u> in them. One should be <u>pure water</u>, another should be a <u>very concentrated sugar solution</u>. Then you can have a few others with concentrations <u>in between</u>.

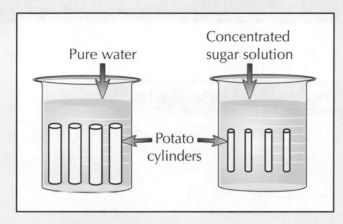

Pure water

Concentrated sugar solution

Potato cylinders

The only thing that you should change is the <u>concentration</u> of the <u>sugar solution</u>. Everything else (e.g. the volume of solution and the time the experiment runs for) must be kept the <u>same</u> in each case or the experiment won't be a <u>fair test</u>.

2) You measure the <u>length</u> of the cylinders, then leave a few cylinders in each beaker for half an hour or so. Then you take them out and measure their lengths <u>again</u>.

3) If the cylinders have drawn in water by osmosis, they'll be a bit <u>longer</u>. If water has been drawn out, they'll have <u>shrunk</u> a bit. Then you can plot a few <u>graphs</u> and things.

Non-living system — *Visking tubing*

1) Tie a piece of wire around <u>one end</u> of some <u>Visking tubing</u> and put a <u>glass tube</u> in the <u>other end</u> — fix the tubing around it with wire. Then <u>pour</u> some sugar solution down the glass tube into the Visking tubing.

2) Put the Visking tubing in a <u>beaker</u> of pure water — <u>measure</u> where the sugar solution comes up to on the <u>glass tube</u>.

3) Leave the tubing <u>overnight</u>, then <u>measure</u> where the liquid is in the glass tube. <u>Water</u> should be <u>drawn into</u> the Visking tubing by osmosis and this will <u>force</u> the liquid <u>up</u> the glass tube.

Visking tubing is a partially permeable membrane.

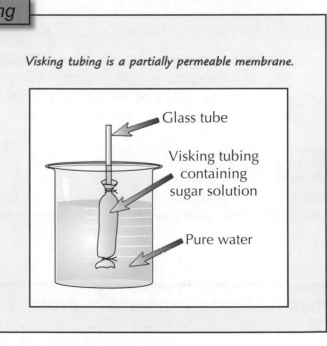

Glass tube

Visking tubing containing sugar solution

Pure water

Active Transport

The movement of substances has been too <u>passive</u> for my liking. It's time to get <u>active</u>.

Active Transport is the Opposite of Diffusion

Here's what you <u>need to know</u>:

> **<u>ACTIVE TRANSPORT</u>** is the <u>movement of particles</u> against a concentration gradient (i.e. from an area of <u>lower concentration</u> to an area of <u>higher concentration</u>) <u>using energy</u> released during respiration.

Active Transport is Used by Living Organisms

<u>Active transport</u>, like diffusion and osmosis, is used to <u>move substances in and out of cells</u>.

Example 1:

Active transport is used in the <u>digestive system</u> when there is a <u>low concentration</u> of nutrients in the <u>gut</u>, but a <u>high concentration</u> of nutrients in the <u>blood</u>:

1) When there's <u>a higher concentration</u> of nutrients in the gut they <u>diffuse naturally</u> into the blood.

2) <u>BUT</u> — sometimes there's a <u>lower concentration</u> of nutrients in the gut than there is in the blood.

3) This means that the <u>concentration gradient</u> is the wrong way. The nutrients should go <u>the other way</u> if they followed the rules of diffusion.

4) The answer is that <u>active transport</u> is responsible.

5) Active transport allows nutrients to be taken into the blood, despite the fact that the <u>concentration gradient</u> is the wrong way. This is essential to stop us starving. But active transport needs <u>ENERGY</u> from <u>respiration</u> to make it work.

Example 2:

Active transport is also used by <u>plants</u> — it's how they get <u>minerals</u> from the <u>soil</u> (lower mineral concentration) into their <u>root hair cells</u> (higher mineral concentration).

Active transport is an active process — it requires energy

Active transport involves moving substances against the concentration gradient, so it needs energy to make it work. Think of it like this: if you're trying to walk along a crowded street, it's hard to walk in the opposite direction to the one most people are travelling in. You have to push your way through — and that requires energy. The energy for active transport comes from respiration.

Movement of Substances

This page is all about the factors that affect the movement of substances <u>in and out of cells</u>. It might not be fun, but it will be <u>useful</u>. Read on...

Three Main Factors Affect The Movement of Substances

The <u>rates</u> of diffusion, osmosis and active transport <u>vary</u> — they're affected by these <u>factors</u>:

1) Surface Area to Volume Ratio

1) This can be a bit <u>tricky</u> to get your head around, but it's easier if you think of cells as <u>cubes</u> for now.

2) The <u>rate</u> of diffusion, osmosis and active transport is <u>higher</u> in cells (or cubes) with a <u>larger</u> <u>surface area to volume ratio</u>.

3) The <u>smaller</u> cube has a <u>larger</u> surface area to volume ratio — this means <u>substances</u> would <u>move</u> into and out of this cube <u>faster</u>.

Surface area (cm²)	2 x 2 x 6 = 24	3 x 3 x 6 = 54
Volume (cm³)	2 x 2 x 2 = 8	3 x 3 x 3 = 27
Surface area to volume ratio	24 : 8 = <u>3 : 1</u>	54 : 27 = <u>2 : 1</u>

2) Temperature

As the particles in a substance get <u>warmer</u> they have <u>more energy</u> — so they <u>move faster</u>. This means as <u>temperature increases</u>, substances move in and out of cells <u>faster</u>.

3) Concentration Gradient

1) Substances move in and out of a cell <u>faster</u> if there's a <u>bigger difference in concentration</u> between the inside and outside of the cell (see page 11).

2) If there is a <u>high concentration</u> on one side, there are more particles there to <u>move across</u>.

3) This <u>only</u> increases the rate of <u>diffusion</u> and <u>osmosis</u> though — concentration gradients <u>don't affect</u> the rate of <u>active transport</u>.

Surface area to volume ratios crop up a lot in Biology...

...so it's a good idea to try to understand them now. Just remember that generally speaking, a <u>smaller</u> object has a <u>larger</u> surface area to volume ratio than a bigger object. Anything that increases the surface area of an object more than the volume will increase the ratio.

Warm-Up and Exam Questions

More questions I'm afraid. There are quite a few of them, but that's because they're pretty important...

Warm-Up Questions

1) Describe the lock and key model of enzyme activity.
2) What is meant by the term osmosis?
3) Explain how water moves into and out of human body cells.
4) What process releases the energy needed for active transport?

Exam Questions

1   The graph shows the results from an investigation into the effect
    of temperature on the rate of an enzyme-catalysed reaction.

    a)   What is the optimum temperature
         for this enzyme?

         (1 mark)

    b)   Describe the results
         shown on the graph.

         (2 marks)

    c)   Explain why the rate of the
         reaction is zero at **45 °C**.

         (3 marks)

2   Raw meat can contain *Salmonella* bacteria.
    This bacterium can cause illness if it enters the human digestive system.

    a)   Enzymes within the bacterial cells act as biological catalysts.
         What is meant by the term **biological catalyst**?

         (1 mark)

    b)   The metabolic reactions in *Salmonella* bacteria are fastest between 35 and 37 °C.
         Explain why people are advised to store raw meat at
         temperatures much lower than 35 °C.

         (2 marks)

3   a)   Copy and complete the following sentence about diffusion, using suitable words.

         When particles diffuse, they move from an area of ....concentration
         to an area of .... concentration.

         (1 mark)

    The diagram on the right shows a cell and the surrounding
    tissue fluid. Oxygen moves in and out of the cell by diffusion.

    b)   What effect will diffusion have on the oxygen
         concentration inside this cell?

         (1 mark)

Exam Questions

PAPER 2

4   Celia has a sample of an enzyme. She times how long it takes the enzyme to break down a substance at different pH levels. The results of Celia's experiment are shown in the graph.

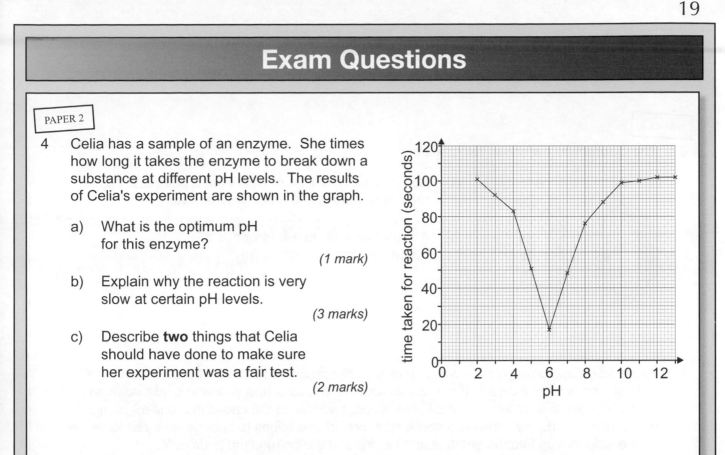

a)   What is the optimum pH for this enzyme?

(1 mark)

b)   Explain why the reaction is very slow at certain pH levels.

(3 marks)

c)   Describe **two** things that Celia should have done to make sure her experiment was a fair test.

(2 marks)

5   Two germinating barley seedlings were placed in solutions that contained a known concentration of potassium ions, as shown in the diagram below. Each seedling was grown at a different temperature. The uptake of potassium ions was measured.

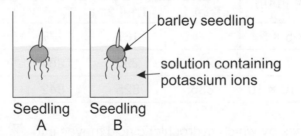

Seedling   Seedling
A   B

Barley seedlings take up potassium ions by active transport.

a)   Explain what is meant by the term **active transport**.

(2 marks)

The graph shows the uptake of potassium ions by the barley seedlings.

b)   Suggest which seedling was grown at the higher temperature. Explain your answer.

(2 marks)

c)   What effect would increasing the concentration of the potassium ion solution have on the uptake of potassium ions via active transport?

(1 mark)

Exam Questions

PAPER 2

6   The diagram below shows two plant cells.

A   B

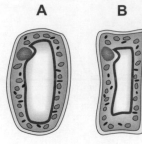

a)   Suggest which cell (**A** or **B**) is from a plant that has been well watered. Explain your answer.

(3 marks)

b)   A plant may start to wilt (droop) if it is not well watered. Explain why.

(2 marks)

7   Pablo made up some gelatine with cresol red solution and ammonium hydroxide. Cresol red solution is a pH indicator that is red in alkaline solutions and yellow in acidic solutions. He cut the gelatine into cubes of different sizes, and placed the cubes in a beaker of dilute hydrochloric acid. He measured how long it took for the cubes to change from red to yellow as the acid moved into the gelatine and neutralised the ammonium hydroxide. His results are shown in the table.

Size (mm)	Time taken for cube to become yellow (s)			
	Trial 1	Trial 2	Trial 3	Trial 4
5 × 5 × 5	174	167	177	182
7 × 7 × 7	274	290	284	292
10 × 10 × 10	835	825	842	838

a)   Name the process by which hydrochloric acid moves into the gelatine cubes in this experiment.

(1 mark)

b)   Calculate the average time for a 10 × 10 × 10 mm gelatine cube to become yellow in this experiment. Show your working.

(2 marks)

c)   Describe and explain the relationship between the size of the gelatine cube and the time taken for the cube to become yellow.

(3 marks)

8   Soaking an egg in vinegar dissolves its outer shell and leaves the egg surrounded by a partially permeable membrane. Some students use eggs which have been prepared in this way to investigate osmosis. They remove two eggs from the vinegar and place one of the eggs in a jar of water and the other in a jar of weak sugar solution.

a)   Describe **one** way in which the students could measure the effect of osmosis.

(2 marks)

b)   Suggest what the results of this experiment would be.

(2 marks)

Revision Summary for Section 1

If you're still in a state of shock from opening the book and revising for the first time, don't be worried. Do your best to answer the following questions and if you get any wrong, just flick back to the stuff that's not quite sunk in yet — then learn it until you remember it.

1) What are the eight basic characteristics that all living organisms share?

2) Name three organelles that are found in both animal and plant cells.

3) Name two organelles that are only found in plant cells. Describe their functions.

4) What is a tissue?

5) What is an organ? And an organ system?

6) What are plant cell walls made of?

7) How do most animals store carbohydrate?

8) Give two examples of fungi.

9) Explain what is meant by the term 'saprotrophic nutrition'.

10) Give two examples of protoctists.

11) Give three features of viruses.

12) What are pathogens? Name two pathogens.

13) What name is given to biological catalysts?

14) What is a catalyst?

15) An enzyme with an optimum temperature of 37 °C is heated to 60 °C. Suggest what will happen to it.

16) Briefly describe an experiment to show how temperature can affect enzyme activity.

17) What is diffusion?

18) A solution of pure water is separated from a concentrated sugar solution by a partially permeable membrane. In which direction will molecules flow, and what substance will these molecules be?

19) Why are turgid cells important to plants?

20) Describe an experiment using a non-living system that shows diffusion taking place. Then, as a treat, do the same for osmosis.

21) How is active transport different from diffusion in terms of:

    a) energy requirements,

    b) concentration gradients?

22) Describe how surface area to volume ratio affects the movement of substances in and out of cells.

Biological Molecules

Biological molecules are things like carbohydrates, lipids and proteins. They're generally long, complex molecules made up from smaller basic units. And, unsurprisingly, they're what this page is all about...

Learn The Structure of Carbohydrates, Lipids and Proteins

Carbohydrates are Made Up of Simple Sugars

- Carbohydrate molecules contain the elements carbon, hydrogen and oxygen.
- Starch and glycogen are large, complex carbohydrates, which are made up of many smaller units (e.g. glucose or maltose molecules) joined together in a long chain.

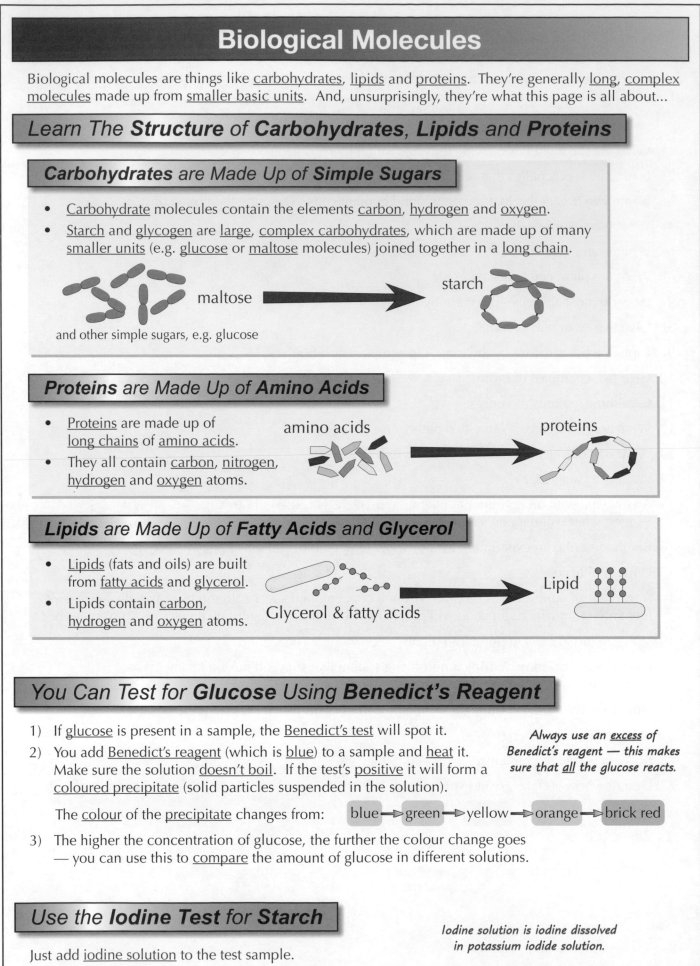

maltose → starch

and other simple sugars, e.g. glucose

Proteins are Made Up of Amino Acids

- Proteins are made up of long chains of amino acids.
- They all contain carbon, nitrogen, hydrogen and oxygen atoms.

amino acids → proteins

Lipids are Made Up of Fatty Acids and Glycerol

- Lipids (fats and oils) are built from fatty acids and glycerol.
- Lipids contain carbon, hydrogen and oxygen atoms.

Glycerol & fatty acids → Lipid

You Can Test for Glucose Using Benedict's Reagent

1) If glucose is present in a sample, the Benedict's test will spot it.
2) You add Benedict's reagent (which is blue) to a sample and heat it. Make sure the solution doesn't boil. If the test's positive it will form a coloured precipitate (solid particles suspended in the solution).

    Always use an excess of Benedict's reagent — this makes sure that all the glucose reacts.

    The colour of the precipitate changes from: blue → green → yellow → orange → brick red

3) The higher the concentration of glucose, the further the colour change goes — you can use this to compare the amount of glucose in different solutions.

Use the Iodine Test for Starch

Iodine solution is iodine dissolved in potassium iodide solution.

Just add iodine solution to the test sample.
- If starch is present, the sample changes from browny-orange to a dark, blue-black colour.
- If there's no starch, it stays browny-orange.

A Balanced Diet

Your body needs the <u>right fuel</u> or it won't work properly — that means <u>cutting down</u> on the lard.

You Need to **Eat Different Foods** to Get **Different Nutrients**

Nutrient	Found in...		Function(s)
<u>Carbohydrates</u>	Pasta, rice, sugar		Provide <u>energy</u>.
<u>Lipids</u> (fats and oils)	Butter, oily fish		Provide <u>energy</u>, act as an <u>energy store</u> and provide <u>insulation</u>.
<u>Proteins</u>	Meat, fish		Needed for <u>growth</u> and <u>repair</u> of tissue, and to provide energy in emergencies.
<u>Vitamins</u>	A	Liver (yum...)	Helps to <u>improve vision</u> and keep your <u>skin</u> and <u>hair healthy</u>.
	C	Oranges	Needed to <u>prevent scurvy</u>.
	D	Eggs	Needed for <u>calcium absorption</u>.
<u>Mineral ions</u>	Calcium	Milk, cheese	Needed to make <u>bones</u> and <u>teeth</u>.
	Iron	Red meat	Needed to make <u>haemoglobin</u> for healthy <u>blood</u>.
<u>Water</u>	Food and drink		Just about <u>every bodily function</u> relies on water — we need a constant supply to <u>replace</u> water lost through urinating, breathing and sweating.
<u>Dietary fibre</u>	Wholemeal bread		Aids the <u>movement</u> of food through the <u>gut</u>.

Vitamin D is also made by your body when your skin is exposed to sunlight.

A **Balanced Diet** Supplies **All** Your **Essential Nutrients**

1) A balanced diet gives you all the <u>essential nutrients</u> you need — in the <u>right proportions</u>.
2) The <u>six</u> essential nutrients are <u>carbohydrates</u>, <u>proteins</u>, <u>lipids</u>, <u>vitamins</u>, <u>minerals</u> and <u>water</u>.
3) You also need <u>fibre</u> (to keep the gut in good working order).

Energy Requirements Vary in Different People

You get <u>energy</u> from the food you eat, but the <u>amount</u> of energy you need <u>isn't</u> a set thing — it's <u>different</u> for everyone. The energy a person needs depends on things like...

Activity level ⟶ <u>Active people</u> need <u>more energy</u> than people who sit about all day. Bit of an obvious one, really...

Age ⟶ <u>Children</u> and <u>teenagers</u> need <u>more energy</u> than <u>older people</u> — they need energy to <u>grow</u> and they're generally <u>more active</u>.

Pregnancy ⟶ <u>Pregnant women</u> need <u>more energy</u> than other women — they've got to provide the energy their babies need to <u>develop</u>.

Energy from Food

Food Can be Burnt to See How Much Energy it Contains

The posh name for this is <u>calorimetry</u>. You need to know how to do it with a <u>simple experiment</u>:

First You Need a Dry Food, Water and a Flame...

1) You need a <u>food</u> that'll <u>burn easily</u> — something that's <u>dry</u>, e.g. peanuts or pasta, will work best.

2) <u>Weigh</u> a small amount of the food and then <u>skewer</u> it on a <u>mounted needle</u>.

3) Next, add <u>25 cm³</u> of <u>water</u> to a boiling tube (held with a clamp) — this will be used to <u>measure</u> the amount of <u>heat energy</u> that's released when the food is burnt.

4) <u>Measure</u> the <u>temperature</u> of the water, then <u>set fire</u> to the food using a <u>Bunsen burner flame</u>. Make sure the Bunsen isn't near the water or your results might be a bit wonky.

5) Time for the exciting bit — immediately <u>hold</u> the burning food <u>under</u> the boiling tube until it <u>goes out</u>. Then <u>relight</u> the food and <u>hold</u> it under the tube — <u>keep doing this</u> until the food <u>won't</u> catch fire again.

6) The last thing to do is <u>measure</u> the <u>temperature</u> of the water <u>again</u>. Then you're ready for a bit of <u>maths</u>...

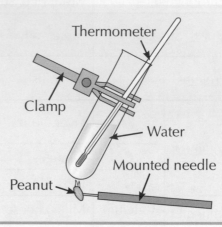

Thermometer

Clamp

Water

Mounted needle

Peanut

...Then You Can Calculate the Amount of Energy in the Food

1) Calculate the Amount of Energy in Joules

$$\text{ENERGY IN FOOD (in J)} = \text{MASS OF WATER (in g)} \times \text{TEMPERATURE CHANGE OF WATER (in °C)} \times 4.2$$

1) <u>1 cm³</u> of water is the same as <u>1 g</u> of water.

2) The <u>4.2</u> in the formula is the <u>amount of energy</u> (in joules) needed to <u>raise</u> the temperature of <u>1 g</u> of water by <u>1 °C</u>.

This is the specific heat capacity of water, otherwise known as a calorie.

2) Calculate the Amount of Energy in Joules per Gram

You need to do this calculation so you can <u>compare</u> the energy values of different foods <u>fairly</u>.

$$\text{ENERGY PER GRAM OF FOOD (in J/g)} = \frac{\text{ENERGY IN FOOD (in J)}}{\text{MASS OF FOOD (in g)}}$$

The Accuracy of the Experiment Can be Increased

1) The experiment <u>isn't perfect</u> — quite a bit of the <u>energy</u> released from burning is <u>lost</u> to the surroundings. It's why the energy value on the <u>packet</u> of the food you used is likely to be <u>much higher</u> than your own.

2) <u>Insulating</u> the boiling tube, e.g. with foil, would minimise heat loss and keep <u>more energy</u> in the water — making your results <u>more accurate</u>.

Paper 2

Enzymes and Digestion

Remember <u>enzymes</u> from p.8-10? (If not go and have a look). Various enzymes are used in <u>digestion</u> — they're produced by specialised cells and then <u>released</u> into the <u>gut</u> to help break down the food.

Digestive Enzymes Break Down Big Molecules into Smaller Ones

1) <u>Starch</u>, <u>proteins</u> and <u>fats</u> are <u>BIG molecules</u>. They're <u>too big</u> to pass through the <u>walls</u> of the digestive system. They're also <u>insoluble</u>.

2) <u>Sugars</u>, <u>amino acids</u>, <u>glycerol</u> and <u>fatty acids</u> are much <u>smaller molecules</u>. They're <u>soluble</u> and can <u>pass easily</u> through the walls of the digestive system.

3) The <u>digestive enzymes</u> break down the BIG molecules into the smaller ones.

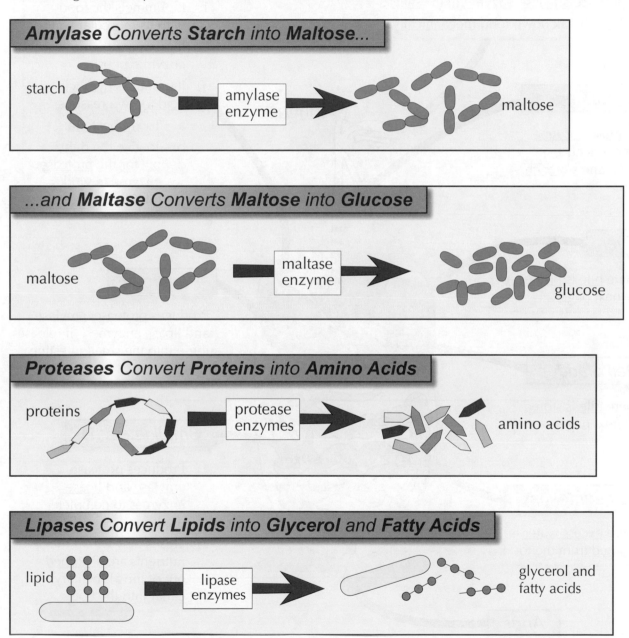

Amylase *Converts* Starch *into* Maltose...

starch   amylase enzyme   maltose

...*and* Maltase *Converts* Maltose *into* Glucose

maltose   maltase enzyme   glucose

Proteases *Convert* Proteins *into* Amino Acids

proteins   protease enzymes   amino acids

Lipases *Convert* Lipids *into* Glycerol *and* Fatty Acids

lipid   lipase enzymes   glycerol and fatty acids

Enzymes break down BIG molecules into LITTLE molecules...

...which lets them pass through the gut wall <u>more easily</u>. You need to know all the examples of <u>enzymes</u> on this page, including which <u>big molecules</u> they break down, and which <u>little molecules</u> the big molecules break into. Scribble them out again and again until you can do it in your sleep...

The Alimentary Canal

So, now you know what the enzymes do, here's a nice big picture of the whole of your gut.

Your **Alimentary Canal** Runs Through Your Body

The alimentary canal is just another name for the gut. You need to know the names and functions of its main parts, plus a few of the organs associated with it:

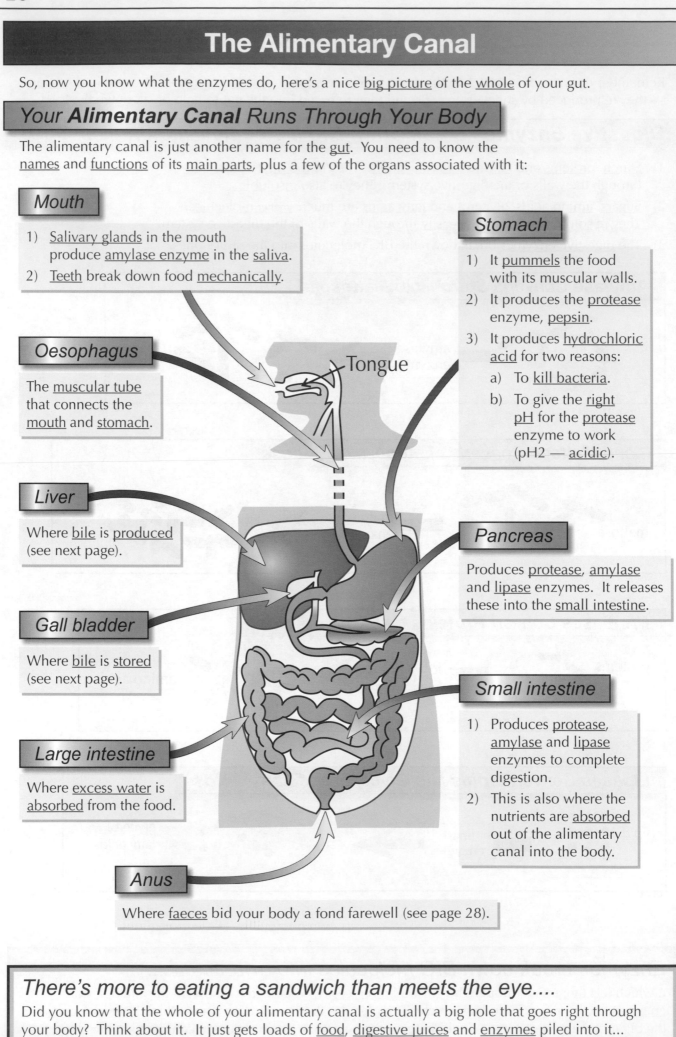

Mouth

1) Salivary glands in the mouth produce amylase enzyme in the saliva.
2) Teeth break down food mechanically.

Oesophagus

The muscular tube that connects the mouth and stomach.

Tongue

Stomach

1) It pummels the food with its muscular walls.
2) It produces the protease enzyme, pepsin.
3) It produces hydrochloric acid for two reasons:
   a) To kill bacteria.
   b) To give the right pH for the protease enzyme to work (pH2 — acidic).

Liver

Where bile is produced (see next page).

Gall bladder

Where bile is stored (see next page).

Pancreas

Produces protease, amylase and lipase enzymes. It releases these into the small intestine.

Small intestine

1) Produces protease, amylase and lipase enzymes to complete digestion.
2) This is also where the nutrients are absorbed out of the alimentary canal into the body.

Large intestine

Where excess water is absorbed from the food.

Anus

Where faeces bid your body a fond farewell (see page 28).

There's more to eating a sandwich than meets the eye....

Did you know that the whole of your alimentary canal is actually a big hole that goes right through your body? Think about it. It just gets loads of food, digestive juices and enzymes piled into it...

More on Digestion

The digestive system is well <u>adapted</u> to its function of <u>breaking down</u> and <u>absorbing food</u>. Here are three examples that show what a clever system it is...

Bile *Neutralises* the Stomach Acid and *Emulsifies* Fats

1) Bile is <u>produced</u> in the <u>liver</u>. It's <u>stored</u> in the <u>gall bladder</u> before it's released into the <u>small intestine</u> (see previous page).

2) The <u>hydrochloric acid</u> in the stomach makes the pH <u>too acidic</u> for enzymes in the small intestine to work properly. Bile is <u>alkaline</u> — it <u>neutralises</u> the acid and makes conditions <u>alkaline</u>. The enzymes in the small intestine <u>work best</u> in these alkaline conditions.

3) Bile also <u>emulsifies</u> fats. In other words it breaks the fat into <u>tiny droplets</u>. This gives a much <u>bigger surface area</u> of fat for the enzyme lipase to work on — which makes its digestion <u>faster</u>.

Food is *Moved* Through The Gut by *Peristalsis*

1) There's <u>muscular</u> tissue all the way down the alimentary canal.

2) Its job is to <u>squeeze</u> balls of food (called boluses) through your gut — <u>otherwise</u> it would get <u>clogged up</u> with bits of old food. Mmm.

3) This squeezing action, which is <u>waves</u> of <u>circular muscle contractions</u>, is called <u>peristalsis</u>.

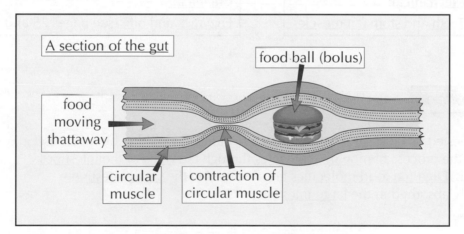

A section of the gut

food ball (bolus)

food moving thattaway

circular muscle

contraction of circular muscle

Villi in the *Small Intestine* Help with *Absorption*

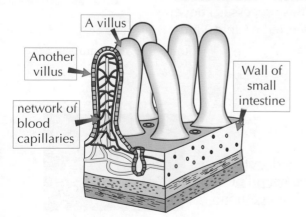

A villus

Another villus

network of blood capillaries

Wall of small intestine

1) The <u>small intestine</u> is <u>adapted</u> for absorption of food.

2) It's very <u>long</u>, so there's time to break down and absorb <u>all</u> the food before it reaches the end.

3) There's a really <u>big surface area</u> for absorption, because the walls of the small intestine are covered in <u>millions and millions</u> of tiny little projections called <u>villi</u>.

4) Each <u>cell</u> on the surface of a villus also has its own <u>microvilli</u> — little projections that increase the surface area even more.

5) Villi have a <u>single permeable</u> layer of surface cells and a very <u>good blood supply</u> to assist <u>quick absorption</u>.

The Digestive Process

If this page was a bit of food, I would suggest you break it down into manageable pieces with your teeth, and then absorb it with your small intestine. But it's not, so you'll have to use your brain...

There are **Five Main Stages** of Digestion

The different <u>stages</u> of digestion happen in the following <u>order</u>:

1) Ingestion

This one is pretty simple — it's putting <u>food</u> (or drink) <u>into your mouth</u>.

2) Digestion

After you've ingested something, you need to <u>digest</u> it. Digestion is the <u>break-down</u> of <u>large</u>, <u>insoluble molecules</u> into <u>small</u>, <u>soluble molecules</u>. Your body has <u>mechanical</u> and <u>chemical</u> ways to digest food:

Mechanical:	**Chemical:**
<u>Teeth</u> and <u>stomach muscles</u>	<u>Enzymes</u> and <u>bile</u> (see pages 25 and 27)

3) Absorption

If all those digested bits just <u>sat</u> in your alimentary canal, it <u>wouldn't</u> be much use. <u>Absorption</u> is the process of <u>moving molecules</u> through the <u>walls</u> of the <u>intestines</u> into the blood. <u>Digested food molecules</u> are absorbed in the <u>small intestine</u> — <u>water</u> is mainly absorbed in the <u>large intestine</u>.

4) Assimilation

When digested molecules have been absorbed, they're <u>moved into body cells</u>. The digested molecules then become <u>part</u> of the cells — this process is known as <u>assimilation</u>. For example, when <u>amino acids</u> (from digested proteins) are assimilated, they're used by cells to make <u>cellular proteins</u>.

5) Egestion

Not everything that you ingest can be digested. All of the <u>undigested stuff</u> forms <u>faeces</u>, which are of <u>no use</u> to your body — you <u>get rid of them</u> via a one-way ticket through the <u>anus</u>. This is known as <u>egestion</u>.

Warm-Up and Exam Questions

That section should have given you plenty of food for thought. Ha ha. Ok — you can stop rolling around on the floor laughing now. It's time to power your way through these questions.

Warm-Up Questions

1) True or false: proteins, lipids and carbohydrates all contain nitrogen.
2) Name the smaller basic units that make up the following molecules: a) a lipid, b) a protein.
3) Describe how you would use Benedict's reagent to test for glucose.
4) Some iodine is added to a sample and the colour changes from browny-orange to blue-black. What does this indicate?

Exam Questions

1 The passage below describes the functions and sources of some different vitamins and minerals that we need for a healthy diet.

a) Copy and complete the passage by writing suitable words in the gaps.

Vitamin A helps to improve .... and keep skin and hair healthy. A good source of vitamin A is .... Vitamin D can be found in foods such as .... It's needed for .... absorption. Your diet should also include things like .... as they contain vitamin C. Calcium is needed to make .... and teeth. A good source of calcium is ....

(7 marks)

b) i) Give **one** reason why dietary fibre is also needed as part of a healthy diet.
(1 mark)

ii) Give **one** example of a food that contains dietary fibre.
(1 mark)

c) Why do we need to drink water as part of a healthy diet?
(1 mark)

PAPER 2

2 Different people have different energy requirements. Calories are a measure of the amount of energy in food.

a) It is suggested that on average, non-pregnant women aged 19-49 need about 2000 calories per day, but most pregnant women in the same age group need 300 calories per day more. Explain why.
(1 mark)

b) It is recommended that a 14 year old girl with an average activity level should eat around 2350 calories per day. A woman over the age of 50 with an average activity level should eat around 1800 calories per day. Explain why there is a difference.
(1 mark)

c) Regardless of energy requirements, it is important that everyone has a balanced diet. What is meant by the term **balanced diet**?
(2 marks)

Exam Questions

3 There are a number of digestive enzymes found in the human body.
Copy and complete the table by writing the correct enzyme or function in the box provided.
The first one has been done for you.

Enzyme	Function
proteases	convert proteins into amino acids
	converts starch into maltose
	converts maltose into glucose
lipases	

(3 marks)

4 The diagram shows the human alimentary canal, with the different parts named or labelled with a letter (**A-F**).

a) Copy and complete the table by writing the letter of the label next to the correct function.
The first one has been done for you.

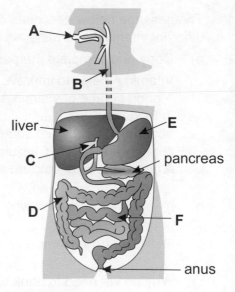

Function	Label letter
Pummels the food, and produces the protease enzyme pepsin.	E
Contains salivary glands, which produce amylase.	
Where nutrients are absorbed from food.	
Where excess water is absorbed from food.	

(3 marks)

b) Describe the function of the pancreas in digestion.

(2 marks)

c) Describe the role of peristalsis in the alimentary canal.

(3 marks)

5 Egestion and digestion are two stages of the digestive process.

a) What is meant by the term **egestion**?

(2 marks)

b) Describe what happens during digestion.

(2 marks)

c) Once food molecules have been absorbed, they're then incorporated into the body's cells. What name is given to this process?

(1 mark)

d) What technical term is used to describe placing food and drink in your mouth?

(1 mark)

Exam Questions

PAPER 2

6 Heidi is carrying out an experiment to find out how much energy there is in a peanut. The experimental set up is shown in the diagram on the right.

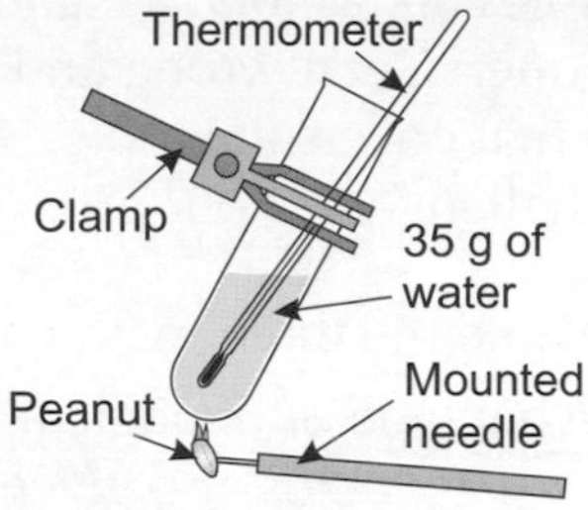

Thermometer

Clamp

35 g of water

Mounted needle

Peanut

a) Give **two** measurements that Heidi should make and record before starting the experiment.

(2 marks)

b) At the end of the experiment, the temperature of the water has risen by 51 °C. Using the formula below, calculate the amount of energy in the peanut.

Energy in food (J) = mass of water (g) × temperature change of water (°C) × 4.2

(1 mark)

c) If the peanut weighed 0.7 g, calculate the energy (in joules) per g of peanuts.

(1 mark)

d) The packet Heidi took the peanut from stated that the energy content of the peanuts is 25 200 J/g. Suggest why the value Heidi measured in her experiment is different from this value.

(2 marks)

e) Suggest **one** way that Heidi could improve the accuracy of her results.

(1 mark)

7 Gallstones are small, solid stones formed mainly of excess cholesterol. They can block the bile ducts (tubes) that connect the liver to the gall bladder and the gall bladder to the small intestine.

a) i) Name the digestive fluid stored in the gall bladder.

(1 mark)

ii) Name the organs in the body where this digestive fluid is produced, and where it acts on food.

(2 marks)

iii) This digestive fluid is alkaline. Explain why this is important.

(2 marks)

b) Suggest why eating fatty foods might cause a problem for people suffering from gallstones.

(4 marks)

8 Coeliac disease is an autoimmune disorder that causes a range of symptoms, including pain in the abdomen, diarrhoea and fatigue. It is caused by the immune system reacting to a protein found in gluten. The reaction can cause villi to become inflamed and flattened.

a) i) Where in the alimentary canal are villi found?

(1 mark)

ii) Describe **three** structural features of normal villi.

(3 marks)

b) Suggest why coeliac disease sufferers might also be diagnosed with vitamin deficiencies.

(2 marks)

Revision Summary for Section 2

By reading this page you are hereby accepting the challenge I have created for you below. The rules are as follows: attempt to answer a question — if you get it right, move on to the next one. Get it wrong and you must shake your fist at the sky before flicking back to the page that covers the topic. Answer all of the questions correctly and you'll have completed the challenge — your prize awaits you on the next page...

1) Name the three main chemical elements that are found in carbohydrates.
2) What type of biological molecules are made up of:
   a) fatty acids and glycerol?
   b) amino acids?
3) What could you use to see if there's starch in a sample?
4) Why does the body need proteins? What foods contain proteins?
5) What nutrients does the body get energy from?
6) Eric has just been to see his doctor. He has been told that he needs to increase the amount of vitamin D in his diet. What foods can Eric get this nutrient from? Why does Eric need vitamin D?
7) Give two reasons why some people need more energy from food than others.
8) Describe a simple experiment to measure the amount of energy in a food.
9) What is the main role of digestive enzymes?
10) Name the enzymes that convert starch into glucose.
11) What do proteases do?
12) When lipids are digested, what molecules are they broken down into?
13) Describe the function(s) of the:
    a) mouth,
    b) oesophagus,
    c) small intestine.
14) Where in the body is bile:
    a) produced?   b) stored?   c) used?
15) What are the two functions of bile?
16) Why is peristalsis needed by the body?
17) Explain how villi help with absorption in the small intestine.
18) What is the difference between ingestion and egestion?
19) Put the following digestive processes in order that they occur:
    a) absorption
    b) assimilation
    c) digestion

Photosynthesis

Plants can make their own food — it's ace. Here's how...

Photosynthesis Produces **Glucose** Using **Sunlight**

1) <u>Photosynthesis</u> is the process that produces '<u>food</u>' in plants. The 'food' it produces is <u>glucose</u>.

2) Photosynthesis happens in the <u>leaves</u> of all <u>green plants</u> — this is largely what the leaves are for.

3) Photosynthesis happens inside the <u>chloroplasts</u>, which are found in leaf cells and in other <u>green</u> parts of a plant. Chloroplasts contain a pigment called <u>chlorophyll</u>, which absorbs <u>sunlight</u> and uses its energy to convert <u>carbon dioxide</u> and <u>water</u> into <u>glucose</u>. <u>Oxygen</u> is also produced.

4) Photosynthesis is an important process because it <u>converts light energy to chemical energy</u>, which is <u>stored</u> in the <u>glucose</u>. This chemical energy is <u>released</u> when glucose is broken down during <u>respiration</u> (see pages 49 to 50).

Learn the **Word** and **Symbol** Equations for **Photosynthesis**:

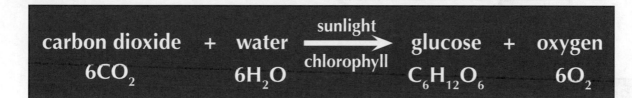

$$\text{carbon dioxide} + \text{water} \xrightarrow[\text{chlorophyll}]{\text{sunlight}} \text{glucose} + \text{oxygen}$$

$$6CO_2 \qquad 6H_2O \qquad\qquad C_6H_{12}O_6 \qquad 6O_2$$

Limiting Factors Affect the **Rate of Photosynthesis**

The <u>rate</u> of photosynthesis <u>varies</u>. It all depends on what the <u>limiting factor</u> is at that moment in time.

1) A limiting factor is something which <u>stops photosynthesis from happening any faster</u>. <u>Light intensity</u>, <u>CO_2 concentration</u> and <u>temperature</u> can all be the limiting factor.

2) The limiting factor depends on the <u>environmental conditions</u>. E.g. in <u>winter</u> low temperatures might be the limiting factor. At <u>night</u>, light is likely to be the limiting factor.

Not Enough **LIGHT** Slows Down the **Rate of Photosynthesis**

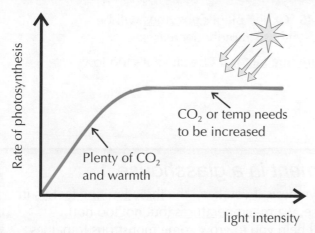

CO$_2$ or temp needs to be increased

Plenty of CO$_2$ and warmth

Rate of photosynthesis

light intensity

<u>Chlorophyll</u> uses <u>light energy</u> to perform photosynthesis. It can only do it as quickly as the light energy is arriving.

1) If the <u>light intensity</u> is increased, the rate of photosynthesis will <u>increase steadily</u>, but only up to a <u>certain point</u>.

2) Beyond that, it won't make any <u>difference</u> because then it'll be either the <u>temperature</u> or the <u>CO_2</u> level which is now the limiting factor.

Photosynthesis

Too Little CO₂ Slows Down the Rate of Photosynthesis

<u>CO₂</u> is one of the <u>raw materials</u> needed for photosynthesis — only <u>0.04%</u> of the air is CO_2, so it's <u>pretty scarce</u> as far as plants are concerned.

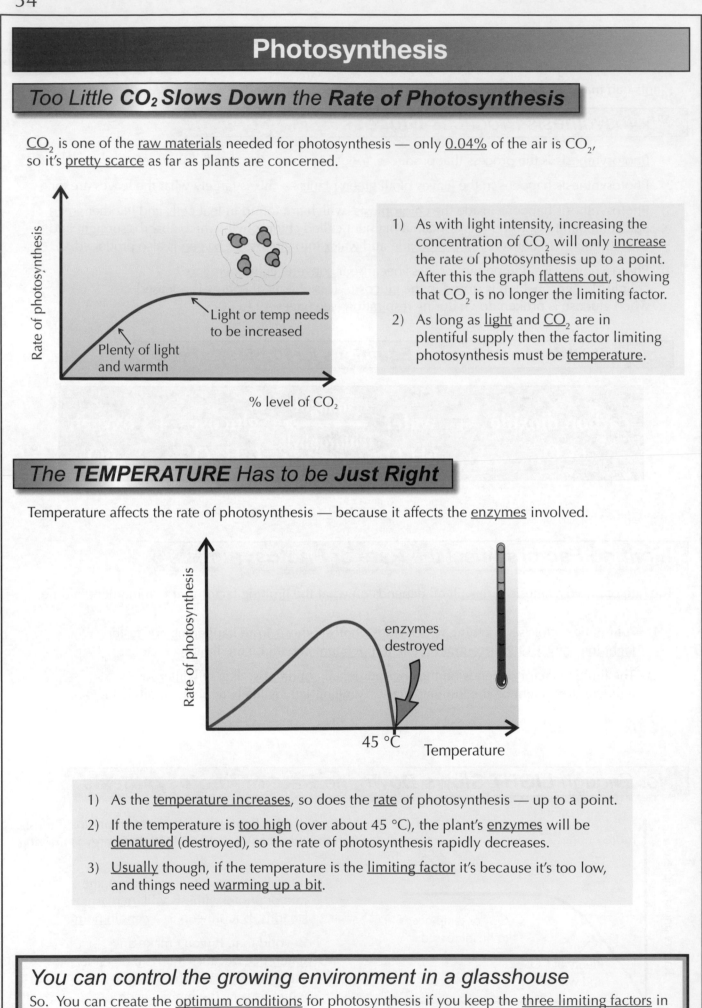

1) As with light intensity, increasing the concentration of CO_2 will only <u>increase</u> the rate of photosynthesis up to a point. After this the graph <u>flattens out</u>, showing that CO_2 is no longer the limiting factor.

2) As long as <u>light</u> and <u>CO₂</u> are in plentiful supply then the factor limiting photosynthesis must be <u>temperature</u>.

Light or temp needs to be increased

Plenty of light and warmth

% level of CO_2

The TEMPERATURE Has to be Just Right

Temperature affects the rate of photosynthesis — because it affects the <u>enzymes</u> involved.

enzymes destroyed

45 °C   Temperature

1) As the <u>temperature increases</u>, so does the <u>rate</u> of photosynthesis — up to a point.

2) If the temperature is <u>too high</u> (over about 45 °C), the plant's <u>enzymes</u> will be <u>denatured</u> (destroyed), so the rate of photosynthesis rapidly decreases.

3) <u>Usually</u> though, if the temperature is the <u>limiting factor</u> it's because it's too low, and things need <u>warming up a bit</u>.

You can control the growing environment in a glasshouse

So. You can create the <u>optimum conditions</u> for photosynthesis if you keep the <u>three limiting factors</u> in balance, which means plenty of <u>light</u> and <u>CO₂</u>, and nice, <u>warm temperatures</u> (but not too hot). You can control all three factors in a glasshouse. This'll help you to grow some monstrous tomatoes.

Adaptations for Photosynthesis

Most photosynthesis takes place in the <u>leaves</u>, so leaves have
a few tricks up their sleeves to make sure it all goes well.

Leaves are Designed for *Making Food* by *Photosynthesis*

The whole structure of leaves is geared towards that.
You need to know all the different parts of a <u>typical leaf</u> shown on the diagram:

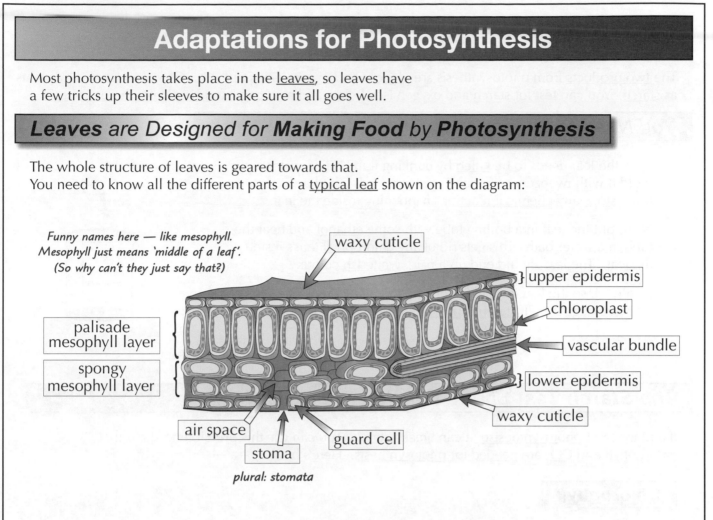

Funny names here — like mesophyll.
Mesophyll just means 'middle of a leaf'.
(So why can't they just say that?)

waxy cuticle

upper epidermis

chloroplast

vascular bundle

palisade
mesophyll layer

spongy
mesophyll layer

lower epidermis

waxy cuticle

air space

guard cell

stoma

plural: stomata

Leaves are **Adapted** *for* **Efficient Photosynthesis**

1) Leaves are <u>broad</u>, so there's a large surface area exposed to <u>light</u>.

2) Most of the chloroplasts are found in the <u>palisade layer</u>. This is so that they're near the top of the leaf where they can get the most <u>light</u>.

3) The <u>upper epidermis</u> is <u>transparent</u> so that light can pass through it to the <u>palisade layer</u>.

4) Leaves have a network of <u>vascular bundles</u> — these are the transport vessels <u>xylem</u> and <u>phloem</u> (see page 41). They <u>deliver water</u> and other <u>nutrients</u> to every part of the leaf and take away the <u>glucose</u> produced by photosynthesis. They also help to <u>support</u> the leaf structure.

5) The <u>waxy cuticle</u> helps to <u>reduce water loss</u> by evaporation.

6) The <u>adaptations</u> of leaves for efficient <u>gas exchange</u> (see page 53) also make <u>photosynthesis</u> more efficient. E.g. the lower surface is full of little holes called <u>stomata</u>, which let CO_2 diffuse directly into the leaf.

Efficient photosynthesis means maximum 'food' production

Think back to the photosynthesis equation on page 33. Plants need three main things from their environment in order to photosynthesise: <u>carbon dioxide</u>, <u>water</u> and <u>light</u>. So <u>leaves</u> are <u>adapted</u> to make sure a plant gets as much of them as possible. Pretty straightforward really.

Photosynthesis Experiments

The two products from photosynthesis are glucose and oxygen (see page 33). Glucose is stored by plants as starch. You can test for starch and oxygen (see below and next page) to investigate photosynthesis.

You Need to Know How to **Test a Leaf** for Starch

1) First, the leaf needs to be killed by dunking it in boiling water (hold it with tweezers or forceps) — this sounds a bit harsh, but it stops any chemical reactions happening inside the leaf.

2) Next, put the leaf in a boiling tube with some ethanol and heat the tube in a water bath. This gets rid of any chlorophyll that's inside the leaf. The leaf should end up a pale, white-ish colour.

3) Finally, rinse the leaf in cold water and add a few drops of iodine solution to it (see page 22). If starch is present inside the leaf, it will turn blue-black.

The **Starch Test** Shows Whether **Photosynthesis** is **Taking Place**

If a plant can't photosynthesise, it can't make starch. You can use this principle to show that chlorophyll and CO_2 are needed for photosynthesis. Here's how...

Chlorophyll

You can show that chlorophyll is needed for photosynthesis using variegated (green and white) leaves. Only the green parts of the leaf contain chlorophyll.

1) Take a variegated leaf from a plant that's been exposed to light for a bit. Make sure you record which bits are green and which bits aren't.

2) Test the leaf for starch as above — you'll see that only the bits that were green turn blue-black.

3) This suggests that only the parts of the leaf that contained chlorophyll are able to photosynthesise and produce starch.

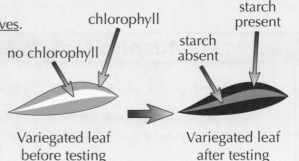

The white parts of the leaf go brown because the brown iodine solution stains them.

CO_2

1) You can show that CO_2 is needed for photosynthesis with the apparatus shown on the right.

2) The soda lime will absorb CO_2 out of the air in the jar.

3) If you leave the plant in the jar for a while and then test a leaf for starch, it won't turn blue-black.

4) This shows that no starch has been made in the leaf, which means that CO_2 is needed for photosynthesis.

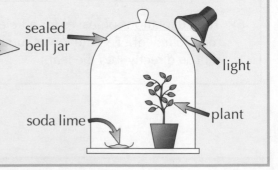

For both of these tests, it's important that any variables that could affect the results, e.g. the temperature, are controlled.

More Photosynthesis Experiments

More starch testing on this page I'm afraid. But there's also a bit about how oxygen production can show the rate of photosynthesis. Don't say I don't mix things up a bit for you...

Another Starch Test...

Remember, if a plant can't photosynthesise, it can't make starch. You can use this principle to show that light is needed for photosynthesis. Here's how:

1) To show that light is needed for photosynthesis you need a plant that's been grown without any light, e.g. in a cupboard.

2) Cut a leaf from the plant and test it for starch using iodine solution (see previous page) — the leaf won't turn blue-black.

3) This shows that light is needed for photosynthesis, as no starch has been made.

Even though the plant is kept in the dark, you need to make sure it's warm enough to photosynthesise and that there's plenty of CO_2 — or it won't be a fair test.

Oxygen Production Shows the Rate of Photosynthesis

Canadian pondweed can be used to measure the effect of light intensity on the rate of photosynthesis. The rate at which the pondweed produces oxygen corresponds to the rate at which it's photosynthesising — the faster the rate of oxygen production, the faster the rate of photosynthesis.

Here's how the experiment works:

1) A source of white light is placed at a specific distance from the pondweed.

2) The pondweed is left to photosynthesise for a set amount of time. As it photosynthesises, the oxygen released will collect in the capillary tube.

3) At the end of the experiment, the syringe is used to draw the gas bubble in the tube up alongside a ruler and the length of the gas bubble is measured. This is proportional to the volume of O_2 produced.

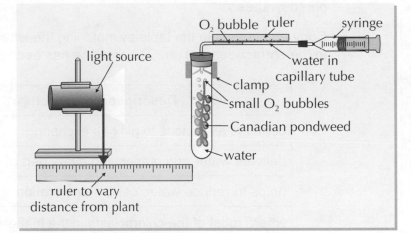

4) For this experiment, any variables that could affect the results should be controlled, e.g. the temperature and time the pondweed is left to photosynthesise.

5) The experiment is then repeated with the light source placed at different distances from the pondweed.

> The apparatus above can be altered to measure the effect of temperature and CO_2 on photosynthesis, e.g. the test tube of pondweed is put into a beaker of water at a set temperature and CO_2 is bubbled into the test tube (then the experiment's repeated with different temperatures of water / concentrations of CO_2).

Warm-Up and Exam Questions

So, here we go again — another set of questions to test your knowledge. But don't roll your eyes, I promise they'll be really, really enjoyable. OK, don't hold me to that, but make sure you do them...

Warm-Up Questions

1) What is meant by a limiting factor for the rate of photosynthesis?
2) Explain why the rate of photosynthesis decreases if the temperature is too high.
3) Outline an experiment you could do to show that carbon dioxide is needed for photosynthesis.
4) What can you measure to show the rate of photosynthesis?

Exam Questions

1 The diagram shows a cross-section through a typical leaf. Some of the structures in the leaf are labelled **A** to **E**.

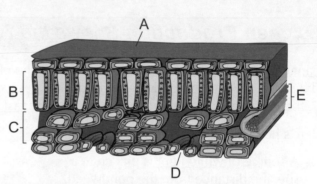

a) The table below contains descriptions of how the structures labelled in the diagram make the leaf well-adapted for efficient photosynthesis.

Copy and complete the table by matching the letters in the diagram to the correct description. The first one has been done for you.

Description of structure	Letter
contains air spaces to aid gas exchange	**C**
delivers water and nutrients to every part of the leaf	
helps to reduce water loss by evaporation	
where most of the chloroplasts in the leaf are located, to maximise the amount of light they receive	
allows carbon dioxide to diffuse directly into the leaf	

(4 marks)

b) Explain how photosynthesis is involved in creating a store of chemical energy for the plant.

(2 marks)

c) Write down the word and balanced symbol equations for photosynthesis.

(4 marks)

Exam Questions

2   Seth investigated the effect of different concentrations of carbon dioxide on the rate
of photosynthesis of his Swiss cheese plant. The results are shown on the graph below.

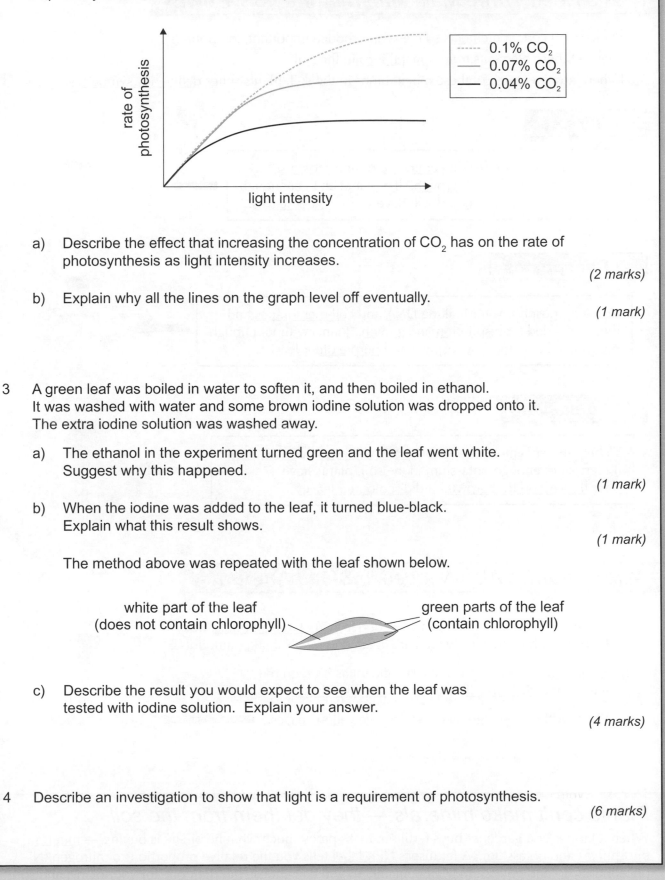

a)   Describe the effect that increasing the concentration of CO_2 has on the rate of
photosynthesis as light intensity increases.

(2 marks)

b)   Explain why all the lines on the graph level off eventually.

(1 mark)

3   A green leaf was boiled in water to soften it, and then boiled in ethanol.
It was washed with water and some brown iodine solution was dropped onto it.
The extra iodine solution was washed away.

a)   The ethanol in the experiment turned green and the leaf went white.
Suggest why this happened.

(1 mark)

b)   When the iodine was added to the leaf, it turned blue-black.
Explain what this result shows.

(1 mark)

The method above was repeated with the leaf shown below.

white part of the leaf
(does not contain chlorophyll)

green parts of the leaf
(contain chlorophyll)

c)   Describe the result you would expect to see when the leaf was
tested with iodine solution. Explain your answer.

(4 marks)

4   Describe an investigation to show that light is a requirement of photosynthesis.

(6 marks)

Minerals for Healthy Growth

Plants are important in <u>food chains</u> and <u>nutrient cycles</u> because they can take <u>minerals</u> from the soil and <u>energy</u> from the Sun and turn it into food. And then, after all that hard work, we eat them.

Plants Need *Three* Main *Mineral Ions* For *Growth*

1) Plants need certain <u>elements</u> so they can produce important compounds.
2) They get these elements from <u>mineral ions</u> in the <u>soil</u>.
3) If there aren't enough of these mineral ions in the soil, plants suffer <u>deficiency symptoms</u>.

1) Nitrates

Contain nitrogen for making <u>amino acids</u> and <u>proteins</u>. These are needed for <u>cell growth</u>. If a plant can't get enough nitrates it will be <u>stunted</u> and will have <u>yellow older leaves</u>.

2) Phosphates

Contain phosphorus for making <u>DNA</u> and <u>cell membranes</u> and they're needed for <u>respiration</u> and <u>growth</u>. Plants without enough phosphate have <u>poor root growth</u> and <u>purple older leaves</u>.

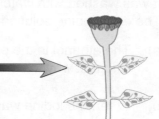

3) Potassium

To help the <u>enzymes</u> needed for <u>photosynthesis</u> and <u>respiration</u>. If there's not enough potassium in the soil, plants have <u>poor flower and fruit growth</u> and <u>discoloured leaves</u>.

Magnesium is Also Needed in *Small Amounts*

1) The three main mineral ions are needed in fairly <u>large amounts</u>, but there are other elements which are needed in much <u>smaller</u> amounts.

2) <u>Magnesium</u> is one of the most significant as it's required for making <u>chlorophyll</u> (needed for <u>photosynthesis</u>).

3) Plants without enough magnesium have <u>yellow leaves</u>.

Plants can't make minerals — they get them from the soil

When a farmer or a gardener buys fertiliser, that's pretty much what he or she is buying — <u>nitrates</u>, <u>phosphates</u> and <u>potassium</u>. A fertiliser's <u>NPK label</u> tells you the relative proportions of nitrogen (<u>N</u>), phosphorus (<u>P</u>) and potassium (<u>K</u>) it contains, so you can choose the <u>right one</u> for your plants and soil. Don't forget about <u>magnesium</u>, though — it's dead important for making <u>chlorophyll</u>.

Transport in Plants

Like all multicellular organisms, plants need a way of transporting substances from A to B.

Multicellular Organisms Need Transport Systems

1) The cells in all living organisms need a variety of substances to live, e.g. plant cells need things like water, minerals and sugars. They also need to get rid of waste substances.

2) In unicellular organisms, these substances can diffuse directly into and out of the cell across the cell membrane. The diffusion rate is quick because of the short distances substances have to travel.

3) But in multicellular organisms (like animals and plants) direct diffusion from the outer surface would be too slow — that's because substances would have to travel large distances to reach every single cell.

However, carbon dioxide diffuses into plants at the leaves (where it's needed).

4) So multicellular organisms need transport systems to move substances to and from individual cells quickly.

Plants Have Two Main Transport Systems

Plants have two systems transporting stuff around. Both go to every part of the plant, but they're totally separate.

Water and minerals

Xylem tubes transport water and minerals:

The xylem carry water and mineral salts from the roots up the shoot to the leaves in the transpiration stream (see next page).

Paper 2

Phloem tubes transport food:

1) The phloem transport sugars, like sucrose, and amino acids from where they're made in the leaves to other parts of the plant.

2) This movement of food substances around the plant is known as translocation.

Paper 2

Sucrose and amino acids

Root Hairs Take In Water

1) The cells on plant roots grow into long 'hairs' which stick out into the soil.

2) Each branch of a root will be covered in millions of these microscopic hairs.

3) This gives the plant a big surface area for absorbing water from the soil.

Root hair cells also take in minerals — this is done by active transport (see page 16).

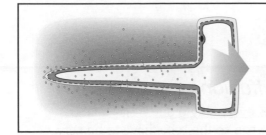

Water is taken in by osmosis (see p.12-13).

There's usually a higher concentration of water in the soil than there is inside the plant, so the water is drawn into the root hair cell by osmosis.

Transpiration

If you don't water a house plant for a few days it starts to go <u>all droopy</u>. Then it <u>dies</u>. Plants need water.

Transpiration is the Loss of Water from the Plant

1) Transpiration is caused by the <u>evaporation</u> and <u>diffusion</u> (see page 11) of water from a plant's surface.

2) Most transpiration happens at the <u>leaves</u>.

3) Evaporation creates a slight <u>shortage</u> of water in the leaf, and so more water is drawn up from the rest of the plant through the <u>xylem vessels</u> (see previous page) to replace it.

4) This in turn means more water is drawn up from the <u>roots</u>, and so there's a constant <u>transpiration stream</u> of water through the plant.

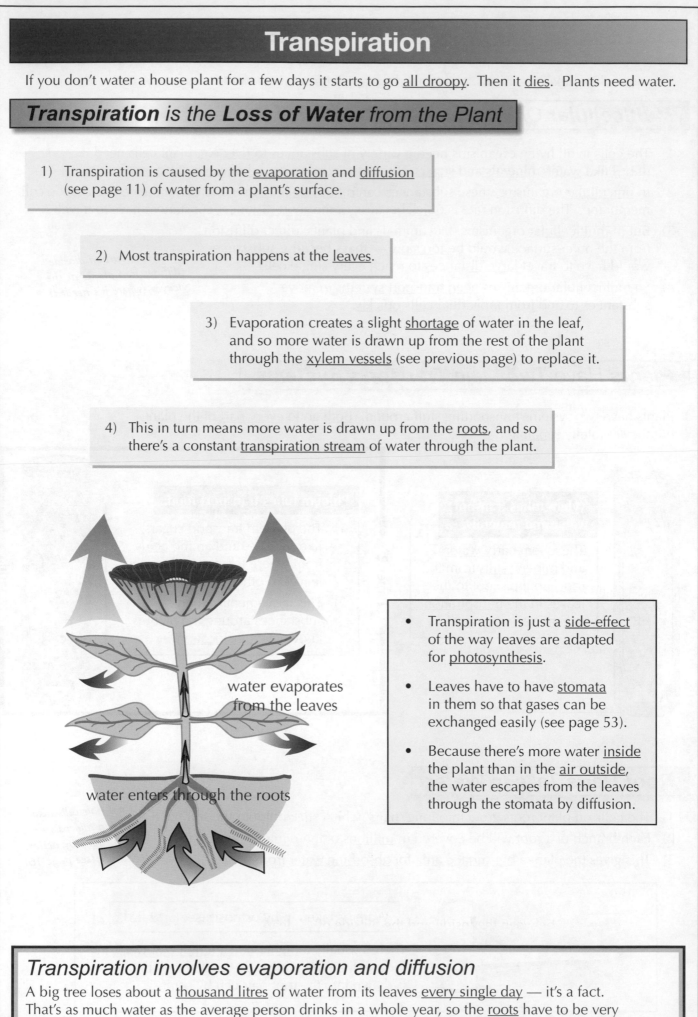

water evaporates from the leaves

water enters through the roots

- Transpiration is just a <u>side-effect</u> of the way leaves are adapted for <u>photosynthesis</u>.

- Leaves have to have <u>stomata</u> in them so that gases can be exchanged easily (see page 53).

- Because there's more water <u>inside</u> the plant than in the <u>air outside</u>, the water escapes from the leaves through the stomata by diffusion.

Transpiration involves evaporation and diffusion

A big tree loses about a <u>thousand litres</u> of water from its leaves <u>every single day</u> — it's a fact. That's as much water as the average person drinks in a whole year, so the <u>roots</u> have to be very effective at drawing in water from the soil. Which is why they have all those root <u>hairs</u>, you see.

Transpiration

The rate of transpiration varies according to the environmental conditions...

Transpiration Rate is Affected by Four Main Things

Light Intensity

1) The <u>brighter</u> the light, the <u>greater</u> the transpiration rate.
2) <u>Stomata</u> begin to <u>close</u> as it gets darker. Photosynthesis can't happen in the dark, so they don't need to be open to let <u>CO_2</u> in. When the stomata are closed, very little water can escape.

Temperature

1) The <u>warmer</u> it is, the <u>faster</u> transpiration happens.
2) When it's warm the water particles have <u>more energy</u> to evaporate and diffuse out of the stomata.

Wind Speed

1) The <u>higher</u> the wind speed around a leaf, the <u>greater</u> the transpiration rate.
2) If wind speed around a leaf is <u>low</u>, the water vapour just <u>surrounds the leaf</u> and doesn't move away. This means there's a <u>high concentration</u> of water particles outside the leaf as well as inside it, so <u>diffusion</u> doesn't happen as quickly.
3) If it's windy, the water vapour is <u>swept away</u>, maintaining a <u>low concentration</u> of water in the air outside the leaf. Diffusion then happens quickly, from an area of high concentration to an area of low concentration.

Humidity

1) The <u>drier</u> the air around a leaf, the <u>faster</u> transpiration happens.
2) This is like what happens with air movement. If the air is <u>humid</u> there's a lot of water in it already, so there's not much of a <u>difference</u> between the inside and the outside of the leaf.
3) Diffusion happens <u>fastest</u> if there's a <u>really high concentration</u> in one place, and a <u>really low concentration</u> in the other.

Measuring Transpiration

It's time for another <u>experiment</u> — you get to use a piece of equipment you've probably never heard of...

A *Potometer* can be Used to *Estimate Transpiration Rate*

A <u>potometer</u> is a special piece of apparatus used to <u>estimate transpiration rates</u>. It actually <u>measures water uptake</u> by a plant, but it's <u>assumed</u> that water uptake by the plant is <u>directly related</u> to water loss by the leaves (transpiration). Here's how to use a potometer:

1) <u>Cut</u> a shoot <u>underwater</u> to prevent air from entering the xylem.
   Cut it at a <u>slant</u> to increase the surface area available for water uptake.

2) <u>Assemble</u> the potometer <u>in water</u> and insert the shoot <u>under water</u>, so no <u>air</u> can enter.

3) Remove the apparatus from the water but keep the end of the capillary tube <u>submerged</u> in a beaker of water.

   Setting up a potometer is tough — if there are air bubbles in the apparatus or the plant's xylem it will affect your results.

4) Check that the apparatus is <u>watertight</u> and <u>airtight</u>.

5) <u>Dry</u> the leaves, allow time for the shoot to <u>acclimatise</u> and then <u>shut</u> the tap.

6) Remove the end of the capillary tube from the beaker of water until <u>one air bubble</u> has formed, then put the end of the tube <u>back into the water</u>.

7) Record the <u>starting position</u> of the air bubble.

8) Start a <u>stopwatch</u> and record the <u>distance moved</u> by the bubble per unit time, e.g. per hour.

9) Keep the <u>conditions constant</u> throughout the experiment, e.g. the <u>temperature</u> and <u>air humidity</u>.

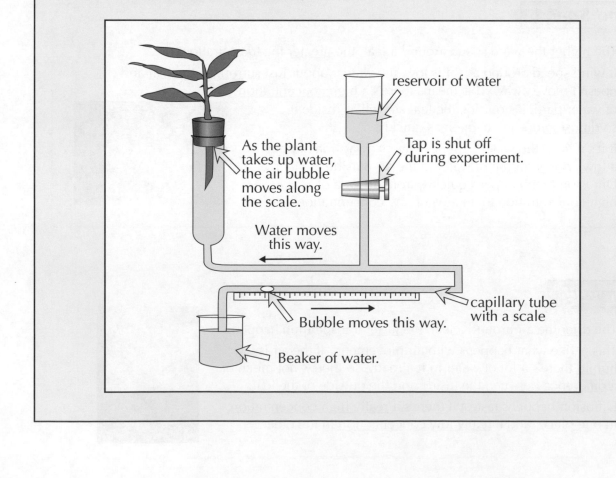

As the plant takes up water, the air bubble moves along the scale.

reservoir of water

Tap is shut off during experiment.

Water moves this way.

Bubble moves this way.

capillary tube with a scale

Beaker of water.

Measuring Transpiration

Now you know how to use a potometer, you can start to mix things up a bit.
Here's your chance to find out exactly how much the four factors on p.43 affect transpiration rate.

See How **Environmental Conditions** Affect Transpiration Rates

1) You can use a potometer to <u>estimate</u> how different factors affect the transpiration rate.

2) The set up on the previous page will be your <u>control</u> — you can <u>vary</u> an <u>environmental condition</u> (see below), run the experiment again and <u>compare</u> the results to the <u>control</u> to see how the change <u>affected</u> the transpiration rate.

Light Intensity

You could use a <u>lamp</u> to <u>increase</u> the <u>intensity of light</u> that hits the plant — this should <u>increase</u> the transpiration rate. To <u>decrease</u> the light intensity, put the potometer in a <u>cupboard</u> (this should <u>decrease</u> the transpiration rate).

Temperature

You could increase or decrease the temperature by putting the potometer in a <u>room</u> that's <u>warmer</u> or <u>colder</u> than where you did the control experiment. An <u>increase</u> in temperature should <u>increase</u> the transpiration rate and a <u>decrease</u> in temperature should <u>lower</u> it.

Wind Speed

You could use a <u>fan</u> to <u>increase</u> the wind speed around the plant — this should <u>increase</u> the transpiration rate.

Humidity

You could <u>increase</u> the humidity of the air around the plant by <u>spraying a little water</u> into a clear <u>plastic bag</u> before <u>sealing</u> it around the plant. This should <u>decrease</u> the rate of transpiration.

Make sure you know how to use a potometer

The <u>tricky bit</u> is setting up the apparatus — keeping air out and water in is harder than it sounds, but if you're only writing about the experiment in an exam, you <u>don't</u> have to worry about that. Phew. Only the questions to go, then it's the end of Section 3. What a relief.

Warm-Up and Exam Questions

Just a few simple warm-up questions and a few slightly harder exam questions stand between you and mastering transport in plants...

Warm-Up Questions

1) What do plants need nitrates for?
2) Explain why small, unicellular organisms do not need a transport system, but large, multicellular organisms (such as plants) do.
3) State the four main factors that affect the rate of transpiration in plants.

Exam Questions

1 Plants absorb water and mineral ions through their root hair cells.

a) Name and describe the process by which water is drawn into a root hair cell from the soil.

(2 marks)

b) Name the vessels that transport water and mineral ions from the roots of a plant to the leaves.

(1 mark)

PAPER 2

2 Aphids are insects which feed on plant sap. Sap is the name given to the liquids carried around the plant in transport vessels.

a) The sap the aphids feed on contains sucrose. What type of transport vessel does the sap come from?

(1 mark)

b) Name **one** other nutrient that the aphid will be able to obtain from the plant sap.

(1 mark)

3 A scientist planted 10 seedlings of the same variety in a growth medium containing a complete supply of minerals. He then planted a further 10 seedlings in a growth medium deficient in magnesium. The seedlings were left to grow under carefully controlled conditions.

a) At the end of the investigation, the seedlings grown without magnesium had yellow leaves. The seedlings grown in a complete supply of minerals did not. Suggest why the magnesium-deficient plants had yellow leaves.

(1 mark)

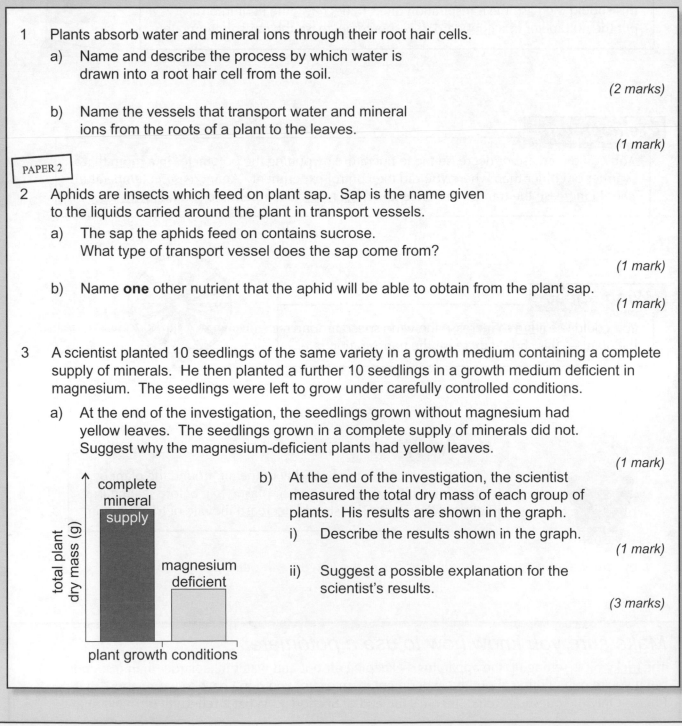

b) At the end of the investigation, the scientist measured the total dry mass of each group of plants. His results are shown in the graph.

i) Describe the results shown in the graph.

(1 mark)

ii) Suggest a possible explanation for the scientist's results.

(3 marks)

Exam Questions

4 A scientist measured the rate of transpiration in two plants over 48 hours. The results are shown in the graph.

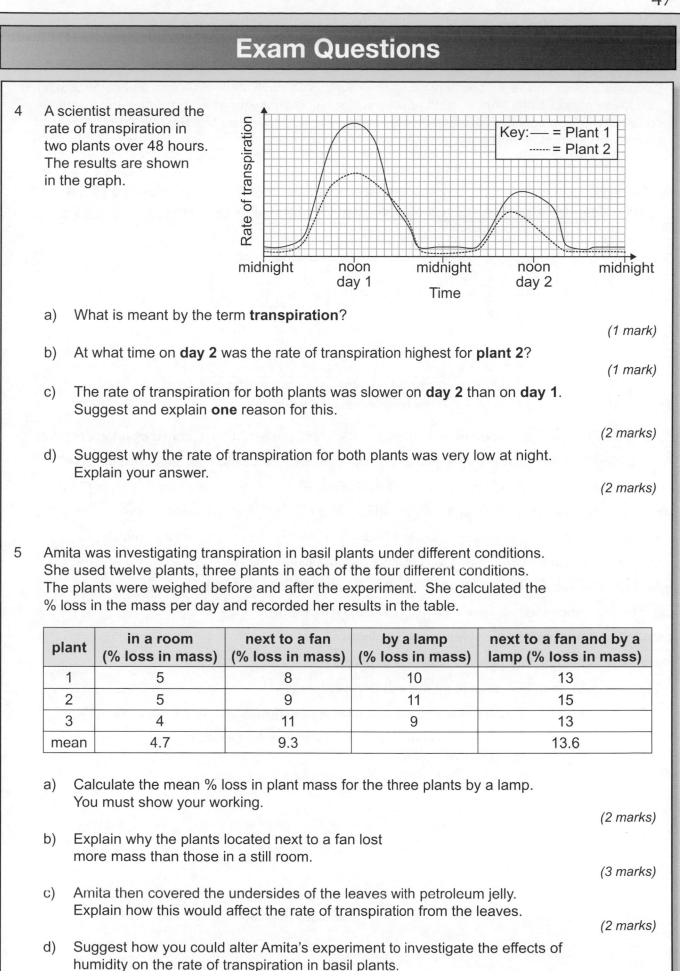

a) What is meant by the term **transpiration**?

(1 mark)

b) At what time on **day 2** was the rate of transpiration highest for **plant 2**?

(1 mark)

c) The rate of transpiration for both plants was slower on **day 2** than on **day 1**. Suggest and explain **one** reason for this.

(2 marks)

d) Suggest why the rate of transpiration for both plants was very low at night. Explain your answer.

(2 marks)

5 Amita was investigating transpiration in basil plants under different conditions. She used twelve plants, three plants in each of the four different conditions. The plants were weighed before and after the experiment. She calculated the % loss in the mass per day and recorded her results in the table.

plant	in a room (% loss in mass)	next to a fan (% loss in mass)	by a lamp (% loss in mass)	next to a fan and by a lamp (% loss in mass)
1	5	8	10	13
2	5	9	11	15
3	4	11	9	13
mean	4.7	9.3		13.6

a) Calculate the mean % loss in plant mass for the three plants by a lamp. You must show your working.

(2 marks)

b) Explain why the plants located next to a fan lost more mass than those in a still room.

(3 marks)

c) Amita then covered the undersides of the leaves with petroleum jelly. Explain how this would affect the rate of transpiration from the leaves.

(2 marks)

d) Suggest how you could alter Amita's experiment to investigate the effects of humidity on the rate of transpiration in basil plants.

(2 marks)

Revision Summary for Section 3

Congratulations. You've successfully navigated your way through another section and come through it in one piece (hopefully). Anyway, it's now time to see if, during your journey through the loveliness of section three, you actually absorbed the stuff on the pages. Have a bash at the questions below and cement this section in your brain.

1) What are the two products of photosynthesis?

2)* The graph shows how the rate of photosynthesis in plants is affected by increasing the level of carbon dioxide. Look at the graph and answer the two questions below.

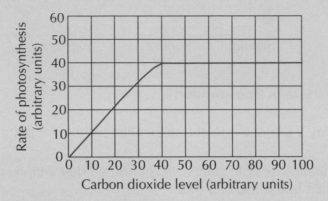

    a) At what level of carbon dioxide is the plant's rate of photosynthesis limited by another factor?

    b) Suggest two possible limiting factors on the plant's rate of photosynthesis above this level.

3) How does being broad help a leaf to photosynthesise?

4) Describe one other way that leaves are adapted for efficient photosynthesis.

5) Briefly describe an experiment to show that chlorophyll is required for photosynthesis.

6) Name the three main mineral ions plants need for healthy growth.

7) How can you tell by looking at a plant that it isn't getting enough magnesium?

8) Which mineral ion is needed by plants to make chlorophyll?

9) What is the function of xylem vessels in plants?

10) What is the function of phloem vessels in plants?

11) How does water get into a plant through its root hair cells?

12) How is the transpiration rate affected by: a) increased temperature, b) increased humidity?

13) Describe an experiment that you could do to measure how temperature affects the transpiration rate of a plant.

* Answers on p.205

Respiration

You need <u>energy</u> to keep your body going. Energy comes from <u>food</u>, and it's <u>released</u> by <u>respiration</u>.

Respiration is NOT "Breathing In and Out"

1) Respiration is <u>NOT</u> breathing in and breathing out, as you might think.
2) <u>Respiration</u> actually goes on in <u>every cell</u> in your body.
3) It's the process of <u>releasing energy</u> from <u>glucose</u>.
4) Energy is released as <u>chemical energy</u> and <u>heat</u>.

> • The <u>chemical energy</u> is used to do things like <u>create large molecules</u> from smaller ones (e.g. proteins from amino acids) and <u>contract muscles</u>.
>
> • The <u>heat energy</u> helps to <u>maintain</u> a steady <u>body temperature</u>.

5) There are <u>two types</u> of respiration, <u>aerobic</u> and <u>anaerobic</u>.

> <u>RESPIRATION</u> is the process of <u>RELEASING ENERGY</u> from <u>GLUCOSE</u>, which happens constantly <u>IN EVERY LIVING CELL</u>.

*The **Heat** Produced by **Respiration** can be Measured*

Here's an experiment that you can do to <u>measure</u> the <u>heat</u> that <u>respiration</u> gives off.

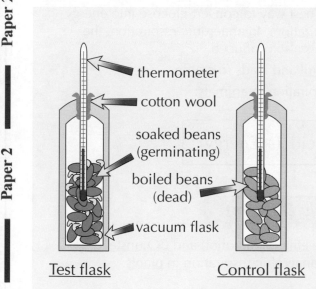

thermometer

cotton wool

soaked beans (germinating)

boiled beans (dead)

vacuum flask

<u>Test flask</u>   <u>Control flask</u>

• First, <u>soak</u> some <u>dried beans</u> in <u>water</u> for a day or two. They will start to <u>germinate</u> (you should see little sprouts coming out of them). Germinating beans will <u>respire</u>.

• <u>Boil</u> a <u>similar-sized</u>, second bunch of dried beans. This will <u>kill the beans</u> and make sure they <u>can't respire</u>. The dead beans will act as your <u>control</u>.

• Add each set of beans to a <u>vacuum flask</u>, making sure there's some <u>air</u> left in the flasks (so the germinating beans can <u>respire aerobically</u>).

• Place a <u>thermometer</u> into each flask and seal the top with <u>cotton wool</u>.

• Record the <u>temperature</u> of each flask daily for a week.

> The beans are well-insulated in the flasks, so when the germinating beans <u>respire</u> and produce <u>heat</u>, the <u>test flask's temperature</u> will <u>increase</u> compared to the control flask.

Respiration releases energy from glucose

Make sure you understand what the two flasks of beans show. The <u>control</u> flask of boiled beans is there to show that it's the <u>respiring, germinating beans</u> in the test flask that are <u>producing the heat</u>.

Paper 2   Paper 2   Paper 2   Paper 2   Paper 2   Paper 2

Respiration

You need to know all about <u>aerobic respiration</u> and <u>anaerobic respiration</u>...

Aerobic Respiration Needs Plenty of Oxygen

1) <u>Aerobic respiration</u> is what happens when there's <u>plenty of oxygen</u> available.
2) <u>Aerobic</u> just means "<u>with oxygen</u>" and it's the most efficient way to release <u>energy</u> from <u>glucose</u>.
3) This is the type of respiration that you're using <u>most of the time</u>.
   You need to learn <u>the word equation</u> and <u>the balanced chemical equation</u>:

$$\text{Glucose} + \text{Oxygen} \implies \text{Carbon dioxide} + \text{Water} \ (+ \textit{Energy})$$
$$C_6H_{12}O_6 + 6O_2 \implies 6CO_2 + 6H_2O \ (+ \textit{Energy})$$

This is the reverse of the photosynthesis equation (see page 33).

Anaerobic Respiration Doesn't Use Oxygen At All

1) When you do really <u>vigorous exercise</u> your body can't supply enough <u>oxygen</u> to your muscles for aerobic respiration — even though your <u>heart rate</u> and <u>breathing rate</u> increase as much as they can. Your muscles have to start <u>respiring anaerobically</u> as well.
2) Anaerobic just means "<u>without</u> oxygen". It's <u>NOT</u> the best way to convert glucose into energy because it releases much <u>less energy</u> than aerobic respiration. In anaerobic respiration, the glucose is only <u>partially</u> broken down, and <u>lactic acid</u> is also produced.
3) The <u>lactic acid</u> builds up in the muscles — it gets <u>painful</u> and leads to <u>cramp</u>.
   You need to learn <u>the word equation</u> for anaerobic respiration in <u>animals</u>:

$$\text{Glucose} \implies \text{Lactic Acid} \ (+ \text{Energy})$$

Anaerobic Respiration in Plants is Slightly Different

<u>Plants</u> can respire <u>without oxygen</u> too, but they produce <u>ethanol</u> (alcohol) and CO_2 <u>instead</u> of lactic acid. You need to learn <u>the word equation</u> for anaerobic respiration in <u>plants</u>:

$$\text{Glucose} \implies \text{Ethanol} + \text{Carbon Dioxide} \ (+ \text{Energy})$$

Fungi like yeast also do anaerobic respiration like this — people use yeast to produce beer (see page 146).

Only aerobic respiration uses oxygen...

So when you're just sitting about, you use <u>aerobic respiration</u> to get all your energy — but when you do hard exercise, you can't get enough oxygen to your muscles, so you use <u>anaerobic respiration</u> too.

Investigating Respiration

Not convinced about <u>carbon dioxide</u> being produced by <u>respiration</u>?
Well here's how to <u>detect</u> it yourself...

Carbon Dioxide Production can be Detected using an Indicator

1) You can use <u>hydrogen-carbonate solution</u> to show that
living organisms produce <u>CO_2</u> as they respire.

2) Normally this solution is <u>orange</u>, but it <u>changes colour</u>
to a <u>lovely yellow</u> in the presence of <u>carbon dioxide</u>.

3) Here's how you can set up an experiment to demonstrate
<u>carbon dioxide production</u> by some <u>beans</u>:

> Firstly, prepare one set of <u>germinating beans</u> and one set of <u>boiled beans</u> (the control)
> as described in the experiment on page 49.
>
> Now, set up the experiment as shown in the diagrams below:
>
> • Put some <u>hydrogen-carbonate indicator</u> into two <u>test tubes</u>.
>
> • Place a <u>platform</u> made of <u>gauze</u> into each test tube and put
> one set of beans on the platform in each tube.
>
> • <u>Seal</u> the test tubes with a <u>rubber bung</u>.
>
> • Leave the apparatus for a <u>set period</u> of <u>time</u> (e.g. an hour).

Results:

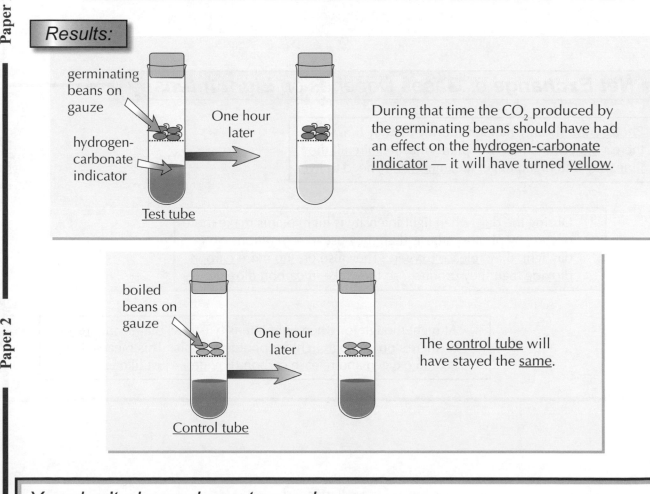

germinating
beans on
gauze

hydrogen-
carbonate
indicator

One hour
later

Test tube

During that time the CO_2 produced by
the germinating beans should have had
an effect on the <u>hydrogen-carbonate</u>
<u>indicator</u> — it will have turned <u>yellow</u>.

boiled
beans on
gauze

One hour
later

Control tube

The <u>control tube</u> will
have stayed the <u>same</u>.

You don't always have to use beans...

You can also do this experiment with <u>small organisms</u> like woodlice or maggots (the control for these
would be glass beads though). Try <u>drawing the diagrams</u> above to get this experiment in your head.

Gas Exchange — Flowering Plants

Diffusion is the net movement of particles from an area of higher concentration to an area of lower concentration. Now's a good time to flick back to page 11 if you don't have a clue what I'm on about...

Plants Exchange Gases By Diffusion

1) When plants photosynthesise they use up CO_2 from the atmosphere and produce O_2 as a waste product.

2) When plants respire they use up O_2 and produce CO_2 as a waste product.

3) So there are lots of gases moving to and fro in plants, and this movement happens by diffusion.

Example:

1) When the plant is photosynthesising it uses up lots of CO_2, so there's hardly any inside the leaf. Luckily this makes more CO_2 move into the leaf by diffusion (from an area of higher concentration to an area of lower concentration).

2) At the same time lots of O_2 is being made as a waste product of photosynthesis. Some is used in respiration, and the rest diffuses out through the stomata (moving from an area of higher concentration to an area of lower concentration).

The Net Exchange of Gases Depends on Light Intensity

1) Photosynthesis only happens during the day (i.e. when there's light available). But plants must respire all the time, day and night, to get the energy they need to live.

2) During the day (when light intensity is high) plants make more oxygen by photosynthesis than they use in respiration. So in daylight, they release oxygen. They also use up more carbon dioxide than they produce, so they take in carbon dioxide.

3) At night though (or when light intensity is low) plants only respire — there's not enough light for photosynthesis. This means they take in oxygen and release carbon dioxide — just like us.

Gases move in and out of plants by diffusion...

Which gases move in or out depends on the time of day. Just remember, plants photosynthesise when the Sun is shining, so in the day they'll be taking in lots of carbon dioxide and giving out oxygen.

Gas Exchange — Flowering Plants

Gas exchange in plants takes place in the leaves...

Leaves are **Adapted** for **Efficient Gas Exchange**

1) Leaves are <u>broad</u>, so there's a large surface area for <u>diffusion</u>. They're also <u>thin</u>, which means <u>gases</u> only have to travel a <u>short distance</u> to reach the cells where they're needed.

2) There are <u>air spaces</u> inside the leaf. This lets gases like carbon dioxide and oxygen move easily between cells. It also increases the surface area for <u>gas exchange</u>.

3) The lower surface is full of little holes called <u>stomata</u>. They're there to let gases like <u>CO_2</u> and <u>O_2</u> diffuse in and out. They also allow <u>water</u> to escape — which is known as <u>transpiration</u> (see page 42).

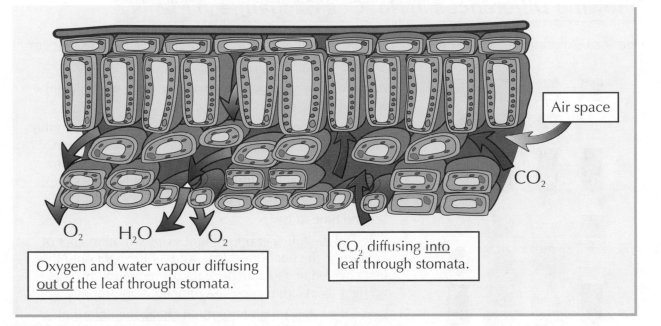

Air space

CO_2

O_2 H_2O O_2

Oxygen and water vapour diffusing <u>out of</u> the leaf through stomata.

CO_2 diffusing <u>into</u> leaf through stomata.

Stomata can be **Opened** and **Closed**

1) <u>Stomata</u> begin to <u>close</u> as it gets dark. Photosynthesis can't happen in the dark, so they don't need to be open to let <u>CO_2</u> in. When the stomata are <u>closed</u>, water <u>can't escape</u>. This stops the plant <u>drying out</u>.

2) Stomata also <u>close</u> when supplies of <u>water</u> from the <u>roots</u> start to <u>dry up</u>. This <u>stops</u> the plant from <u>photosynthesising</u> (bad), but if they <u>didn't close</u>, the plant might dry out and <u>die</u> (worse).

3) The <u>opening</u> and <u>closing</u> of stomata is <u>controlled</u> by the cells that surround them (called <u>guard cells</u>).

Interesting fact — stomata is the plural of stoma...

A biggish tree loses around <u>1000 litres</u> of water from its leaves every day. That's about as much water as the average person drinks in a whole year, so the roots have to draw lots of water from the soil to replace it. No wonder the <u>stomata close</u> when the <u>soil's dry</u> or when it's <u>too dark</u> to photosynthesise.

Gas Exchange — Flowering Plants

Hydrogen-carbonate Indicator and CO₂ Concentration

You can use hydrogen-carbonate indicator to show changes in CO_2 concentration:

You might remember from p.51 that a solution of hydrogen-carbonate indicator in air with a normal CO_2 concentration is orange.

Well if the CO_2 concentration of the air increases, more CO_2 will dissolve in it, and it becomes more yellow.

And if the CO_2 concentration of the air decreases, CO_2 will come out of the solution, and it becomes purple.

Showing Differences in Net Gas Exchange in Plants

Here's an experiment using hydrogen-carbonate indicator to show how light affects gas exchange:

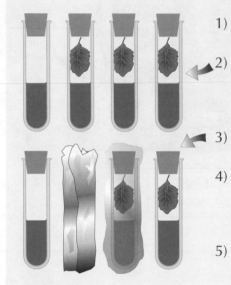

1) Add the same volume of hydrogen-carbonate indicator to four boiling tubes.

2) Put similar-sized, healthy-looking leaves into three of the tubes and seal with a rubber bung. Trap the leaf stem with the bung to stop it falling down into the solution if you need to. Keep the fourth tube empty as a control.

3) Completely wrap one tube in aluminium foil, and a second tube in gauze.

4) Place all the tubes in bright light. This will let plenty of light on to the uncovered leaf, and a little light onto the leaf covered in gauze. The leaf covered in foil will get no light — assuming you've wrapped it up properly.

5) Leave the tubes for an hour, then check the colour of the indicator.

Results

1) There shouldn't be any change in the colour of the control tube.

2) You'd expect the indicator in the darkened tube to go yellow. Respiration will still take place but there will be no photosynthesis, so the CO_2 concentration in the tube will increase.

3) You'd expect the indicator in the shaded tube to stay a similar colour. With a little photosynthesis and some respiration taking place, roughly equal amounts of CO_2 will be taken up and produced by the leaf, so the CO_2 concentration in the tube won't change very much.

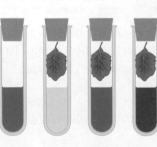

4) You'd expect the indicator in the well-lit tube to go purple. There will be some respiration, but lots of photosynthesis, leading to net uptake of CO_2 by the leaf. This will lower the CO_2 concentration in the tube.

Give it a go, then draw a nice colour-picture of it...

This experiment might sound like a long-winded way to get some coloured tubes, but CO_2 is pretty hard to measure (being generally like the rest of the air), so this is actually a neat way to show it.

Warm-Up and Exam Questions

Right, question time. Give these your best shot...

Warm-Up Questions

1) Give one way that the chemical energy from respiration is used.
2) Write the word equation for anaerobic respiration in humans.
3) Name the two substances produced during anaerobic respiration in plants.
4) True or False? Plants only respire at night.

Exam Questions

1 Respiration is a process carried out by all living cells.
   It can take place aerobically or anaerobically.

   a) State the purpose of respiration.

   (1 mark)

   b) Give **two** differences between aerobic and anaerobic respiration.

   (2 marks)

   c) Write the balanced chemical equation for aerobic respiration.

   (2 marks)

2 Plants exchange gases with the atmosphere. The diagram below shows a cross section
   through part of a leaf, with arrows indicating the movement of two different gases during
   daylight hours.

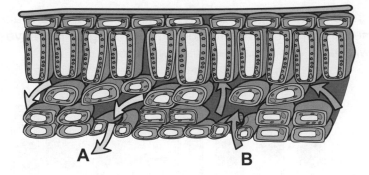

   a) i)   Suggest the gas that is most likely to be represented by each of the letters
            on the diagram.

   (2 marks)

       ii) Name the process by which gases move into and out of leaves.

   (1 mark)

   b) i)   Which process in leaves produces oxygen as a waste product?

   (1 mark)

       ii) Which process in leaves produces carbon dioxide as a waste product?

   (1 mark)

   c) Leaves contain structures called stomata.
       Describe what stomata are and explain their role in gas exchange.

   (2 marks)

   d) Describe and explain **three** ways in which a leaf is adapted for efficient gas exchange.

   (6 marks)

Exam Questions

PAPER 2

3   The following passage describes how changing rates of photosynthesis and respiration affect the net exchange of gases in plants at different times of day. Copy and complete the passage.

> .... only happens during the day, when the
>
> .... is high. During the day, plants make more
>
> .... than they use up in respiration. At night, plants
>
> only ...., so they take in ....
>
> and release ....

(6 marks)

PAPER 2

4   Describe an investigation to show that respiration produces heat.

(6 marks)

PAPER 2

5   Alec has designed an experiment to investigate the effect of light intensity on net gas exchange in plants. He places healthy beech leaves into three tubes containing orange hydrogen-carbonate indicator and seals the tubes with rubber bungs. He prepares a fourth tube containing only indicator as a control.

In order to vary the amount of light reaching the three leaves, Alec wraps tube **A** in gauze to block out some light, and tube **B** in foil to block out all light. He leaves tubes **C** and **D** (the control) unwrapped. His apparatus is shown below.

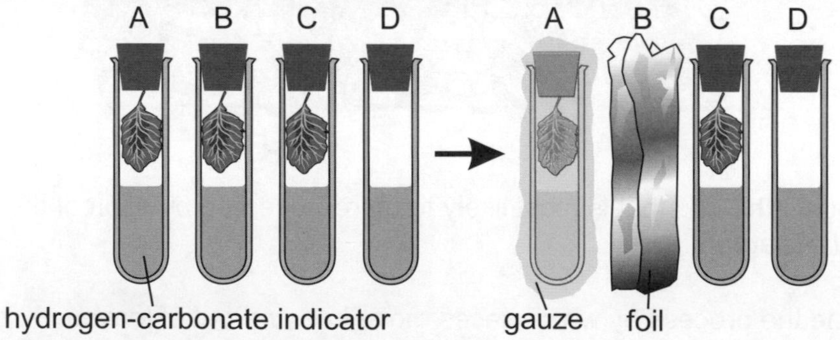

hydrogen-carbonate indicator   gauze   foil

a)   Suggest why Alec sealed the tubes with rubber bungs.

(1 mark)

b)   Explain why Alec included a control tube.

(1 mark)

c)   Alec left the tubes near a bright light for two hours. After this time there was no change in the colour of the indicator solution in tube D. Describe and explain the changes he saw in the indicator solution in the other three tubes, A, B and C, after the two hour period.

(6 marks)

The Respiratory System and Ventilation

The respiratory system lets you breathe in and out. Pretty important. But before we get into the breathing stuff, we need to look more closely at the structure of the thorax...

The **Lungs** Are in the **Thorax**

1) The thorax is the top part of your body.

2) It's separated from the lower part of the body by the diaphragm.

3) The lungs are like big pink sponges and are protected by the ribcage. They're surrounded by the pleural membranes.

4) The air that you breathe in goes through the trachea. This splits into two tubes called bronchi (each one is a bronchus), one going to each lung.

5) The bronchi split into progressively smaller tubes called bronchioles.

6) The bronchioles finally end at small bags called alveoli where the gas exchange takes place (see page 59).

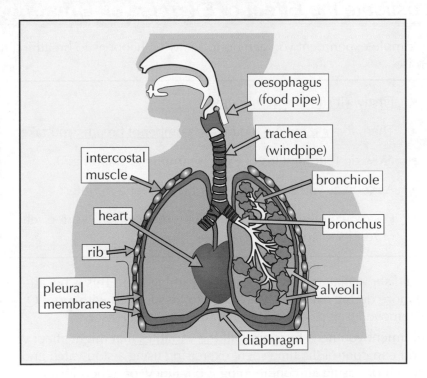

oesophagus (food pipe)

trachea (windpipe)

intercostal muscle

bronchiole

heart

bronchus

rib

pleural membranes

alveoli

diaphragm

Take a deep breath...

...scribble out a picture of the thorax and label it. It doesn't have to be pretty — you just need to make sure you're getting the labels in the right place. Learning the structure of the thorax will make the next few pages about ventilation and gas exchange make a lot more sense. Believe me.

The Respiratory System and Ventilation

You need to get <u>oxygen</u> into your bloodstream to supply your cells for <u>respiration</u>.
You also need to get rid of <u>carbon dioxide</u> from your blood.
This all happens in your <u>lungs</u> when you breathe air <u>in and out</u>...

Breathing In...

1) <u>Intercostal muscles</u> and <u>diaphragm contract</u>.

2) Thorax volume <u>increases</u>.

3) This <u>decreases</u> the pressure, drawing air <u>in</u>.

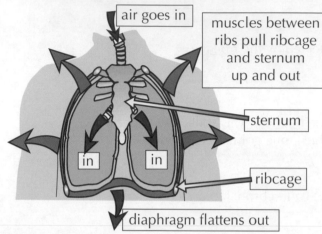

air goes in

muscles between ribs pull ribcage and sternum up and out

sternum

in   in

ribcage

diaphragm flattens out

...and Breathing Out

1) <u>Intercostal muscles</u> and <u>diaphragm relax</u>.

2) Thorax volume <u>decreases</u>.

3) Air is forced <u>out</u>.

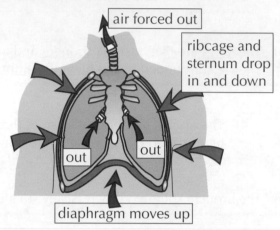

air forced out

ribcage and sternum drop in and down

out   out

diaphragm moves up

You Can Investigate the Effect of Exercise on Breathing Rate

1) There's a really simple experiment you can do to see what happens to breathing rate when you exercise:

> - Firstly, <u>sit still</u> for <u>five minutes</u>.
>
> - Then, for <u>one minute</u>, count the <u>number of breaths</u> you take.
>
> - Now do <u>four minutes</u> of <u>exercise</u> (running, skipping...).
>
> - As soon as you stop <u>count your breaths</u> for a minute.
>
> - Pester <u>two other people</u> to do the same so you get three sets of results to compare.

2) Your results should show that exercise <u>increases breathing rate</u>. This is because your <u>muscles respire more</u> during exercise. They need to be supplied with <u>more O_2</u> and have <u>more CO_2</u> removed (see p.50), so your breathing rate increases.

3) During this experiment you need to <u>control all the variables</u> that might affect your results — e.g. you can control the <u>time spent exercising</u> using a stopwatch and the <u>temperature</u> of the room using air conditioning (ooh, fancy) or a thermostat.

Breathing — changing the size of the space in your lungs

So when you breathe in, you don't have to suck the air in. You just make the <u>space in your lungs bigger</u> and the <u>air rushes in to fill it</u>. Once you've got this page learned, flip over and carry on...

Gas Exchange — Humans

Gas exchange doesn't only happen in plants — it happens in humans too.
Oxygen goes into your bloodstream and you offload nasty 'orrible carbon dioxide...

Alveoli Carry Out Gas Exchange in the Body

1) The lungs contain millions and millions of little air sacs called alveoli where gas exchange happens.

2) The blood passing next to the alveoli has just returned to the lungs from the rest of the body, so it contains lots of carbon dioxide and very little oxygen. Oxygen diffuses out of the alveolus (high concentration) into the blood (low concentration). Carbon dioxide diffuses out of the blood (high concentration) into the alveolus (low concentration) to be breathed out.

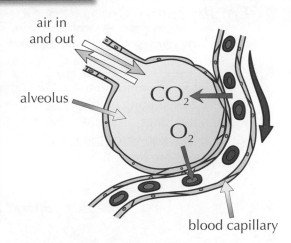

air in and out
alveolus
CO_2
O_2
blood capillary

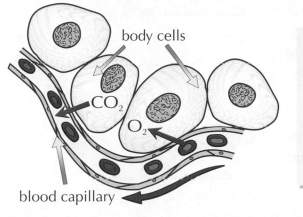

body cells
CO_2
O_2
blood capillary

3) When the blood reaches body cells oxygen is released from the red blood cells (where there's a high concentration) and diffuses into the body cells (where the concentration is low).

4) At the same time, carbon dioxide diffuses out of the body cells (where there's a high concentration) into the blood (where there's a low concentration). It's then carried back to the lungs.

Alveoli are Specialised for Gas Exchange

1) The huge number of microscopic alveoli gives the lungs an enormous surface area.

2) There's a moist lining for gases to dissolve in.

3) The alveoli have very thin walls — only one cell thick, so the gas doesn't have far to diffuse.

4) They have a great blood supply to maintain a high concentration gradient.

5) The walls are permeable — so gases can diffuse across easily.

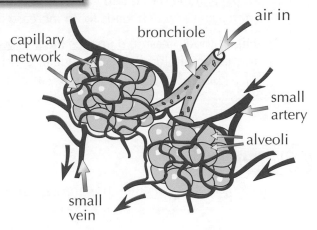

capillary network
bronchiole
air in
small artery
alveoli
small vein

Alveoli are exchange surfaces

A large surface area is a key way that organisms' exchange surfaces are made more effective — molecules can only diffuse through a membrane when they're right next to it, and a large surface area means that a lot more molecules are close to the membrane. Make sure you're clear on this, and the others ways that alveoli are adapted for their function. If you know it, it'll be easy marks in the exam.

Gas Exchange — Humans

Smoking Tobacco Can Cause Quite a Few Problems

Smoking can severely affect your <u>lungs</u> and <u>circulatory system</u>. Here's how:

1) Emphysema, Smoker's Cough and Bronchitis

1) Smoking <u>damages</u> the walls inside the <u>alveoli</u>, <u>reducing</u> the <u>surface area</u> for gas exchange and leading to diseases like <u>emphysema</u>.

2) The <u>tar</u> in cigarettes damages the <u>cilia</u> (little hairs) in your lungs and trachea. These hairs, along with <u>mucus</u>, catch a load of <u>dust</u> and <u>bacteria</u> before they reach the lungs. The cilia also help to keep the <u>trachea clear</u> by sweeping mucus <u>back towards the mouth</u>. When these cilia are damaged, <u>chest infections</u> are more likely.

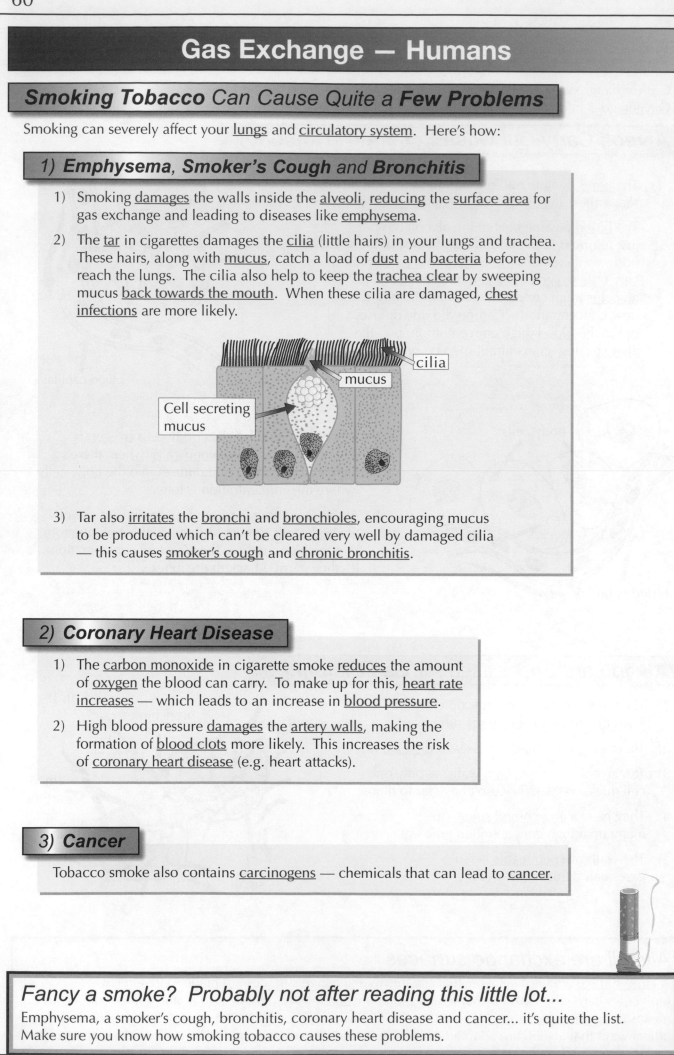

cilia

mucus

Cell secreting mucus

3) Tar also <u>irritates</u> the <u>bronchi</u> and <u>bronchioles</u>, encouraging mucus to be produced which can't be cleared very well by damaged cilia — this causes <u>smoker's cough</u> and <u>chronic bronchitis</u>.

2) Coronary Heart Disease

1) The <u>carbon monoxide</u> in cigarette smoke <u>reduces</u> the amount of <u>oxygen</u> the blood can carry. To make up for this, <u>heart rate increases</u> — which leads to an increase in <u>blood pressure</u>.

2) High blood pressure <u>damages</u> the <u>artery walls</u>, making the formation of <u>blood clots</u> more likely. This increases the risk of <u>coronary heart disease</u> (e.g. heart attacks).

3) Cancer

Tobacco smoke also contains <u>carcinogens</u> — chemicals that can lead to <u>cancer</u>.

Fancy a smoke? Probably not after reading this little lot...

Emphysema, a smoker's cough, bronchitis, coronary heart disease and cancer... it's quite the list. Make sure you know how smoking tobacco causes these problems.

Warm-Up and Exam Questions

The questions on this page are great practice for the exam. I'd give them a go if I were you...

Warm-Up Questions

1) Where in the thorax are the pleural membranes found?
2) True or False? After air enters the body through the nose and mouth, it passes into the trachea.
3) Which muscles contract to increase the volume of the thorax when breathing in?

Exam Questions

1   Gas exchange in humans occurs in the alveoli.

    a)   Describe and explain the exchange of oxygen between an alveolus and a capillary.

                (3 marks)

    b)   The table below lists some of the features of the alveoli.
           Copy and complete the table by explaining how each feature
           helps to make the alveoli well adapted for gas exchange.

Feature	Explanation
Thin outer walls	
Good blood supply	
Permeable outer walls	

                 (3 marks)

2   Describe an investigation to find the effect of exercise on a person's breathing rate.

                 (6 marks)

3   The graph below shows how the percentage of smokers in the UK aged between 35 and 54 has changed since 1950.

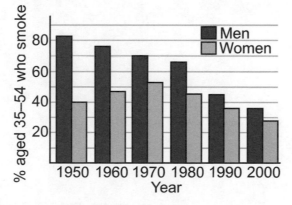

    a)   Describe the main trends shown by the graph.

                 (2 marks)

    b)   Suggest **one** reason for the trend in the number of male smokers.

                 (1 mark)

    c)   Describe and explain **two** ways in which smoking can affect the lungs and circulatory system.

                 (4 marks)

Revision Summary for Section 4

Well that's another section you've got through, nice work. Take a deep breath and have a stretch...
I bet you thought about what's going on in your lungs then, didn't you? Well whilst you're at it, have
a gaze out of the window and have a think about all those plants working their roots off to pump out
oxygen... I'll stop there before I get carried away...

1) Explain what respiration is in a sentence.
2) What is aerobic respiration? Give the word and symbol equations for it.
3) What is anaerobic respiration?
4) What are two drawbacks of anaerobic respiration compared to aerobic respiration?
5) Give the word equations for anaerobic respiration in plants.
6) Name an indicator solution that can be used to detect carbon dioxide.
7) Describe an experiment to detect CO_2 production from respiration.
8) Name the process by which plants exchange gases.
9) Why do plants need to exchange gases with their surroundings?
10) a) At night, there's a lot of O_2 inside the leaf and not a lot of CO_2. True or false?
    b) Explain your answer to part a).
11) Describe an experiment you could use to show the effect of light on gas exchange in leaves.
    What would you use as a control?
12) Name the key structures of the thorax.
13) What happens to the intercostal muscles and diaphragm when you breathe in?
14) What happens to the intercostal muscles and diaphragm when you breathe out?
15) Explain why exercise increases your breathing rate.
16) Describe the path the air takes from when it is inhaled through
    the nose and mouth to when it reaches the alveoli.
17) Describe the gas exchange that happens between the alveoli and the blood.
18) Give four ways that the alveoli's structure is ideal for gas exchange.
19) How does smoking contribute to coronary heart disease?
20) Name two other diseases linked to smoking tobacco.

Functions of the Blood

All multicellular organisms need a transport system (see page 41) and in humans, it's the blood.

Blood has Four Main Components

They are:

PLASMA	PLATELETS	RED BLOOD CELLS	WHITE BLOOD CELLS

Plasma is the Liquid Bit of Blood

It's basically blood minus the blood cells (see below and on the next page). Plasma is a pale yellow liquid which carries just about everything that needs transporting around your body:

1) Red and white blood cells and platelets.

2) Digested food products (like glucose and amino acids) from the gut to all the body cells.

3) Carbon dioxide from the body cells to the lungs.

4) Urea from the liver to the kidneys (where it's removed in the urine, see p.72-73).

5) Hormones, which act as chemical messengers (see page 84).

6) Heat energy.

Platelets are Small Fragments of Cells that Help Blood Clot

Paper 2

1) When you damage a blood vessel, platelets clump together to 'plug' the damaged area.

2) This is known as blood clotting. Blood clots stop you losing too much blood and prevent microorganisms from entering the wound.

3) In a clot, platelets are held together by a mesh of a protein called fibrin (though this process also needs other proteins called clotting factors to work properly).

Paper 2

Red Blood Cells Have the Job of Carrying Oxygen

They transport oxygen from the lungs to all the cells in the body.
A red blood cell is well adapted to its function:

1) Red blood cells are small and have a biconcave shape (which is a posh way of saying they look a little bit like doughnuts, see diagram below) to give a large surface area for absorbing and releasing oxygen.

2) They contain haemoglobin, which is what gives blood its colour — it contains a lot of iron. In the lungs, haemoglobin reacts with oxygen to become oxyhaemoglobin. In body tissues the reverse reaction happens to release oxygen to the cells.

3) Red blood cells don't have a nucleus — this frees up space for more haemoglobin, so they can carry more oxygen.

White Blood Cells and Immunity

Your body is <u>constantly</u> fighting off attack from all sorts of <u>nasties</u> — yep, things really are out to get you.

Your **Immune System** Deals with **Pathogens**

1) <u>Pathogens</u> are microorganisms that <u>cause disease</u>, e.g. certain types of bacteria and viruses (see p.5).

2) Once pathogens have entered your body they'll reproduce rapidly unless they're <u>destroyed</u>. That's the job of your <u>immune system</u>, and <u>white blood cells</u> are the <u>most important part</u> of it.

3) There are two different types of white blood cell you need to know about: <u>phagocytes</u> and <u>lymphocytes</u>.

Phagocytes Ingest **Pathogens**

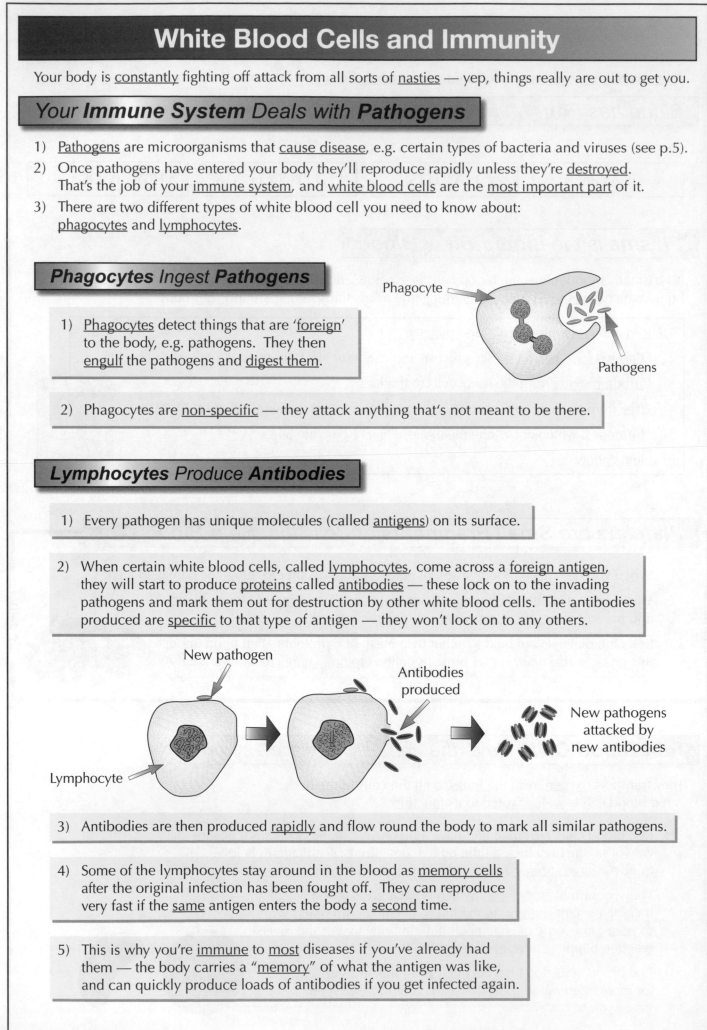

1) <u>Phagocytes</u> detect things that are '<u>foreign</u>' to the body, e.g. pathogens. They then <u>engulf</u> the pathogens and <u>digest them</u>.

Phagocyte

Pathogens

2) Phagocytes are <u>non-specific</u> — they attack anything that's not meant to be there.

Lymphocytes Produce **Antibodies**

1) Every pathogen has unique molecules (called <u>antigens</u>) on its surface.

2) When certain white blood cells, called <u>lymphocytes</u>, come across a <u>foreign antigen</u>, they will start to produce <u>proteins</u> called <u>antibodies</u> — these lock on to the invading pathogens and mark them out for destruction by other white blood cells. The antibodies produced are <u>specific</u> to that type of antigen — they won't lock on to any others.

New pathogen

Antibodies produced

New pathogens attacked by new antibodies

Lymphocyte

3) Antibodies are then produced <u>rapidly</u> and flow round the body to mark all similar pathogens.

4) Some of the lymphocytes stay around in the blood as <u>memory cells</u> after the original infection has been fought off. They can reproduce very fast if the <u>same</u> antigen enters the body a <u>second</u> time.

5) This is why you're <u>immune</u> to <u>most</u> diseases if you've already had them — the body carries a "<u>memory</u>" of what the antigen was like, and can quickly produce loads of antibodies if you get infected again.

Vaccinations and Immunity

Vaccinations have changed the way we fight disease. We don't always have to deal with the problem once it's happened — we can prevent it happening in the first place.

Vaccination — Protects from Future Infections

1) When you're infected with a new pathogen it can take your lymphocytes a while to produce the antibodies to deal with it. In that time you can get very ill, or maybe even die.

2) To avoid this you can be vaccinated against some diseases, e.g. polio or measles.

3) Vaccination involves injecting dead or inactive pathogens into the body. These carry antigens, so even though they're harmless they still trigger an immune response — your lymphocytes produce antibodies to attack them.

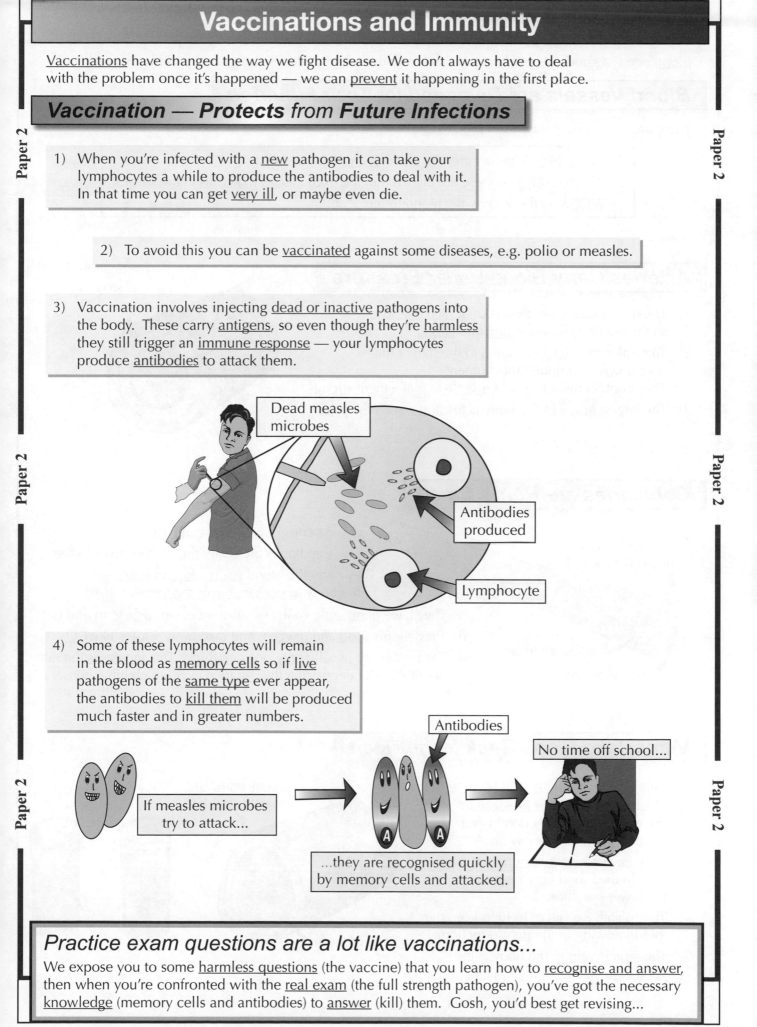

Dead measles microbes

Antibodies produced

Lymphocyte

4) Some of these lymphocytes will remain in the blood as memory cells so if live pathogens of the same type ever appear, the antibodies to kill them will be produced much faster and in greater numbers.

Antibodies

No time off school...

If measles microbes try to attack...

...they are recognised quickly by memory cells and attacked.

Practice exam questions are a lot like vaccinations...

We expose you to some harmless questions (the vaccine) that you learn how to recognise and answer, then when you're confronted with the real exam (the full strength pathogen), you've got the necessary knowledge (memory cells and antibodies) to answer (kill) them. Gosh, you'd best get revising...

Blood Vessels

Blood needs a good set of 'tubes' to carry it round the body. Here's a page on the different types:

Blood Vessels are Designed for Their Function

There are three different types of blood vessel:

1) ARTERIES — these carry the blood away from the heart.
2) CAPILLARIES — these are involved in the exchange of materials at the tissues.
3) VEINS — these carry the blood to the heart.

Arteries Carry Blood Under Pressure

1) The heart pumps the blood out at high pressure so the artery walls are strong and elastic.

2) The walls are thick compared to the size of the hole down the middle (the "lumen"). They contain thick layers of muscle to make them strong.

3) The largest artery in the body is the aorta (see next page).

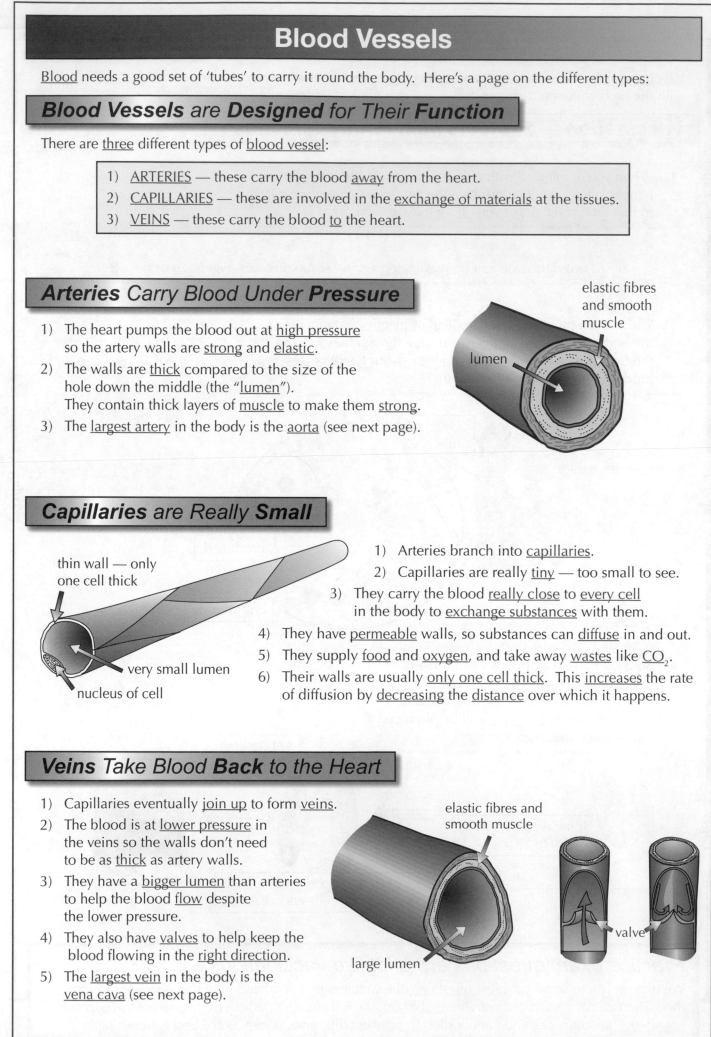

elastic fibres and smooth muscle

lumen

Capillaries are Really Small

thin wall — only one cell thick

very small lumen

nucleus of cell

1) Arteries branch into capillaries.

2) Capillaries are really tiny — too small to see.

3) They carry the blood really close to every cell in the body to exchange substances with them.

4) They have permeable walls, so substances can diffuse in and out.

5) They supply food and oxygen, and take away wastes like CO_2.

6) Their walls are usually only one cell thick. This increases the rate of diffusion by decreasing the distance over which it happens.

Veins Take Blood Back to the Heart

1) Capillaries eventually join up to form veins.

2) The blood is at lower pressure in the veins so the walls don't need to be as thick as artery walls.

3) They have a bigger lumen than arteries to help the blood flow despite the lower pressure.

4) They also have valves to help keep the blood flowing in the right direction.

5) The largest vein in the body is the vena cava (see next page).

elastic fibres and smooth muscle

large lumen

valve

The Heart

Blood doesn't just move around the body <u>on its own</u>, of course. It needs a <u>pump</u>.

Learn This Diagram of the Heart with All Its Labels

1) The <u>right atrium</u> of the heart receives <u>deoxygenated</u> blood from the <u>body</u> (through the <u>vena cava</u>).
   (The plural of atrium is atria.)

2) The deoxygenated blood moves through to the <u>right ventricle</u>, which pumps it to the <u>lungs</u> (via the <u>pulmonary artery</u>).

3) The <u>left atrium</u> receives <u>oxygenated</u> blood from the <u>lungs</u> (through the <u>pulmonary vein</u>).

4) The oxygenated blood then moves through to the <u>left ventricle</u>, which pumps it out round the <u>whole body</u> (via the <u>aorta</u>).

5) The <u>left</u> ventricle has a much <u>thicker wall</u> than the <u>right</u> ventricle. It needs more <u>muscle</u> because it has to pump blood around the <u>whole body</u>, whereas the right ventricle only has to pump it to the <u>lungs</u>. This also means that the blood in the left ventricle is under <u>higher pressure</u> than the blood in the right ventricle.

6) The <u>valves</u> prevent the <u>backflow</u> of blood.

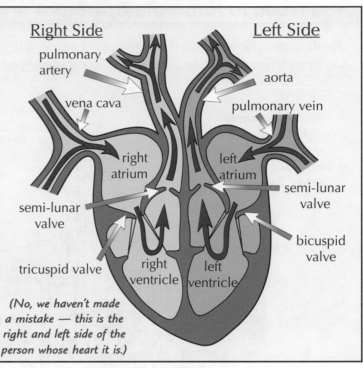

Right Side — Left Side

pulmonary artery
aorta
vena cava
pulmonary vein
right atrium
left atrium
semi-lunar valve
semi-lunar valve
bicuspid valve
tricuspid valve
right ventricle
left ventricle

(No, we haven't made a mistake — this is the right and left side of the person whose heart it is.)

Exercise Increases Heart Rate

1) When you <u>exercise</u>, your muscles need <u>more energy</u>, so you <u>respire more</u>.

2) You need to get <u>more oxygen</u> into the cells and <u>remove</u> more <u>carbon dioxide</u>. For this to happen the blood has to flow faster, so your <u>heart rate increases</u>. Here's how:

There's more on respiration on pages 49 - 50.

- Exercise <u>increases</u> the amount of <u>carbon dioxide</u> in the <u>blood</u>.
- High levels of blood CO_2 are detected by <u>receptors</u> in the <u>aorta</u> and <u>carotid artery</u> (an artery in the neck).
- These receptors <u>send signals</u> to the <u>brain</u>.
- The brain sends signals to the <u>heart</u>, causing it to contract <u>more frequently</u> and with <u>more force</u>.

The Hormonal System Also Helps to Control Heart Rate

1) When an organism is <u>threatened</u> (e.g. by a predator) the <u>adrenal glands</u> release <u>adrenaline</u>.

2) Adrenaline <u>binds</u> to <u>specific receptors</u> in the <u>heart</u>. This causes the cardiac muscle to <u>contract more frequently</u> and with <u>more force</u>, so <u>heart rate increases</u> and the heart <u>pumps more blood</u>.

3) This <u>increases oxygen supply</u> to the <u>tissues</u>, getting the body <u>ready for action</u>.

The Circulation System

The <u>circulation system</u> is made up of the <u>heart</u> (see previous page) and the <u>blood vessels</u>.
It's responsible for getting the <u>blood</u> to where it needs to be, so that useful substances (e.g. <u>glucose</u>
and <u>oxygen</u>) can be delivered and wastes removed.

You Need to Know the Structure of the Circulation System

The diagram below shows the <u>human circulation system</u>.
You need to <u>learn the names</u> of all the <u>blood vessels</u> on it for the exam.

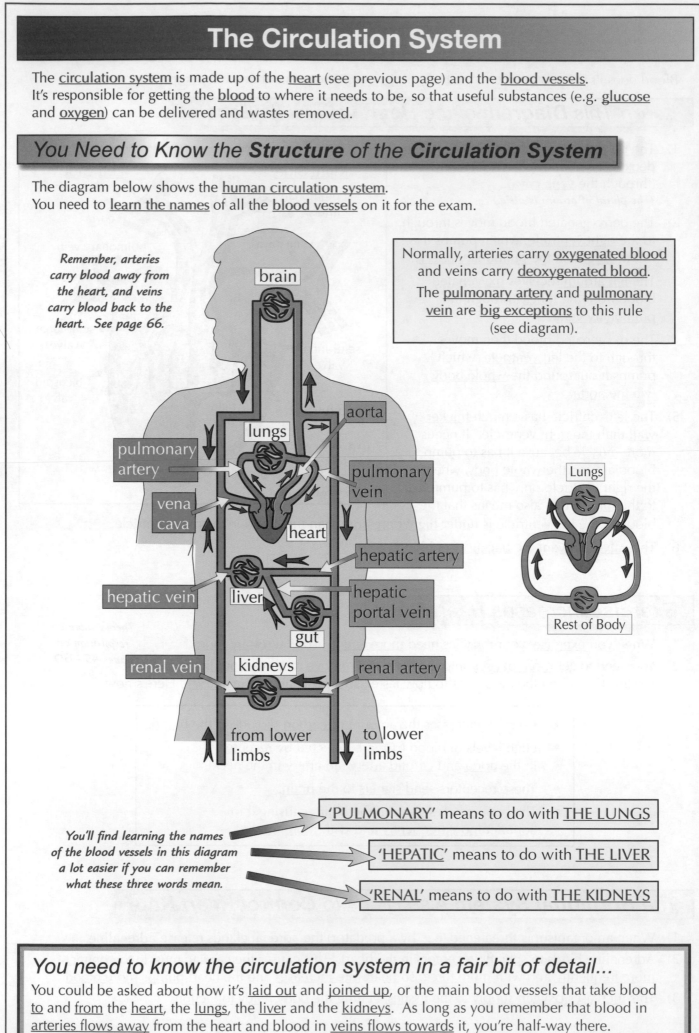

Remember, arteries carry blood away from the heart, and veins carry blood back to the heart. See page 66.

Normally, arteries carry <u>oxygenated blood</u> and veins carry <u>deoxygenated blood</u>.
The <u>pulmonary artery</u> and <u>pulmonary vein</u> are <u>big exceptions</u> to this rule (see diagram).

brain

aorta

lungs

pulmonary artery

pulmonary vein

vena cava

heart

hepatic artery

hepatic vein

liver

hepatic portal vein

gut

renal vein

kidneys

renal artery

from lower limbs

to lower limbs

Lungs

Rest of Body

You'll find learning the names of the blood vessels in this diagram a lot easier if you can remember what these three words mean.

'PULMONARY' means to do with <u>THE LUNGS</u>

'HEPATIC' means to do with <u>THE LIVER</u>

'RENAL' means to do with <u>THE KIDNEYS</u>

You need to know the circulation system in a fair bit of detail...

You could be asked about how it's <u>laid out</u> and <u>joined up</u>, or the main blood vessels that take blood
<u>to</u> and <u>from</u> the <u>heart</u>, the <u>lungs</u>, the <u>liver</u> and the <u>kidneys</u>. As long as you remember that blood in
<u>arteries flows away</u> from the heart and blood in <u>veins flows towards</u> it, you're half-way there.

Warm-Up and Exam Questions

There are some nice diagrams to learn on the previous few pages. If you don't bother, you'll feel pretty silly if you turn over the exam paper and the first question asks you to label a diagram of the heart. Just saying... Anyway, let's see if these questions get your blood pumping...

Warm-Up Questions

1) Name the three main components of the blood that are carried by the plasma.
2) What are the unique molecules found on the surface of pathogens called?
3) Name two gases that diffuse through capillary walls.
4) Name the heart valve found between the left atrium and the left ventricle.

Exam Questions

1 The diagram to the right shows the circulation system with some structures labelled A to H.

Match each of the structures in the box below with the correct letter on the diagram.

> pulmonary artery
>
> hepatic artery
>
> vena cava
>
> kidneys
>
> aorta
>
> hepatic portal vein

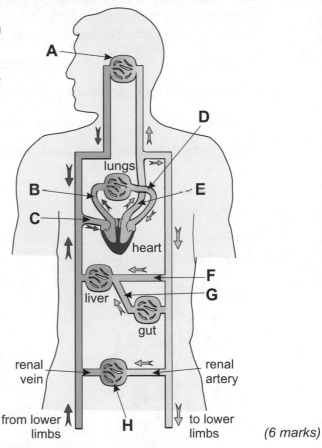

(6 marks)

2 The cell shown below transports oxygen around the body.

View from above

Cut through view

a) Explain how this cell's shape is adapted for transporting oxygen.

(2 marks)

b) Describe and explain **one** other way in which this cell is adapted for carrying oxygen.

(2 marks)

Exam Questions

3   A dog barks at a cat, causing the cat's heart rate to increase
    from 145 beats per minute to 170 beats per minute.

    a)   Explain the process which caused the cat's heart rate to increase.

                                                                              (3 marks)

    b)   Suggest how an increased heart rate prepares the cat for action.

                                                                              (1 mark)

4   White blood cells defend the body against pathogens.

    a)   White blood cells are part of which system of the body? Choose from the following:

             digestive   central nervous   immune   respiratory
              system   system   system   system

                                                                              (1 mark)

    b)   *Campylobacter* is a genus of bacteria that can cause food poisoning.
         Copy and complete the passage by writing a suitable word in each space.

         > When *Campylobacter* bacteria enter the body, non-specific white blood cells
         >
         > called .... recognise the bacteria as foreign to the body.
         >
         > They engulf them and then .... them. Other white blood cells,
         >
         > called .... produce proteins called .... that
         >
         > lock onto the bacteria and mark them out for destruction.

                                                                              (4 marks)

5   The diagram shows the human heart and four blood vessels, as seen from the front.
    The left ventricle has been labelled.

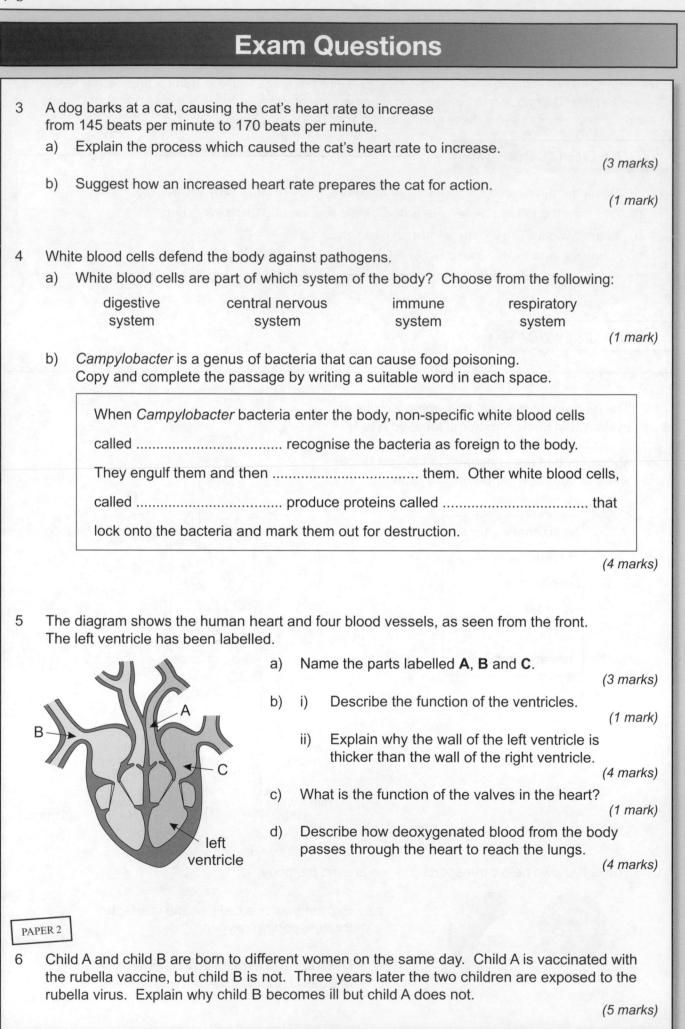

left
ventricle

    a)   Name the parts labelled **A**, **B** and **C**.

                                                                              (3 marks)

    b)   i)   Describe the function of the ventricles.

                                                                              (1 mark)

         ii) Explain why the wall of the left ventricle is
              thicker than the wall of the right ventricle.

                                                                              (4 marks)

    c)   What is the function of the valves in the heart?

                                                                              (1 mark)

    d)   Describe how deoxygenated blood from the body
         passes through the heart to reach the lungs.

                                                                              (4 marks)

PAPER 2

6   Child A and child B are born to different women on the same day. Child A is vaccinated with
    the rubella vaccine, but child B is not. Three years later the two children are exposed to the
    rubella virus. Explain why child B becomes ill but child A does not.

                                                                              (5 marks)

Exam Questions

7   Gareth did an experiment to compare the elasticity of arteries and veins. He dissected out an artery and a vein from a piece of fresh meat. He then took a 5 cm length of each vessel, hung different masses on it, and measured how much it stretched.
His results are shown in the table.

a)   Describe the roles of arteries and veins.

(2 marks)

b)   Suggest **one** way in which Gareth could tell which was the artery and which was the vein when he was dissecting the meat.

(1 mark)

c)   Which vessel stretched more easily? Explain why this was.

(1 mark)

Mass added (g)	Length of blood vessel (mm)	
	Artery	Vein
0	50	50
5	51	53
10	53	56
15	55	59
20	56	-

PAPER 2

8   Bernard-Soulier syndrome is a condition in which the blood fails to clot properly.

a)   Suggest which component of the blood is affected by Bernard-Soulier syndrome.

(1 mark)

b)   Explain why a normally minor injury such as a paper cut could be more serious for a person with Bernard-Soulier syndrome.

(3 marks)

9   Roy conducted an experiment to find out which of his friends has the shortest 'recovery time'. Recovery time is how long it takes the heart rate to return to normal after exercise.
In separate tests, Roy measured the heart rate of three friends by taking their pulses.
He then asked them to run for 2 minutes, after which he measured their heart rate at 15 second intervals until it returned to normal. His results are shown below.

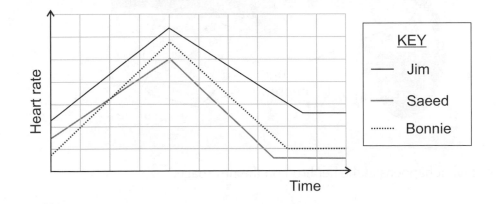

a)   Which of Roy's friends had the shortest recovery time?

(1 mark)

b)   The heart rate increases during exercise so that more oxygen is transported around the body. Suggest why the body requires more oxygen during exercise.

(2 marks)

Excretion — The Kidneys

Excretion (the removal of waste products) is carried out by the skin, the lungs and the kidneys.

The Kidneys are Excretion Organs

The kidneys are part of the urinary system.
They perform three main roles:

1) Removal of urea from the blood.
   Urea is produced in the liver
   from excess amino acids.

2) Adjustment of salt levels in the blood.

3) Adjustment of water content of the blood.

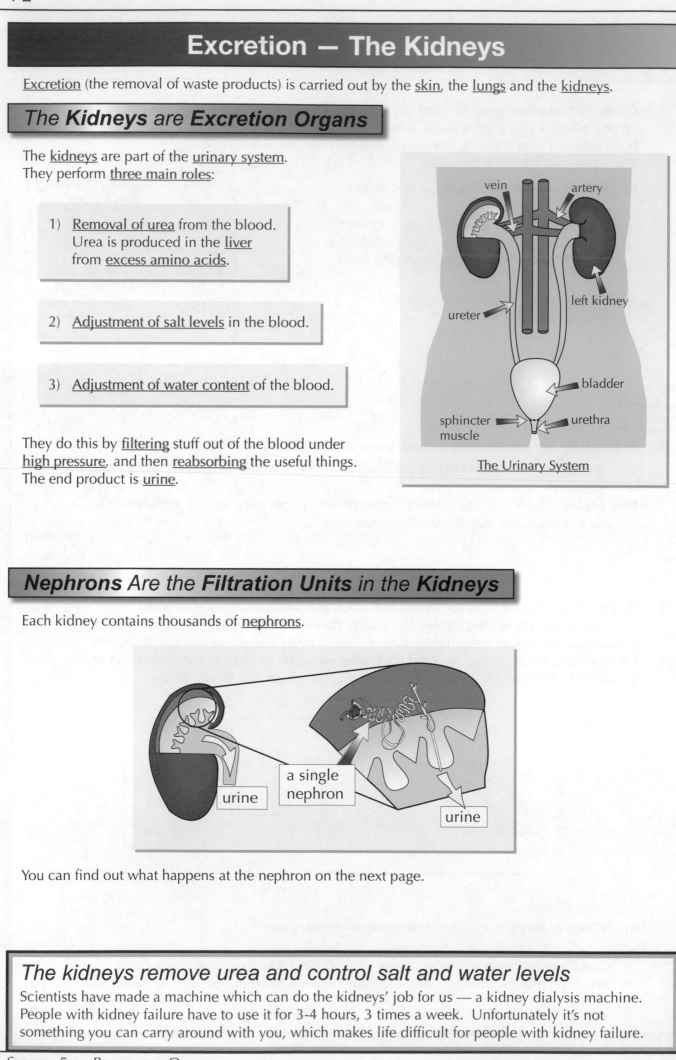

The Urinary System

They do this by filtering stuff out of the blood under
high pressure, and then reabsorbing the useful things.
The end product is urine.

Nephrons Are the Filtration Units in the Kidneys

Each kidney contains thousands of nephrons.

urine

a single nephron

urine

You can find out what happens at the nephron on the next page.

The kidneys remove urea and control salt and water levels

Scientists have made a machine which can do the kidneys' job for us — a kidney dialysis machine.
People with kidney failure have to use it for 3-4 hours, 3 times a week. Unfortunately it's not
something you can carry around with you, which makes life difficult for people with kidney failure.

Excretion — The Kidneys

Here's what happens as <u>blood</u> passes through the <u>nephron</u>...

1) Ultrafiltration:

1) Blood from the <u>renal artery</u> flows through the <u>glomerulus</u> — a bundle of capillaries at the start of the nephron (see diagram).

2) A <u>high pressure</u> is built up which squeezes <u>water</u>, <u>urea</u>, <u>salts</u> and <u>glucose</u> out of the blood and into the <u>Bowman's capsule</u>.

3) The membranes between the blood vessels in the glomerulus and the Bowman's capsule act like <u>filters</u>, so <u>big</u> molecules like <u>proteins</u> and <u>blood cells</u> are <u>not</u> squeezed out. They stay in the blood. The <u>filtered liquid</u> in the Bowman's capsule is known as the <u>glomerular filtrate</u>.

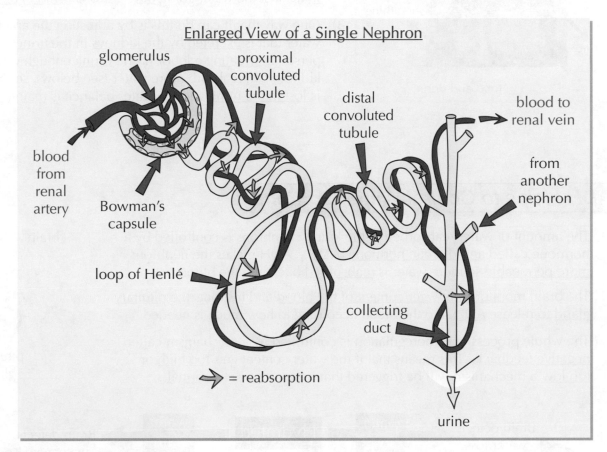

Enlarged View of a Single Nephron

2) Reabsorption:

As the filtrate flows along the nephron, <u>useful</u> substances are <u>selectively reabsorbed</u> back into the blood:

1) <u>All</u> the <u>glucose</u> is reabsorbed from the <u>proximal convoluted tubule</u>. This involves the process of <u>active transport</u> (see p.16) against the concentration gradient.

2) <u>Sufficient salt</u> is reabsorbed. Excess salt isn't.

3) <u>Sufficient water</u> is reabsorbed from the <u>collecting duct</u> into the bloodstream.

It's called selective reabsorption because only some substances are reabsorbed.

3) Release of wastes:

The remaining substances (including <u>water</u>, <u>salts</u> and <u>urea</u>) form <u>urine</u>. This continues out of the <u>nephron</u>, through the ureter and down to the <u>bladder</u>, where it is stored before being released via the <u>urethra</u>.

Osmoregulation — The Kidneys

The kidneys are <u>really important</u> organs. Not only do they filter the blood (see previous page), they also play a key role in controlling the amount of water inside your body. Whether you're interested in it or not, I'm afraid <u>you need to know this page</u> for your exam — so <u>pay attention</u>.

The Kidneys Also Adjust the Body's Water Content

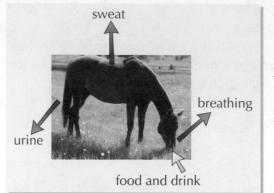

sweat

breathing

urine

food and drink

1) Water is taken into the body as <u>food and drink</u> and is <u>lost</u> from the body in <u>three main ways</u>: sweating, breathing and weeing (see page 86).

2) The body has to <u>constantly balance</u> the water coming <u>in</u> against the water going <u>out</u> — this is <u>osmoregulation</u>.

3) One way that it can do this is by adjusting the amount of water that is <u>excreted by the kidneys</u> in the <u>urine</u>. E.g. if a person is <u>sweating</u> a lot or hasn't <u>drunk</u> enough water, the kidneys can reabsorb more water (see below), so that less is <u>lost in the urine</u> and the water balance is <u>maintained</u>.

ADH Helps to Control Water Content

1) The amount of water reabsorbed in the kidney nephrons is <u>controlled</u> by a hormone called <u>anti-diuretic hormone</u> (ADH). ADH makes the nephrons <u>more permeable</u> so more water is <u>reabsorbed</u> back into the blood.

2) The brain <u>monitors the water content of the blood</u> and instructs the <u>pituitary gland</u> to release <u>ADH</u> into the blood according to how much is needed.

3) The whole process of osmoregulation is controlled by a mechanism called <u>negative feedback</u>. This means that if the water content gets <u>too high</u> or <u>too low</u> a mechanism will be triggered that brings it back to <u>normal</u>.

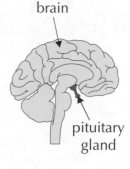

brain

pituitary gland

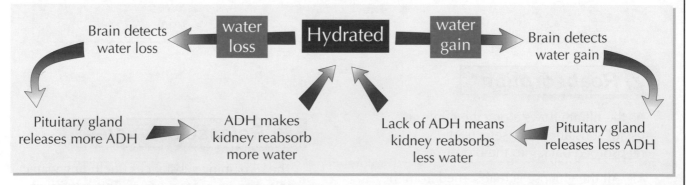

Brain detects water loss

water loss

Hydrated

water gain

Brain detects water gain

Pituitary gland releases more ADH

ADH makes kidney reabsorb more water

Lack of ADH means kidney reabsorbs less water

Pituitary gland releases less ADH

Don't try to kid-me that you know it all — learn it properly...

So the kidneys make sure you don't end up like a dry sponge or a massive water balloon — thank goodness. Make sure you remember which way round ADH works. Basically, low blood water content means increased ADH production and more water reabsorbed in the kidneys. High blood water content means decreased ADH production and less water reabsorbed. What could be simpler...

Warm-Up and Exam Questions

Reckon you know your distal convoluted tubule from your loop of Henlé? Let's see shall we...

Warm-Up Questions

1) Where is urea produced?
2) Is blood entering the glomerulus under high pressure or low pressure?
3) Where is urine stored before being released from the body?

Exam Questions

1   The diagram below shows a single nephron.

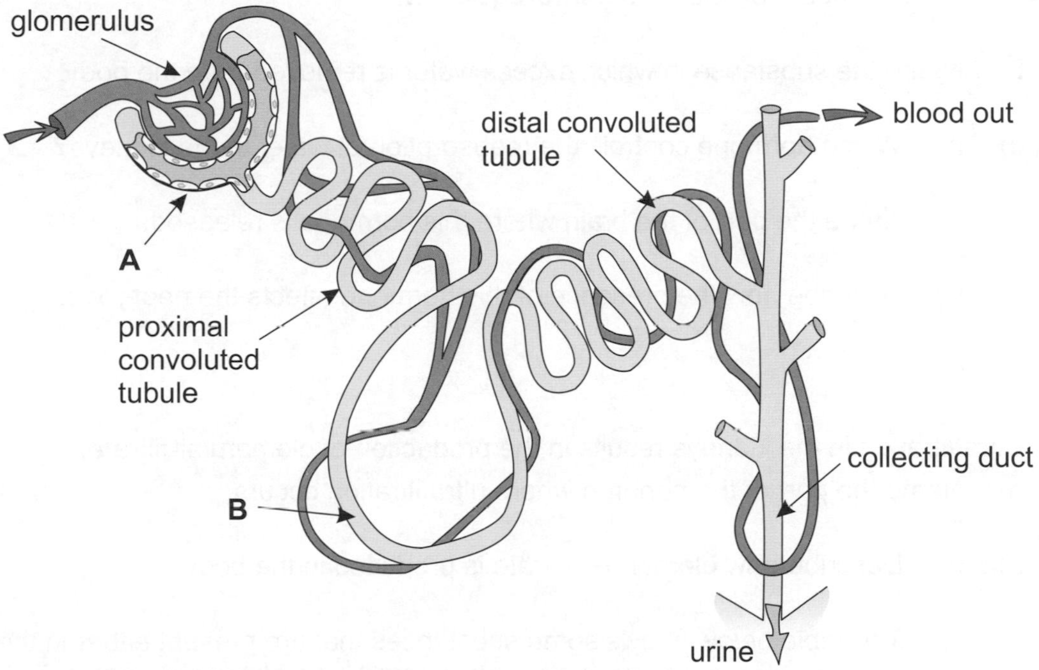

a)   Name the structures labelled **A** and **B** on the diagram.

(2 marks)

b)   Copy and complete the following passage by writing a suitable word or words in the gaps.

> As the glomerular filtrate passes along the nephron, useful substances are taken
> back into the blood in a process known as .... reabsorption.
> Glucose is reabsorbed back into the blood from the ....
> .... is reabsorbed from the collecting duct.

(3 marks)

c)   After passing through the collecting duct, any waste substances that are left are released in the form of urine. Name **two** substances that are found in urine.

(2 marks)

Exam Questions

2 The kidneys are excretion organs which make up part of the urinary system.

   a) Name the parts labelled **A**, **B** and **C** on the diagram on the right.

   (3 marks)

   b) Name one other organ of the human body that's involved in the excretion of waste substances.

   (1 mark)

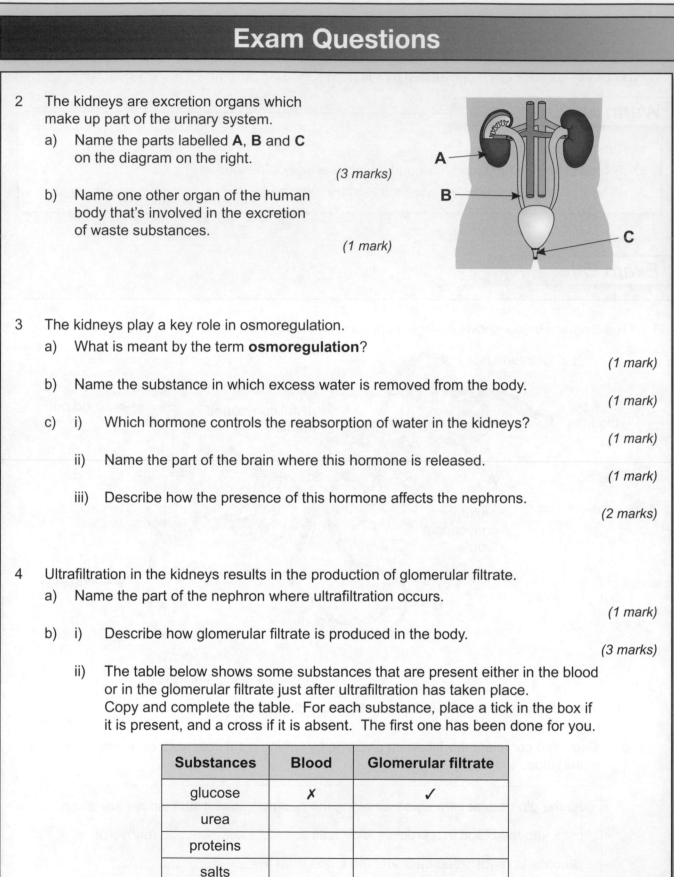

3 The kidneys play a key role in osmoregulation.

   a) What is meant by the term **osmoregulation**?

   (1 mark)

   b) Name the substance in which excess water is removed from the body.

   (1 mark)

   c) i) Which hormone controls the reabsorption of water in the kidneys?

   (1 mark)

   ii) Name the part of the brain where this hormone is released.

   (1 mark)

   iii) Describe how the presence of this hormone affects the nephrons.

   (2 marks)

4 Ultrafiltration in the kidneys results in the production of glomerular filtrate.

   a) Name the part of the nephron where ultrafiltration occurs.

   (1 mark)

   b) i) Describe how glomerular filtrate is produced in the body.

   (3 marks)

   ii) The table below shows some substances that are present either in the blood or in the glomerular filtrate just after ultrafiltration has taken place. Copy and complete the table. For each substance, place a tick in the box if it is present, and a cross if it is absent. The first one has been done for you.

Substances	Blood	Glomerular filtrate
glucose	✗	✓
urea		
proteins		
salts		

   (3 marks)

5 Sian went for a 10 mile run on a warm day. When she got home she noticed that her urine was darker in colour than normal. Explain why she produced darker coloured urine.

   (5 marks)

Revision Summary for Section 5

This revision summary should be able to give you an idea of which pages you understand and which ones you're finding a bit trickier. If you get stuck, have another read through the section.

1) What are the four main components of blood?

2) Name six things that blood plasma transports around the body.

3) What are platelets? What role do they play in the body?

4) Explain how red blood cells are adapted to their function.

5) How do phagocytes defend the body from pathogens?

6) How do lymphocytes defend the body from pathogens?

7) Explain the role of memory cells in the immune system's response against pathogens.

8) Explain how vaccination stops you getting infections.

9) Why do arteries need very muscular, elastic walls?

10) Explain how capillaries are adapted to their function.

11)*The diagram below shows cross sections through an artery, a capillary and a vein.
    Which one is the vein? How can you tell?

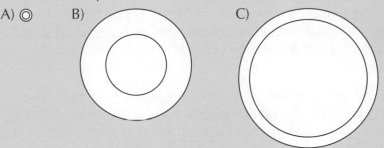

A) ◎   B)   C)

DRAWN TO SCALE (sort of)

12) Draw and label a simple diagram of the heart.

13) Name the blood vessel that joins to the right ventricle of the heart. Where does it take the blood?

14) How does heart rate change during exercise? Why?

15) What hormone causes heart rate to rise?

16) What are the names of the main blood vessels that carry blood to and from the kidneys?

17) What is the name of the blood vessel that carries blood away from the liver?

18) What are the names of the two main blood vessels associated with the lungs?

19) Draw and label a diagram of the urinary system.

20) Describe the process of ultrafiltration.

21) What happens in the collecting duct of a nephron?

22) Describe the path taken by urine once it leaves the nephron.

*Answer on page 207

The Nervous System and Responding to Stimuli

Right, it's time to get your brain cells fired up and take a hit of adrenaline — this section's a corker.

Responding to their Environment Helps Organisms Survive

1) Animals increase their chances of survival by responding to changes in their external environment, e.g. by avoiding places that are too hot or too cold.

2) They also respond to changes in their internal environment to make sure that the conditions are always right for their metabolism (all the chemical reactions that go on inside them).

3) Plants also increase their chances of survival by responding to changes in their environment (see pages 88-89).

4) Any change in the internal or external environment is called a STIMULUS.

The plural of 'stimulus' is 'stimuli'.

Receptors Detect Stimuli and Effectors Produce a Response

1) RECEPTORS detect stimuli. Receptors in the SENSE ORGANS (the eyes, ears, nose, tongue and skin) are groups of cells that detect external stimuli. E.g. rod and cone cells in the eye detect changes in light (see page 80).

2) EFFECTORS are cells that bring about a response to stimuli. They include muscle cells and cells found in glands, e.g. the pancreas. Effectors respond in different ways — muscle cells contract, whereas glands secrete hormones.

3) Receptors communicate with effectors via the nervous system (see below), the hormonal system (see page 84) or sometimes both.

The Central Nervous System (CNS) Coordinates Information

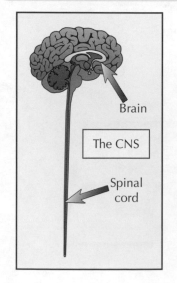

Brain

The CNS

Spinal cord

1) The nervous system is made up of all the neurones (nerve cells) in your body. There are three main types of neurone — sensory neurones, relay neurones and motor neurones.

2) The CENTRAL NERVOUS SYSTEM (CNS) consists of the brain and spinal cord only.

3) When receptors in a sense organ detect a stimulus, they send electrical impulses along sensory neurones to the CNS.

4) The CNS then sends electrical impulses to an effector along a motor neurone. The effector then responds accordingly.

5) The job of the CNS is to COORDINATE the response. Coordinated responses always need a stimulus, a receptor and an effector.

6) Because neurones transmit information using high speed electrical impulses, the nervous system is able to bring about very rapid responses.

Reflexes

Your brain can <u>decide</u> how to respond to a stimulus <u>pretty quickly</u>. But sometimes waiting for your brain to make a decision is just <u>too slow</u>. That's why you have <u>reflexes</u>.

Reflexes Help Prevent Injury

1) <u>Reflexes</u> are <u>automatic</u> responses to certain stimuli — they can reduce the chances of being injured.

2) For example, if someone shines a <u>bright light</u> in your eyes, your <u>pupils</u> automatically get smaller so that less light gets into the eye — this stops it getting <u>damaged</u> (see next page).

3) Or if you get a shock, your body releases the <u>hormone</u> adrenaline automatically — it doesn't wait for you to <u>decide</u> that you're shocked.

4) The route taken by the information in a reflex (from receptor to effector) is called a <u>reflex arc</u>.

The Reflex Arc Goes Through the Central Nervous System

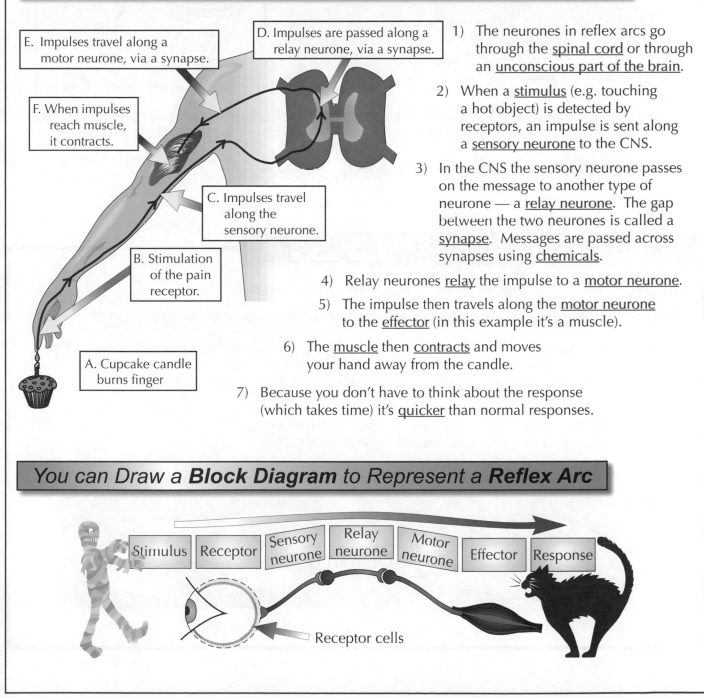

E. Impulses travel along a motor neurone, via a synapse.

D. Impulses are passed along a relay neurone, via a synapse.

F. When impulses reach muscle, it contracts.

C. Impulses travel along the sensory neurone.

B. Stimulation of the pain receptor.

A. Cupcake candle burns finger

1) The neurones in reflex arcs go through the <u>spinal cord</u> or through an <u>unconscious part of the brain</u>.

2) When a <u>stimulus</u> (e.g. touching a hot object) is detected by receptors, an impulse is sent along a <u>sensory neurone</u> to the CNS.

3) In the CNS the sensory neurone passes on the message to another type of neurone — a <u>relay neurone</u>. The gap between the two neurones is called a <u>synapse</u>. Messages are passed across synapses using <u>chemicals</u>.

4) Relay neurones <u>relay</u> the impulse to a <u>motor neurone</u>.

5) The impulse then travels along the <u>motor neurone</u> to the <u>effector</u> (in this example it's a muscle).

6) The <u>muscle</u> then <u>contracts</u> and moves your hand away from the candle.

7) Because you don't have to think about the response (which takes time) it's <u>quicker</u> than normal responses.

You can Draw a Block Diagram to Represent a Reflex Arc

Stimulus | Receptor | Sensory neurone | Relay neurone | Motor neurone | Effector | Response

Receptor cells

The Eye

The eye is a good example of a sense organ, and there are several parts you need to learn about.

Learn the Eye with All Its Labels

1) The CONJUNCTIVA lubricates and protects the surface of the eye.

2) The CORNEA refracts (bends) light into the eye. The cornea is transparent and has no blood vessels to supply it with oxygen, so oxygen diffuses in from the outer surface.

3) The IRIS controls the diameter of the PUPIL (the hole in the middle) and therefore how much light enters the eye.

4) The LENS focuses the light onto the RETINA (the light-sensitive part — it's covered in light receptors called rods and cones).

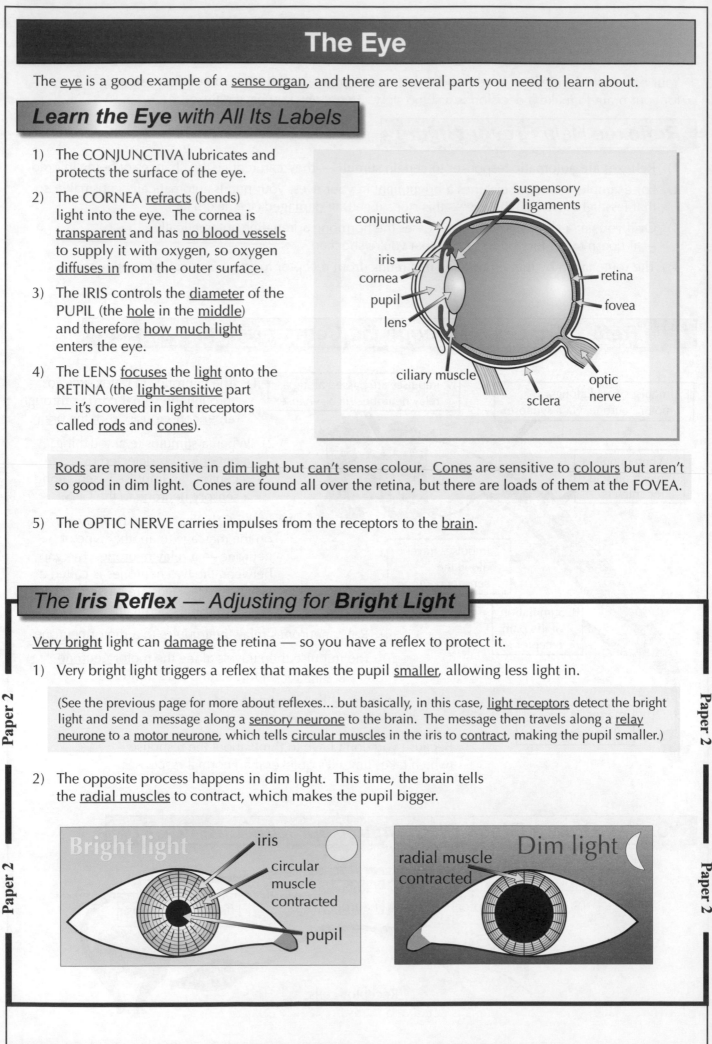

Rods are more sensitive in dim light but can't sense colour. Cones are sensitive to colours but aren't so good in dim light. Cones are found all over the retina, but there are loads of them at the FOVEA.

5) The OPTIC NERVE carries impulses from the receptors to the brain.

The Iris Reflex — Adjusting for Bright Light

Very bright light can damage the retina — so you have a reflex to protect it.

1) Very bright light triggers a reflex that makes the pupil smaller, allowing less light in.

(See the previous page for more about reflexes... but basically, in this case, light receptors detect the bright light and send a message along a sensory neurone to the brain. The message then travels along a relay neurone to a motor neurone, which tells circular muscles in the iris to contract, making the pupil smaller.)

2) The opposite process happens in dim light. This time, the brain tells the radial muscles to contract, which makes the pupil bigger.

The Eye

Another page, another reflex. This one's known as <u>accommodation</u>.

Focusing on Near and Distant Objects — Another **Reflex**

The eye focuses light by <u>changing</u> the <u>shape</u> of the <u>lens</u> — this is known as <u>accommodation</u>.

To Look at **Distant Objects**:

The <u>ciliary muscles relax</u>, which allows the <u>suspensory ligaments</u> to <u>pull tight</u>.
This makes the lens go <u>thin</u> (less curved).

ciliary muscle

suspensory ligaments

To Look at **Near Objects**:

The <u>ciliary muscles contract</u>, which <u>slackens</u> the <u>suspensory ligaments</u>.
The lens becomes <u>fat</u> (more curved).

As you get older, your eye's <u>lens</u> loses <u>flexibility</u>, so it can't easily spring back to a round shape.
This means light can't be <u>focused</u> well for near viewing, so older people often have to use reading glasses.

Long- and **Short-Sightedness** Can Be **Corrected**

1) <u>Long-sighted</u> people are <u>unable to focus</u> on <u>near</u> objects.

2) This occurs when the <u>cornea</u> or <u>lens</u> doesn't <u>bend</u> the light enough or the <u>eyeball</u> is too <u>short</u>.

3) The images of near objects are brought into focus <u>behind</u> the <u>retina</u>.

Uncorrected   Corrected

object   image   lens   image

4) <u>Short-sighted</u> people are <u>unable to focus</u> on <u>distant</u> objects.

5) This occurs when the <u>cornea</u> or <u>lens</u> bends the light <u>too much</u> or the <u>eyeball</u> is too <u>long</u>.

6) The images of distant objects are brought into focus <u>in front</u> of the <u>retina</u>.

Uncorrected   Corrected

image   image

object   object

A thinner (less curved) lens is used to look at distant objects...

...while a fatter (more curved) lens is needed to focus on nearby objects. The ciliary muscles and suspensory ligaments contract and relax to change the shape of the lens. And remember: it's a reflex.

Paper 2

Warm-Up and Exam Questions

Welcome to the first set of questions in this section. I can't guarantee you a laugh per minute, but it's one of the best ways of figuring out just what you know. So it's a case of grin and bear it, I'm afraid...

Warm-Up Questions

1) What are the five sense organs in the human body?
2) Name the two parts of the body which make up the central nervous system.
3) In what form is information transmitted along nerve cells?
4) Why are reflexes useful?
5) Give an example of a reflex.

Exam Questions

1 Animals are able to detect changes in their environment. These changes are known as stimuli.

   a) Suggest why it's important for animals to be able to
      detect changes in their external environment.

      (1 mark)

   b) Cells in the sense organs detect stimuli. What name is given to these cells?

      (1 mark)

   c) Suggest what the **stimulus**, **sense organ** and **effectors** are in this scenario:
      When a hungry animal sees a source of food, it moves towards it.

      (3 marks)

   d) The nervous system coordinates responses to stimuli. Name the other
      communication system in the body that coordinates responses to stimuli.

      (1 mark)

2 Ffion picked up a plate in the kitchen without realising it was hot, then immediately dropped it.
   The diagram below shows the reflex arc for this incident.

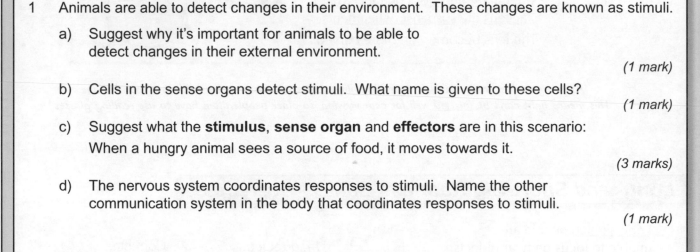

   a) Name the **three** types of neurone labelled **X**, **Y** and **Z**.

      (3 marks)

   b) What name is given to the small gap between neurones, marked **W** on the diagram?

      (1 mark)

   c) State what the effectors are in this reflex arc and describe their response.

      (2 marks)

Exam Questions

3   The diagram below shows a cross section through the eye.

a)   Name the parts labelled **A** and **B**.

(2 marks)

b)   Describe the function of the iris.

(1 mark)

c)   i)   Name the **two** types of light
receptor found on the retina.

(2 marks)

ii)   Name the part of the retina that
has the greatest number of
colour-sensitive light receptors.

(1 mark)

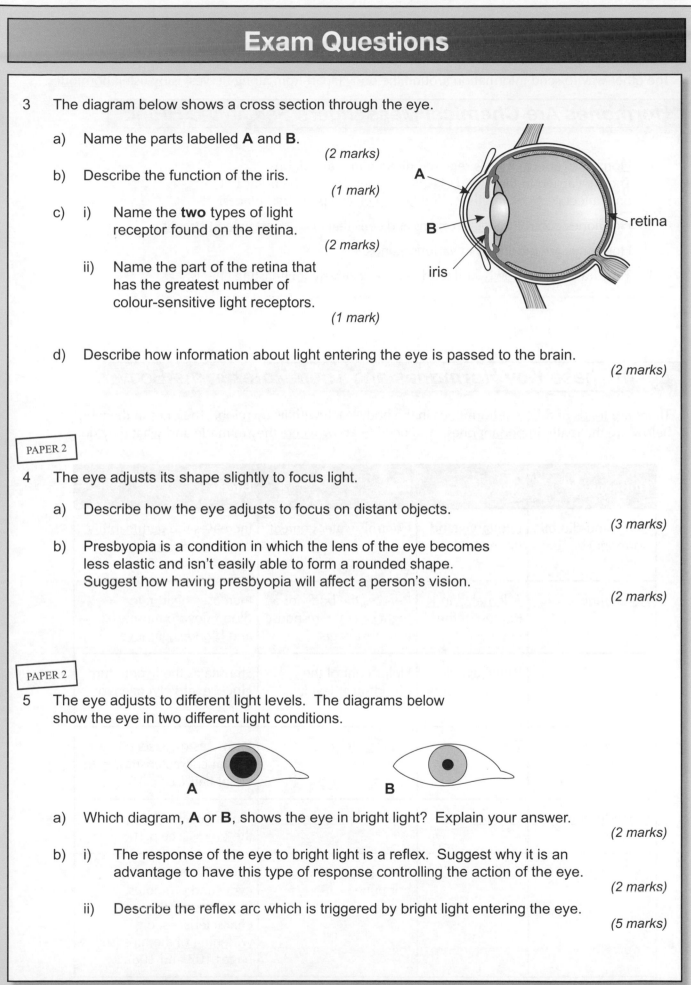

d)   Describe how information about light entering the eye is passed to the brain.

(2 marks)

PAPER 2

4   The eye adjusts its shape slightly to focus light.

a)   Describe how the eye adjusts to focus on distant objects.

(3 marks)

b)   Presbyopia is a condition in which the lens of the eye becomes
less elastic and isn't easily able to form a rounded shape.
Suggest how having presbyopia will affect a person's vision.

(2 marks)

PAPER 2

5   The eye adjusts to different light levels. The diagrams below
show the eye in two different light conditions.

a)   Which diagram, **A** or **B**, shows the eye in bright light? Explain your answer.

(2 marks)

b)   i)   The response of the eye to bright light is a reflex. Suggest why it is an
advantage to have this type of response controlling the action of the eye.

(2 marks)

ii)   Describe the reflex arc which is triggered by bright light entering the eye.

(5 marks)

Hormones

The other way to send information around the body (apart from along nerves) is by using <u>hormones</u>.

Hormones Are Chemical Messengers Sent in the Blood

1) <u>Hormones</u> are <u>chemicals</u> released directly into the <u>blood</u>.
   They're carried in the <u>blood plasma</u> to other parts of the body, but
   only affect particular cells (called <u>target cells</u>) in particular places.

2) Hormones control things in organs and cells that need <u>constant adjustment</u>.

3) Hormones are produced in various <u>glands</u>.

4) They travel quite <u>slowly</u> and tend to have relatively <u>long-lasting</u> effects.

Learn These Key Hormones and Their Roles in the Body

There are <u>loads</u> of <u>different hormones</u> in the body, each with its <u>own job</u>. The ones in the table below are the really <u>important</u> ones. You need to know <u>where</u> they're made and <u>what</u> they do.

Hormone	Source	Role	Effects
<u>ADH</u> (anti-diuretic hormone)	<u>Pituitary gland</u> (in the brain)	Controls <u>water content</u>.	Increases the <u>permeability</u> of the <u>kidney tubules</u> to water (see p.74).
<u>Adrenaline</u>	<u>Adrenal glands</u> (on top of the kidneys)	Readies the body for a '<u>fight or flight</u>' response (see next page).	Increases <u>heart rate</u>, <u>blood flow</u> to muscles and <u>blood sugar level</u>.
<u>Insulin</u>	<u>Pancreas</u>	Helps control the <u>blood sugar level</u>.	Stimulates the <u>liver</u> to turn <u>glucose</u> into <u>glycogen</u> for storage.
<u>Testosterone</u>	<u>Testes</u>	Main <u>male sex hormone</u>.	Promotes <u>male</u> secondary sexual characteristics, e.g. facial hair (see p.107).
<u>Progesterone</u>	<u>Ovaries</u>	Supports <u>pregnancy</u>.	Maintains the <u>lining</u> of the <u>uterus</u> (see p.108).
<u>Oestrogen</u>	<u>Ovaries</u>	Main <u>female sex hormone</u>.	Controls the <u>menstrual cycle</u> and promotes <u>female</u> secondary sexual characteristics, e.g. widening of the hips (see pages 107 and 108).

Hormones and Nerves

Now you know that there are <u>two</u> ways information can be sent round the body — via the <u>nervous</u> or <u>hormonal</u> systems — here's a recap of the differences between them...

Hormones *and* **Nerves** *Do* **Similar Jobs**, *but there are* **Differences**

<u>Hormones</u> and <u>nerves</u> do similar jobs — they both <u>carry information</u> and <u>instructions</u> about the body. But there are some important <u>differences</u> between them that you need to know too:

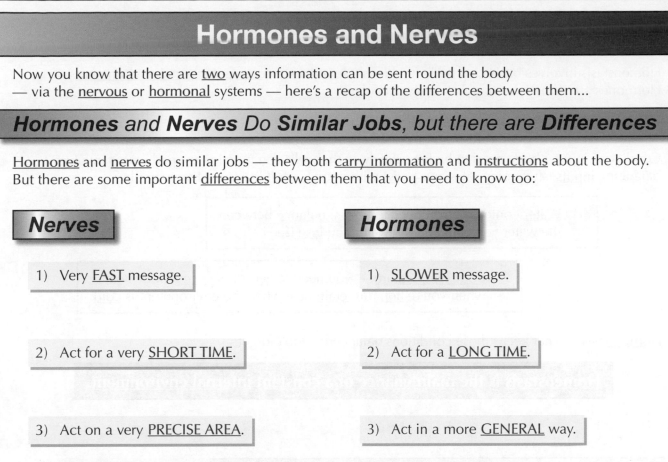

Nerves

1) Very <u>FAST</u> message.

2) Act for a very <u>SHORT TIME</u>.

3) Act on a very <u>PRECISE AREA</u>.

Hormones

1) <u>SLOWER</u> message.

2) Act for a <u>LONG TIME</u>.

3) Act in a more <u>GENERAL</u> way.

If you're not sure whether a response is nervous or hormonal, have a think about the <u>speed</u> of the reaction and <u>how long it lasts</u>:

1) If the Response is **Really Quick**, It's Probably **Nervous**

Some information needs to be passed to effectors <u>really quickly</u> (e.g. <u>pain</u> signals, or information from your eyes telling you about the <u>lion</u> heading your way), so it's no good using hormones to carry the message — they're <u>too slow</u>.

2) But if a Response **Lasts For a Long Time**, It's Probably **Hormonal**

For example, when you get a <u>shock</u>, a hormone called <u>adrenaline</u> is released into the bloodstream (causing the fight-or-flight response, where your body is hyped up ready for action). You can tell it's a <u>hormonal response</u> (even though it kicks in pretty quickly) because you feel a bit wobbly for a while <u>afterwards</u>.

Nerves, hormones — no wonder revision makes me tense...

Hormones control various <u>organs</u> and <u>cells</u> in the body, though they tend to control things that aren't <u>immediately</u> life-threatening. For example, they take care of all things to do with sexual development, pregnancy, birth, breast-feeding, blood sugar level, water content... and so on. Pretty amazing really.

Homeostasis

Homeostasis involves balancing body functions to maintain a "constant internal environment". Hormones are sometimes (but not always) involved.

Homeostasis — it's all about Balance

Conditions in your body need to be kept steady so that cells can function properly. This involves balancing inputs (stuff going into your body) with outputs (stuff leaving). For example...

> 1) Water content — you need to keep a balance between the water you gain and the water you lose (see below).

> 2) Body temperature — you need to get rid of excess body heat when you're hot, but retain heat when the environment is cold.

Homeostasis is what keeps these conditions balanced. Don't forget:

Homeostasis is the maintenance of a constant internal environment.

Water Is Lost from the Body in Various Ways

Water is taken into the body as food and drink and is lost from the body in the following ways:

1) through the SKIN as SWEAT...
2) via the LUNGS in BREATH...
3) via the kidneys as URINE.

Some water is also lost in faeces.

The balance between sweat and urine can depend on what you're doing, or what the weather's like...

- On a HOT DAY, or when you're EXERCISING, you sweat a lot.
- You will produce less urine, but this will be more concentrated (and hence a deeper colour).
- You will also lose more water through your breath when you exercise because you breathe faster.

- On a COLD DAY, or when you're NOT EXERCISING, you don't sweat much.
- You'll produce more urine, which will be pale (since the waste carried in the urine is more diluted).

Body Temperature is Kept at About 37 °C

1) All enzymes work best at a certain optimum temperature (see page 9). The enzymes in the human body work best at about 37 °C — and so this is the temperature your body tries to maintain.

2) A part of the brain acts as your own personal thermostat. It's sensitive to the blood temperature in the brain, and it receives messages from temperature receptors in the skin that provide information about skin temperature.

3) Based on the signals from these receptors, your central nervous system can activate the necessary effectors to make sure your body temperature stays just right.

More on Homeostasis

Homeostasis is so <u>important</u> for organisms (and for science students)
that I just couldn't <u>resist</u> writing a second page on it for you.

The **Skin** Helps to **Maintain Body Temperature**

To <u>stay</u> at a <u>cosy-but-not-too-warm</u> 37 °C your body has a few <u>tricks</u> up its sleeve:

When You're **TOO HOT**:

1) <u>Lots of sweat</u> is produced — when it <u>evaporates</u> it <u>transfers heat</u> from you to the environment, cooling you down.

2) <u>Blood vessels</u> close to the surface of the skin <u>widen</u> — this is called <u>vasodilation</u>. It allows more blood to flow near the surface, so it can radiate more heat into the surroundings.

3) <u>Hairs</u> lie flat.

When You're **TOO COLD**:

1) <u>Very little sweat</u> is produced.

2) <u>Blood vessels</u> near the surface <u>constrict</u> (<u>vasoconstriction</u>) so that less heat can be transferred from the blood to the surroundings.

3) You <u>shiver</u>, and the movement generates heat in the muscles. <u>Exercise</u> does the same.

4) <u>Hairs</u> stand on end to trap an insulating layer of air which helps keep you warm.

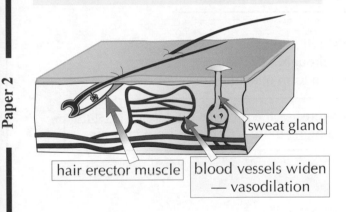

hair erector muscle | blood vessels widen — vasodilation | sweat gland

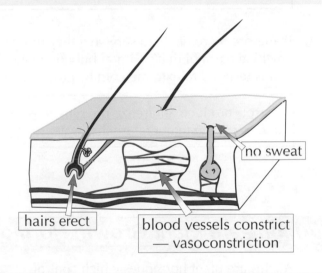

hairs erect | blood vessels constrict — vasoconstriction | no sweat

Smaller Organisms Can **Cool Down Quicker**

1) <u>Smaller organisms</u> have <u>bigger surface area to volume ratios</u> (see page 17).

2) Organisms with bigger surface area to volume ratios can <u>gain</u> (or <u>lose</u>) <u>heat faster</u> because there is <u>more area</u> for the heat to transfer across.

3) This allows <u>small organisms</u> to lose body heat more easily in <u>hot climates</u> and reduces the chance of them <u>overheating</u>. It also means that they're very <u>vulnerable</u> in <u>cold environments</u>.

4) Organisms with <u>smaller</u> surface area to volume ratios gain (or <u>lose</u>) heat <u>more slowly</u> because there is <u>less area</u> for the heat to transfer across.

5) This is why animals living in <u>cold</u> conditions have a <u>compact</u> (rounded) shape to keep their <u>surface area</u> to a minimum, <u>reducing heat loss</u>.

Responses in Plants

You're <u>nearly</u> done for this section. Just a <u>little bit</u> about plants still to go — they're just as important...

Plants *Need to* Respond to Stimuli *Too*

1) Plants, like animals, <u>increase</u> their chances of <u>survival</u>
   by responding to changes in their environment, e.g:

> • They sense the direction of <u>light</u> and <u>grow</u> towards it
>   to <u>maximise</u> light absorption for <u>photosynthesis</u>.
> • They can sense <u>gravity</u>, so their roots and shoots <u>grow</u> in the <u>right direction</u>.
> • <u>Climbing</u> plants have a sense of <u>touch</u>, so they can find things to climb and <u>reach</u> the <u>sunlight</u>.

2) Plants are more likely to survive if they respond to
   the presence of <u>predators</u> to avoid being eaten, e.g.:

> <u>White clover</u> is a plant that can produce substances that are <u>toxic</u> to
> <u>cattle</u>. Cattle start to <u>eat</u> lots of white clover when fields are <u>overgrazed</u>
> — the white clover <u>responds</u> by <u>producing toxins</u>, to <u>avoid</u> being <u>eaten</u>.

3) Plants are more likely to survive if they respond to abiotic stress —
   anything harmful that's natural but non-living, like a drought. E.g. some
   plants respond to extreme cold by producing their own form of antifreeze:

> <u>Carrots</u> produce <u>antifreeze proteins</u> at low temperatures — the proteins <u>bind</u> to <u>ice crystals</u>
> and <u>lower</u> the <u>temperature</u> that water <u>freezes</u> at, <u>stopping</u> more ice crystals from <u>growing</u>.

Auxins *are Plant* Growth Hormones

1) <u>Auxins</u> are <u>plant hormones</u> which control
   <u>growth</u> at the <u>tips</u> of <u>shoots</u> and <u>roots</u>.

2) They move through the plant in <u>solution</u> (dissolved in water).

3) Auxin is produced in the <u>tips</u> and <u>diffuses backwards</u>
   to stimulate the <u>cell elongation process</u> which
   occurs in the cells <u>just behind</u> the tips.

4) Auxin <u>promotes</u> growth in the <u>shoot</u>,
   but actually <u>inhibits</u> growth in the <u>root</u>.

5) Auxins are involved in the <u>growth</u> responses of plants
   to <u>light</u> (phototropism) and <u>gravity</u> (geotropism).
   There's more on these on the next page.

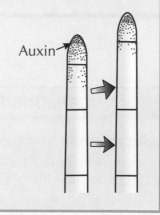

Auxin

I bet I can guess your response to learning about plants...

Everyone seems to think that plants are <u>boring</u>, but they're actually pretty <u>amazing</u>. They can sense
their environment and respond to it accordingly — and they don't even have a nervous system.

Responses in Plants

Remember: auxins are plant hormones that control the growth responses of plants to light (phototropism) and gravity (geotropism).

Auxins Change the Direction of Root and Shoot Growth

Shoots are POSITIVELY PHOTOTROPIC (grow towards light)

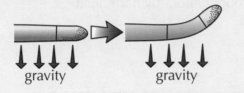

1) When a shoot tip is exposed to light, it accumulates more auxin on the side that's in the shade than the side that's in the light.

2) This makes the cells grow (elongate) faster on the shaded side, so the shoot bends towards the light.

Shoots are NEGATIVELY GEOTROPIC (grow away from gravity)

gravity   gravity

1) When a shoot is growing sideways, gravity produces an unequal distribution of auxin in the tip, with more auxin on the lower side.

2) This causes the lower side to grow faster, bending the shoot upwards.

Roots are POSITIVELY GEOTROPIC (grow towards gravity)

1) A root growing sideways will also have more auxin on its lower side.

2) But in a root the extra auxin inhibits growth. This means the cells on top elongate faster, and the root bends downwards.

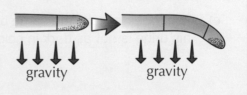

gravity   gravity

Roots grow towards gravity...

...but shoots grow away from gravity. Shoots also grow towards the light.   Try to get the basic facts about auxin from this page and the previous one into your head. Then if you're ever asked to explain the results of an auxin-related experiment in the exam you'll be sorted.

SECTION 6 — COORDINATION AND RESPONSE

Warm-Up and Exam Questions

There's no point in whizzing through the section and glancing over the questions. Do the warm-up questions and go back over any bits you don't know. Then practise and practise the exam questions.

Warm-Up Questions

1) State the sources of the following hormones: a) oestrogen b) progesterone c) adrenaline.
2) Name the hormone that prepares the body for the 'fight or flight' response.
3) What effect does the hormone ADH have on the body?
4) Why is human body temperature maintained at around 37 °C?
5) What are auxins?

Exam Questions

1   Responses to stimuli can be either nervous or hormonal.

    a)   i)   Name the main male sex hormone and state its source.

(2 marks)

         ii)   Describe the role and effect of the hormone insulin.

(2 marks)

    b)   Describe the differences between responses brought about by hormones
        and those brought about by the nervous system.

(4 marks)

2   Tom goes for a bike ride. It is a hot day and he has to work hard on some steep hills.
    Homeostasis helps to regulate the water content in his body.

    a)   What is meant by the term **homeostasis**?

(1 mark)

    b)   i)   Describe **two** ways in which Tom's body loses water while he is cycling.

(2 marks)

         ii)   When Tom returns home, he notices that his urine is dark in colour.
             Suggest why.

(2 marks)

    c)   Tom does exactly the same bike ride the following day, but notices afterwards that
        his urine is not as dark in colour this time. Suggest **one** possible reason for this.

(1 mark)

3   Plants increase their chances of survival if they can respond to environmental changes.
    Copy and complete the passage below by writing a suitable word or words in the spaces.

Plant shoots grow towards .... to maximise photosynthesis.

This growth response is known as ....

Plants can also sense .... so their shoots and roots grow in the right direction.

(3 marks)

Exam Questions

4   Changes in the skin are an important part of temperature regulation. The diagram shows a cross section through the skin of a person who is cold.

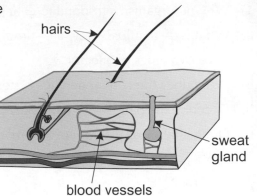

hairs

sweat gland

blood vessels

a)   In the diagram, the blood vessels close to the surface of the skin have narrowed. Give the scientific name for this process and explain why it happens.

(2 marks)

b)   Describe and explain the response of a sweat gland when a person is cold.

(2 marks)

5   Temperatures in a sauna can reach up to 100 °C.

a)   Explain why a person using a sauna may be advised to drink water regularly.

(2 marks)

b)   Suggest how the blood vessels close to the surface of the skin would respond to being in a sauna. Explain your answer.

(3 marks)

6   Cedrick placed some germinating beans on the surface of some damp soil and left them for five days. The appearance of the beans before and after the five day period is shown below.

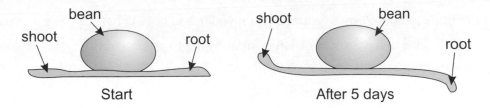

bean

shoot

root

Start

shoot

bean

root

After 5 days

a)   Name the hormone responsible for the observed changes.

(1 mark)

b)   i)   What is meant by the term **negative geotropism**?

(1 mark)

ii)   Which part of the seedling is demonstrating negative geotropism after five days?

(1 mark)

c)   After the five day period, Cedrick turned the seeds upside down, as shown to the right. State the direction in which the root will grow after the seed is turned upside down. Explain your answer.

shoot

bean

root

(3 marks)

Revision Summary for Section 6

That was an OK section, kind of interesting, I reckon. These questions will show what you know and what you don't... if you get stuck, have a look back to remind yourself.

1) Why do organisms respond to changes in their environment?

2) What is a stimulus? How are stimuli detected?

3) Give two types of effector.

4) What does the central nervous system do?

5) Describe the pathway of a reflex arc from stimulus to response.

6) Draw a labelled diagram of a human eye.

7) Explain the roles of the following parts of the eye:
   a) cornea
   b) iris
   c) lens

8) Describe the iris reflex. Why is this needed?

9) How does accommodation of the eye work? Is the lens fat or thin to look at distant objects?

10) Define the term 'hormone'.

11) What is the role of the hormone adrenaline? What effects does it have on the body?

12) Where is insulin made?

13) List three differences between nervous and hormonal responses.

14) Write down two conditions that the body needs to keep fairly constant.

15) Give three ways in which water is lost from the body.

16) Describe how the amount and concentration of urine you produce varies depending on how much exercise you do and how hot it is.

17) At what temperature do most of the enzymes in the human body work best?

18) Describe how body temperature is reduced when you're too hot. What happens if you're too cold?

19) Do larger animals tend to have small or large surface area to volume ratios? How does this affect their temperature control?

20) Give two ways in which plants respond to stimuli.

21) What is: a) positive phototropism?   b) positive geotropism?

22) Shoots are negatively geotropic. How are auxins responsible for this?

DNA, Genes and Chromosomes

It's <u>dead important</u> you get to grips with this stuff — you'll need it to understand the <u>rest of the section</u>.

Learn the Relationship Between **DNA**, *Genes* and **Chromosomes**

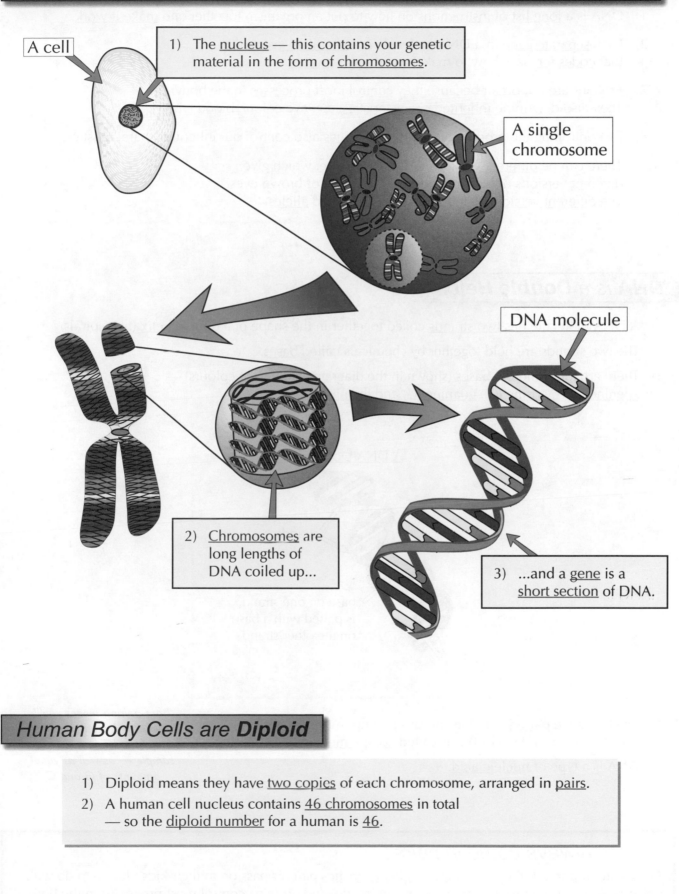

A cell

1) The <u>nucleus</u> — this contains your genetic material in the form of <u>chromosomes</u>.

A single chromosome

DNA molecule

2) <u>Chromosomes</u> are long lengths of DNA coiled up...

3) ...and a <u>gene</u> is a <u>short section</u> of DNA.

Human Body Cells are **Diploid**

1) Diploid means they have <u>two copies</u> of each chromosome, arranged in <u>pairs</u>.

2) A human cell nucleus contains <u>46 chromosomes</u> in total — so the <u>diploid number</u> for a human is <u>46</u>.

DNA, Genes and Chromosomes

Genes are Chemical Instructions

1) DNA is a <u>long list</u> of <u>instructions</u> on how to put an organism together and <u>make it work</u>.

2) Each <u>separate gene</u> in a DNA molecule is a <u>chemical instruction</u> that <u>codes for</u> (says how to make) a particular <u>protein</u>.

3) Proteins are important because they <u>control</u> most <u>processes</u> in the body. They also determine <u>inherited characteristics</u>, e.g. eye colour, blood type.

4) By controlling the production of proteins, <u>genes</u> also control our inherited characteristics.

5) There can be <u>different versions</u> of the <u>same gene</u>, which give different versions of a characteristic — like blue or brown eyes. The <u>different versions</u> of the same gene are called <u>alleles</u>.

DNA is a Double Helix

1) A DNA molecule has <u>two strands</u> coiled together in the shape of a <u>double helix</u> (two spirals).

2) The two strands are held together by chemicals called <u>bases</u>.

3) There are <u>four</u> different bases (shown in the diagram as different colours) — <u>adenine</u> (A), <u>cytosine</u> (C), <u>guanine</u> (G) and <u>thymine</u> (T).

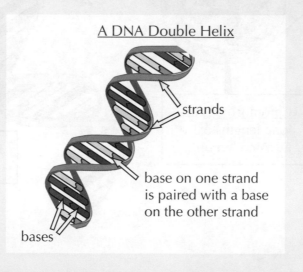

A DNA Double Helix

strands

base on one strand is paired with a base on the other strand

bases

4) The bases are <u>paired</u>, and they always pair up in the same way — it's always A-T and C-G. This is called <u>complementary base-pairing</u>.

5) DNA is a type of <u>nucleic acid</u>.

Base-pairing means you'll always find equal amounts of A and T in a DNA sample — as well as equal amounts of G and C.

Genes always come in pairs...

Genes are important: they control what <u>characteristics</u> parents pass on to their kids. It's all to do with <u>proteins</u> — <u>genes</u> control the <u>proteins</u> that are made, and <u>proteins</u> control most processes in the body.

Asexual Reproduction and Mitosis

There are <u>two ways</u> an organism can <u>reproduce</u> (asexually and sexually) and two ways a cell can <u>divide</u> (mitosis and meiosis). This page, as you might have guessed, is about <u>asexual reproduction</u> and <u>mitosis</u>.

Asexual Reproduction Involves Mitosis

1) An <u>ordinary cell</u> can make a new cell by simply <u>dividing in two</u>. <u>Both new cells</u> are <u>genetically identical</u> to the original cell — they both contain <u>exactly the same</u> genetic information.

2) This type of cell division is known as <u>mitosis</u> (see below).

3) Some organisms <u>produce offspring</u> (children) <u>using mitosis</u>. This is known as <u>asexual reproduction</u>. Organisms which reproduce asexually include <u>bacteria</u> and some <u>plants</u> (see page 103).

> <u>ASEXUAL REPRODUCTION</u> involves only <u>ONE</u> parent. The offspring have <u>identical genes</u> to the parent — so there's <u>no variation</u> between parent and offspring.

Mitosis Produces Genetically Identical Cells

> "MITOSIS is when a cell reproduces itself by <u>splitting</u> to form <u>two cells</u> with <u>identical sets of chromosomes</u>."

So when a <u>diploid cell</u> (see page 93) divides by mitosis, you get <u>two cells</u> that are <u>both diploid</u>. Here's how mitosis works:

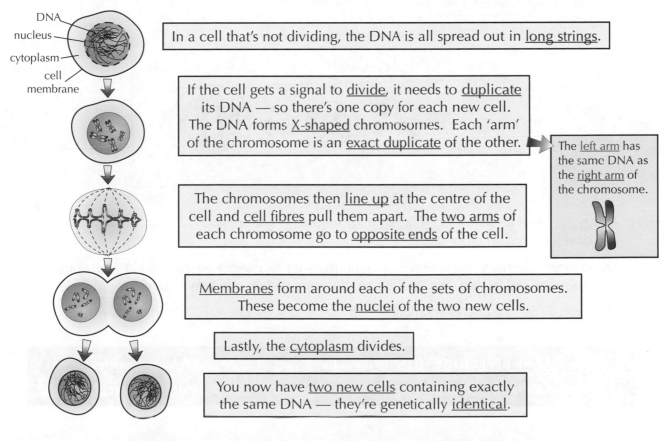

DNA
nucleus
cytoplasm
cell membrane

In a cell that's not dividing, the DNA is all spread out in <u>long strings</u>.

If the cell gets a signal to <u>divide</u>, it needs to <u>duplicate</u> its DNA — so there's one copy for each new cell. The DNA forms <u>X-shaped</u> chromosomes. Each 'arm' of the chromosome is an <u>exact duplicate</u> of the other.

The <u>left arm</u> has the same DNA as the <u>right arm</u> of the chromosome.

The chromosomes then <u>line up</u> at the centre of the cell and <u>cell fibres</u> pull them apart. The <u>two arms</u> of each chromosome go to <u>opposite ends</u> of the cell.

<u>Membranes</u> form around each of the sets of chromosomes. These become the <u>nuclei</u> of the two new cells.

Lastly, the <u>cytoplasm</u> divides.

You now have <u>two new cells</u> containing exactly the same DNA — they're genetically <u>identical</u>.

Mitosis Also Makes New Cells for Growth and Repair

Mitosis isn't just used during asexual reproduction — it's how <u>all plants and animals grow</u> and <u>repair damaged tissue</u>. <u>Cloning</u> (see pages 153 and 154) also involves mitosis.

Sexual Reproduction

Another page, another form of reproduction...

Sexual Reproduction Produces Genetically Different Cells

Sexual reproduction is where genetic information from two organisms (a father and a mother) is combined to produce offspring which are genetically different to either parent.

Sexual Reproduction Involves Gametes...

1) In sexual reproduction the mother and father produce gametes. Gametes are sperm cells and egg cells.

2) Gametes are haploid — this means they have half the number of chromosomes in a normal cell. In humans, each gamete contains 23 chromosomes — so the haploid number is 23.

...and Fertilisation

1) At fertilisation, a male gamete fuses with a female gamete to form a zygote (fertilised egg). The zygote ends up with the full set of chromosomes.

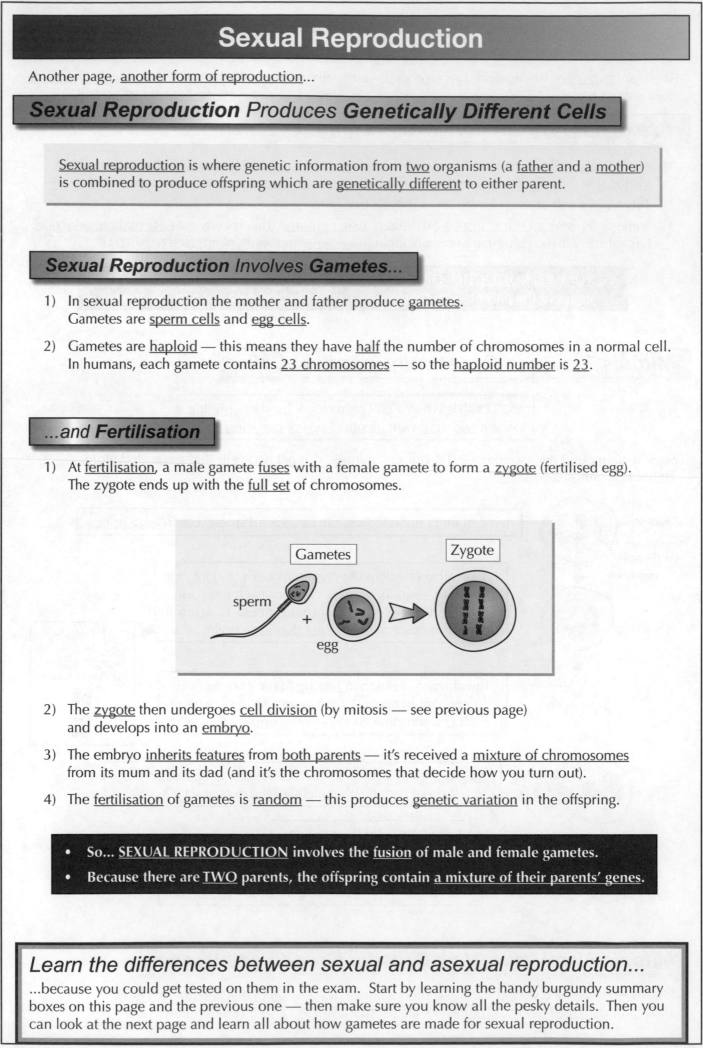

2) The zygote then undergoes cell division (by mitosis — see previous page) and develops into an embryo.

3) The embryo inherits features from both parents — it's received a mixture of chromosomes from its mum and its dad (and it's the chromosomes that decide how you turn out).

4) The fertilisation of gametes is random — this produces genetic variation in the offspring.

- So... SEXUAL REPRODUCTION involves the fusion of male and female gametes.
- Because there are TWO parents, the offspring contain a mixture of their parents' genes.

Learn the differences between sexual and asexual reproduction...

...because you could get tested on them in the exam. Start by learning the handy burgundy summary boxes on this page and the previous one — then make sure you know all the pesky details. Then you can look at the next page and learn all about how gametes are made for sexual reproduction.

Meiosis

This page is a little bit tricky, so take your time.

Gametes are Produced by Meiosis

1) Meiosis is another type of cell division.
2) It's different to mitosis (on page 95) because it doesn't produce identical cells.
3) In humans, meiosis only happens in the reproductive organs (ovaries and testes).

> "MEIOSIS produces four haploid cells whose chromosomes are NOT identical."

Meiosis Involves Two Divisions

Here's how meiosis works:

chromosome pair

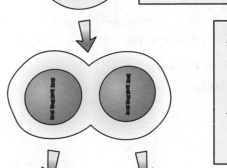

Meiosis — Division 1

1) Before the cell starts to divide, it duplicates its DNA (so there's enough for each new cell). One arm of each chromosome is an exact copy of the other arm.
2) In the first division in meiosis (there are two divisions) the chromosomes line up in pairs in the centre of the cell.

Step 1 is like the start of mitosis. Step 2 is different though.

3) The pairs are then pulled apart, so each new cell only has one copy of each chromosome. Some of the father's chromosomes (shown in blue) and some of the mother's chromosomes (shown in red) go into each new cell.
4) Each new cell will have a mixture of the mother's and father's chromosomes. Mixing up the genes like this creates variation in the offspring.

Meiosis — Division 2

5) In the second division the chromosomes line up again in the centre of the cell. It's a lot like mitosis. The arms of the chromosomes are pulled apart.

6) You get four haploid gametes — each only has a single set of chromosomes. The gametes are all genetically different.

Meiosis produces gametes for sexual reproduction

So. With meiosis you end up with four haploid cells that are all genetically different. With mitosis (page 95), you end up with only two cells and they're genetically identical. Learn all the details on this page and then come up with a rhyme to help you remember the key differences between the two.

Warm-Up and Exam Questions

Take a deep breath and go through these warm-up questions one by one.
If you don't know these basic facts there's no way you'll cope with the exam questions.

Warm-Up Questions

1) Where in the cell are chromosomes found?
2) The body cells of most mammals are diploid. What does this mean?
3) What is the diploid number for humans?
4) An organism is produced through asexual reproduction. How many parents does it have?

Exam Questions

1   Give **two** differences between meiosis and mitosis.

(2 marks)

2   Copy and complete the following passage about sexual reproduction, using suitable words.

During sexual reproduction two parents produce sex cells called ....

These cells are .... , meaning that they have half the number of chromosomes in a normal cell.

In humans, sex cells contain .... chromosomes.

At fertilisation, a male sex cell fuses with a female sex cell to produce a
.... , which undergoes cell division by ....
to produce an embryo.

(5 marks)

3   Genes are short sections of DNA.

a)   Describe the structure of DNA.

(4 marks)

b)   Explain the relationship between genes and the characteristics of an organism.

(2 marks)

c)   Fur length in cats is controlled by a single gene. A female cat gave birth to a litter
of two kittens, shown below. One kitten is long-haired and the other is short-haired.

Explain why the kittens show different characteristics.

(3 marks)

Exam Questions

4   Some species of starfish can produce offspring through a process called fission.
    In this process, the parent's body splits into two parts that undergo
    cell division by mitosis to develop into mature, complete organisms.

   a)   What term is used to describe this form of reproduction?

   (1 mark)

   b)   Suggest how the chromosomes in the offspring will
        compare to those of the parent starfish.

   (1 mark)

   c)   Other than reproduction, suggest **one** function of mitosis in starfish.

   (1 mark)

5   Mosquitoes have three pairs of chromosomes in their body cells.
    Cell A, shown below, is a mosquito cell which is about to divide by meiosis.

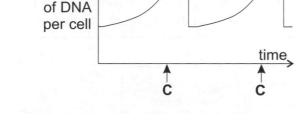

   cell A

   a)   i)   State the haploid number of a cell produced when cell A undergoes meiosis.

   (1 mark)

        ii)   How many cells will be produced in total when cell A undergoes meiosis?

   (1 mark)

   b)   Explain how the processes of meiosis and fertilisation lead to genetic variation
        in the mosquito's offspring.

   (3 marks)

6   The graph below shows how the amount of DNA per cell changes
    as a cell undergoes two cell divisions by mitosis. Point **C** is the
    time when the chromosomes first become visible in the new cells.

   a)   Describe what is happening to the DNA during stage **A**.
        Suggest why this needs to happen.

   (2 marks)

   b)   Suggest what happens at time **B**.

   (1 mark)

   c)   How many cells are there after the first cell division?

   (1 mark)

Sexual Reproduction in Plants

Some types of plants reproduce <u>asexually</u> (see page 95), whilst others reproduce <u>sexually</u> (see below).

The **Flower** Contains both **Male** and **Female Gametes**

Flowering plants have both <u>male</u> and <u>female structures</u> — they're contained in the <u>flower</u>:

The **Stamen** is the **Male** Reproductive Part

The <u>stamen</u> consists of the <u>anther</u> and <u>filament</u>.

The ANTHER contains <u>pollen grains</u> — these produce the <u>male gametes</u> (sperm).

The FILAMENT is the <u>stalk</u> that <u>supports</u> the anther.

The **Carpel** is the **Female** Reproductive Part

The <u>carpel</u> consists of the <u>ovary</u>, <u>style</u> and <u>stigma</u>.

The STIGMA is the <u>end</u> bit that the <u>pollen</u> grains <u>attach</u> to.

The STYLE is the rod-like section that <u>supports</u> the stigma.

The OVARY contains the <u>female gametes</u> (eggs) inside <u>ovules</u>.

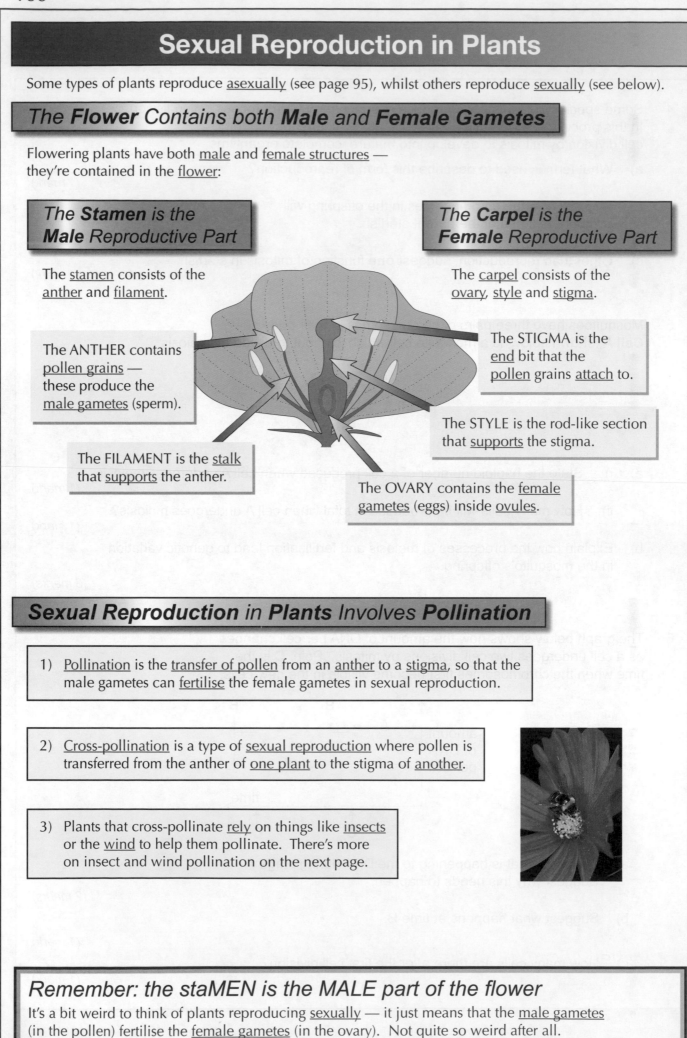

Sexual Reproduction in Plants Involves Pollination

1) <u>Pollination</u> is the <u>transfer of pollen</u> from an <u>anther</u> to a <u>stigma</u>, so that the male gametes can <u>fertilise</u> the female gametes in sexual reproduction.

2) <u>Cross-pollination</u> is a type of <u>sexual reproduction</u> where pollen is transferred from the anther of <u>one plant</u> to the stigma of <u>another</u>.

3) Plants that cross-pollinate <u>rely</u> on things like <u>insects</u> or the <u>wind</u> to help them pollinate. There's more on insect and wind pollination on the next page.

Remember: the staMEN is the MALE part of the flower

It's a bit weird to think of plants reproducing <u>sexually</u> — it just means that the <u>male gametes</u> (in the pollen) fertilise the <u>female gametes</u> (in the ovary). Not quite so weird after all.

Plant Pollination

As you saw on the previous page, <u>sexual reproduction</u> in plants involves the transfer of pollen from an <u>anther</u> to a <u>stigma</u>. This is called <u>pollination</u> and plants sometimes need a bit of outside help, e.g. from <u>bees</u> and <u>butterflies</u> or a <u>gust of wind</u>, to get it done.

Some Plants are **Adapted** for **Insect Pollination**

Here's how plants can be <u>adapted</u> for <u>pollination by insects</u>...

1) They have <u>brightly coloured petals</u> to <u>attract insects</u>.

2) They also have <u>scented flowers</u> and <u>nectaries</u> (glands that secrete <u>nectar</u>) to <u>attract insects</u>.

3) They make <u>big, sticky pollen grains</u> — the grains <u>stick to insects</u> as they go from plant to plant.

4) The <u>stigma</u> is also <u>sticky</u> so that any <u>pollen</u> picked up by insects on other plants will <u>stick to the stigma</u>.

Other Plants are **Adapted** for **Wind Pollination**

Features of plants that are <u>adapted</u> for <u>pollination by wind</u> include...

1) <u>Small</u>, <u>dull petals</u> on the flower (they don't need to attract insects).

2) <u>No nectaries</u> or strong <u>scents</u> (for the same reason).

3) A <u>lot</u> of <u>pollen</u> grains — they're <u>small</u> and <u>light</u> so that they can easily be <u>carried</u> by the wind.

4) <u>Long filaments</u> that <u>hang</u> the anthers <u>outside</u> the flower, so that a lot of the <u>pollen</u> gets <u>blown away</u> by the wind.

5) A <u>large</u> and <u>feathery stigma</u> to <u>catch pollen</u> as it's carried past by the wind. The stigma often <u>hangs outside</u> the flower too.

Pollination is the transfer of pollen from an anther to a stigma

Flowers like <u>roses</u> (big, bright petals, a strong scent) are pollinated by <u>insects</u>. The <u>feathery looking flowers</u> you sometimes see in long <u>grass</u>, and fluffy willow <u>catkins</u>, are pollinated by the <u>wind</u>. If you're given a picture of a flower in the exam, you should be able to say whether it's most likely to be insect- or wind-pollinated and explain your answer. So get learning this page.

Fertilisation and Germination in Plants

Once the pollen has found its way to a lovely stigma, it's time for <u>fertilisation</u> to take place...

Fertilisation is the Fusion of Gametes

1) A <u>pollen</u> grain lands on the <u>stigma</u> of a flower, usually with help from insects or the wind (see previous page).

2) A <u>pollen tube</u> grows out of the pollen grain and down through the <u>style</u> to the <u>ovary</u> and into the <u>ovule</u>.

3) A <u>nucleus</u> from the male gamete <u>moves down the tube</u> to join with a female gamete in the <u>ovule</u>. <u>Fertilisation</u> is when the two nuclei <u>fuse</u> together to make a zygote. This divides by mitosis to form an <u>embryo</u>.

4) Each <u>fertilised</u> female gamete forms a <u>seed</u>. The <u>ovary</u> develops into a <u>fruit</u> around the seed.

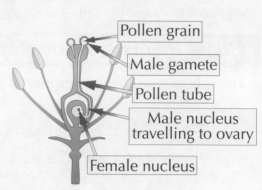

Flowering plants can only be fertilised by pollen grains from the same species (or a closely related species).

Germination is when Seeds Start to Grow

A seed will often lie <u>dormant</u> until the <u>conditions</u> around it are right for <u>germination</u>. Seeds need the right <u>conditions</u> to start germinating:

1) <u>Water</u> — to <u>activate</u> the enzymes that <u>break down</u> the <u>food</u> reserves in the seed.

2) <u>Oxygen</u> — for respiration (see pages 49 and 50), which provides the <u>energy</u> for growth.

3) A suitable <u>temperature</u> — for the enzymes inside the seed to work. This depends on what <u>type</u> of seed it is.

Germination only starts when <u>all</u> these conditions are suitable.

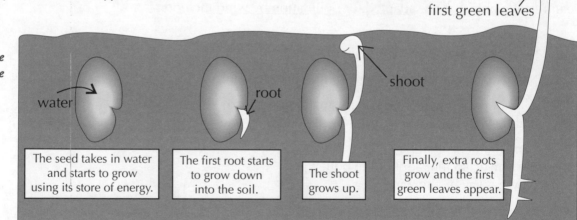

first green leaves

shoot

root

water

The seed takes in water and starts to grow using its store of energy.

The first root starts to grow down into the soil.

The shoot grows up.

Finally, extra roots grow and the first green leaves appear.

Germinating Seeds get Energy from Food Stores

1) A developed seed contains an <u>embryo</u> and a store of <u>food reserves</u>, wrapped in a <u>hard seed coat</u>.

2) When a seed starts to <u>germinate</u>, it gets <u>glucose</u> for respiration from its own <u>food store</u>. This gives it the <u>energy</u> it needs to grow.

3) Once the plant has grown enough to produce <u>green leaves</u> (see above), it can get its own food for energy from <u>photosynthesis</u> (see page 33).

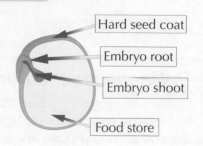

Hard seed coat

Embryo root

Embryo shoot

Food store

Asexual Reproduction in Plants

Some plants reproduce <u>asexually</u>. They do this in the wild (<u>naturally</u>) and when we force them to (<u>artificially</u>). Artificial asexual reproduction is also called <u>cloning</u>.

Plants Can **Reproduce Asexually** Using **Natural Methods**...

Plants have several different ways of reproducing asexually.
Some plants do so by growing <u>new plants</u> from their stems...

Example: Strawberry Plants

1) The parent strawberry plant sends out <u>runners</u> — <u>fast-growing stems</u> that grow out <u>sideways</u>, just above the ground.

2) The runners <u>take root</u> at various points (a short distance away) and <u>new plants</u> start to grow.

3) The new plants are <u>clones</u> of the <u>parent</u> strawberry plant, so there's <u>no</u> genetic variation between them.

Some plants reproduce asexually <u>and</u> sexually, e.g. strawberry plants send out runners and produce fruit (seeds).

runner

new plant

parent plant

Scientifica/Visuals Unlimited, Inc./Getty Images

...or We Can **Clone** Them Using **Artificial Methods**

Asexual reproduction can be used to <u>clone plants</u>. And it's not all high-tech crazy science stuff either — gardeners have been using <u>cuttings</u> for a long time.

1) Gardeners can take <u>cuttings</u> from good parent plants, and then plant them to produce <u>genetically identical copies</u> (clones) of the parent plant.

2) These plants can be produced <u>quickly and cheaply</u>.

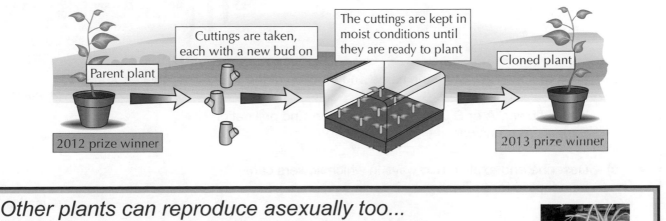

Parent plant

2012 prize winner

Cuttings are taken, each with a new bud on

The cuttings are kept in moist conditions until they are ready to plant

Cloned plant

2013 prize winner

Other plants can reproduce asexually too...

...for example, <u>potatoes</u>, <u>daffodils</u> and <u>spider plants</u>. Spider plants grow tufty bits at the end of their shoots called <u>plantlets</u> — each plantlet is a <u>clone</u> of the original plant. The clone grows roots and becomes a <u>new plant</u>. Plantlets

Warm-Up and Exam Questions

There's no better preparation for exam questions than doing... err... practice exam questions.
Hang on, what's this I see...

Warm-Up Questions

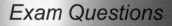

1) Name the two structures that make up a flower's stamen.
2) What is: a) the stigma?   b) the style?
3) What is germination?
4) Give three conditions that are needed for germination to happen.
5) Give one method gardeners use to artificially clone plants.

Exam Questions

1   Flowering plants contain both male and female organs.
    They are able to reproduce sexually via pollination.

   a)   Describe what happens during pollination.

(3 marks)

   b)   Cross-pollination is the term used to describe sexual reproduction involving two
    different plants. Suggest what is meant by the term **self-pollination**.

(1 mark)

2   The diagram below shows cross-sections through two flowers.

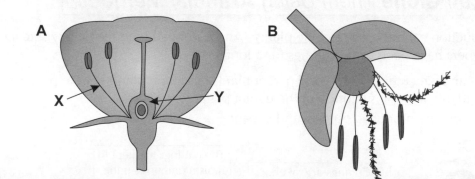

   a)   Look at flower **A**. State the name and function of the structures labelled **X** and **Y**.

(4 marks)

   b)   Which flower, **A** or **B**, is better adapted for wind pollination?
    Explain your answer.

(2 marks)

   c)   Describe and explain **two** ways in which flowers can
    be adapted for pollination by insects.

(2 marks)

Exam Questions

3   Some plants, such as daffodils and strawberry plants, can reproduce asexually.

a)   Strawberry plants reproduce asexually using runners. Explain what is meant by the
     term **runners** and describe how they allow plants to reproduce.

(2 marks)

b)   A strawberry plant is genetically susceptible to a particular virus.
     Explain why any offspring the plant produces through
     asexual reproduction will also be susceptible to the virus.

(1 mark)

4   Copy and complete the following passage about fertilisation in plants, using suitable words.

A pollen grain from one plant lands on the stigma of another plant.

A .... grows out of the pollen grain, down through the

.... to the ovary and into the ovule.

A .... from the male gamete travels to the ovule to fertilise the

female gamete, producing a .... that divides to form an embryo.

The fertilised female gamete forms a .... while the ovary

develops into a ....

(6 marks)

PAPER 2

5   Lauren set up a controlled experiment to investigate the conditions needed for germination.

She placed moist cotton wool and soaked alfalfa seeds in two large sealed flasks.
Flask **A** contained sodium pyrogallate solution, which absorbs oxygen from the air.
Flask **B** contained sodium hydroxide solution, which absorbs carbon dioxide from the air.

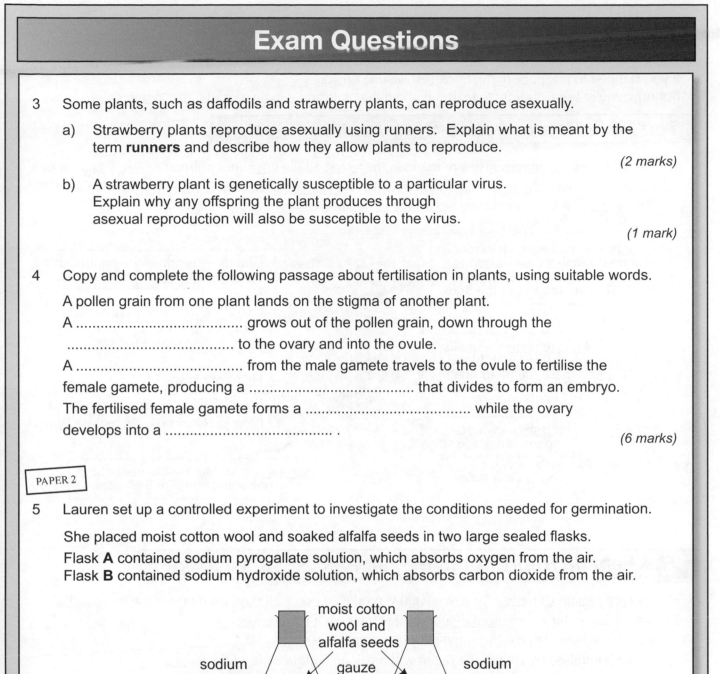

After 24 hours, Lauren found that the seeds had germinated in flask **B** only.

a)   Explain why germination did not occur in flask **A**.

(2 marks)

b)   How did the germinating alfalfa seeds obtain energy
     for growth during the experiment?

(1 mark)

c)   Lauren left flask B for a further 6 days.

     She observed that the seedlings produced green leaves after 4 days,
     but then showed no further growth despite still being alive.

     Suggest why the seedlings in flask **B** stopped growing
     after they had produced green leaves.

(3 marks)

Human Reproductive Systems

If you skipped to this page in the book first, shame on you...
But now you're here, it's time to learn all about the <u>male</u> and <u>female reproductive systems</u>.

The **Male Reproductive System** Makes **Sperm**

1) Sperm are <u>male gametes</u>. They're made in the <u>testes</u>, <u>all the time</u> after puberty.
2) Sperm mix with a <u>liquid</u> to make <u>semen</u>, which is <u>ejaculated</u> from the penis into the <u>vagina</u> of the female during <u>sexual intercourse</u>.

See page 96 for more on gametes.

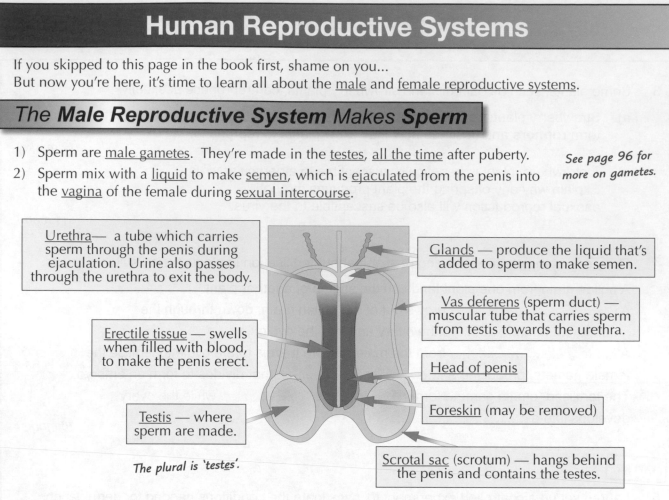

Urethra— a tube which carries sperm through the penis during ejaculation. Urine also passes through the urethra to exit the body.

Glands — produce the liquid that's added to sperm to make semen.

Erectile tissue — swells when filled with blood, to make the penis erect.

Vas deferens (sperm duct) — muscular tube that carries sperm from testis towards the urethra.

Head of penis

Testis — where sperm are made.

Foreskin (may be removed)

Scrotal sac (scrotum) — hangs behind the penis and contains the testes.

The plural is 'testes'.

The **Female Reproductive System** Makes **Ova (Eggs)**

1) Ova are <u>female gametes</u>. An <u>ovum</u> (egg) is produced <u>every 28 days</u> from one of the two <u>ovaries</u>.
2) It then passes into the <u>Fallopian tube</u> — this is where it might <u>meet</u> <u>sperm</u> that have entered the vagina during <u>sexual intercourse</u>.
3) If it <u>isn't fertilised</u> by sperm, the ovum will <u>break up</u> and pass out of the <u>vagina</u>.
4) If it <u>is fertilised</u>, the ovum starts to divide.
5) The new cells will travel down the Fallopian tube to the <u>uterus</u> (womb) and attach to the <u>endometrium</u> (uterus lining). A fertilised ovum develops into an <u>embryo</u>.

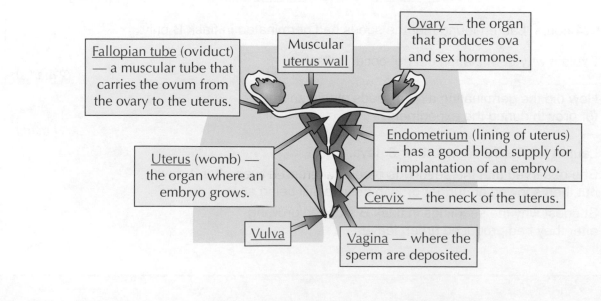

Ovary — the organ that produces ova and sex hormones.

Fallopian tube (oviduct) — a muscular tube that carries the ovum from the ovary to the uterus.

Muscular uterus wall

Endometrium (lining of uterus) — has a good blood supply for implantation of an embryo.

Uterus (womb) — the organ where an embryo grows.

Cervix — the neck of the uterus.

Vulva

Vagina — where the sperm are deposited.

Puberty and the Menstrual Cycle

You need to learn the science behind what happens at puberty. Read on my friend...

Hormones Promote Sexual Characteristics at Puberty

At puberty, your body starts releasing <u>sex hormones</u> — <u>testosterone</u> in men and <u>oestrogen</u> in women. These trigger off the <u>secondary sexual characteristics</u>:

Oestrogen in women causes...

1) <u>Extra hair</u> on underarms and pubic area.
2) <u>Hips</u> to <u>widen</u>.
3) Development of <u>breasts</u>.
4) <u>Ovum</u> release and <u>start of periods</u>.

See page 84 for more on hormones.

Testosterone in men causes...

1) <u>Extra hair</u> on face and body.
2) <u>Muscles</u> to <u>develop</u>.
3) <u>Penis and testicles</u> to enlarge.
4) <u>Sperm</u> production.
5) <u>Deepening</u> of <u>voice</u>.

The Menstrual Cycle is a Monthly Sequence of Events

1) Starting in <u>puberty</u>, females undergo a monthly sequence of events — the <u>menstrual cycle</u>. This involves the body <u>preparing</u> the <u>uterus</u> (womb) in case it receives a <u>fertilised ovum</u> (egg).

2) The menstrual cycle has <u>four stages</u>.

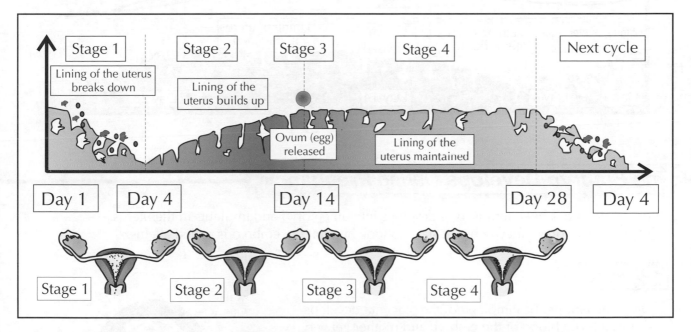

<u>STAGE 1:</u> <u>Day 1 is when bleeding starts</u>. The uterus lining breaks down for about four days.

<u>STAGE 2:</u> <u>The uterus lining builds up again</u>, from day 4 to day 14, into a thick spongy layer full of blood vessels, ready to receive a fertilised ovum (egg).

<u>STAGE 3:</u> <u>An ovum develops and is released</u> from the ovary at day 14.

<u>STAGE 4:</u> <u>The wall is then maintained</u> for about 14 days until day 28. If no fertilised ovum has landed on the uterus wall by day 28, the spongy lining starts to break down and the whole cycle starts again.

The Menstrual Cycle and Pregnancy

Oestrogen and Progesterone Control the Menstrual Cycle

These two hormones are produced in the <u>ovaries</u>, and they control the main events of the cycle:

1) OESTROGEN:
- Causes the lining of the uterus to <u>thicken</u> and <u>grow</u>.
- Stimulates the <u>release of an ovum</u> at day 14.

It's actually a hormone called LH which stimulates ovum release. But oestrogen stimulates production of LH in the first place, so this is more or less true.

2) PROGESTERONE:
- <u>Maintains</u> the lining of the uterus.
- When the level of progesterone <u>falls</u>, the lining <u>breaks down</u>.

If a fertilised ovum implants in the uterus (i.e. the woman becomes <u>pregnant</u>) then the level of <u>progesterone</u> will <u>stay high</u> to maintain the lining of the uterus during pregnancy.

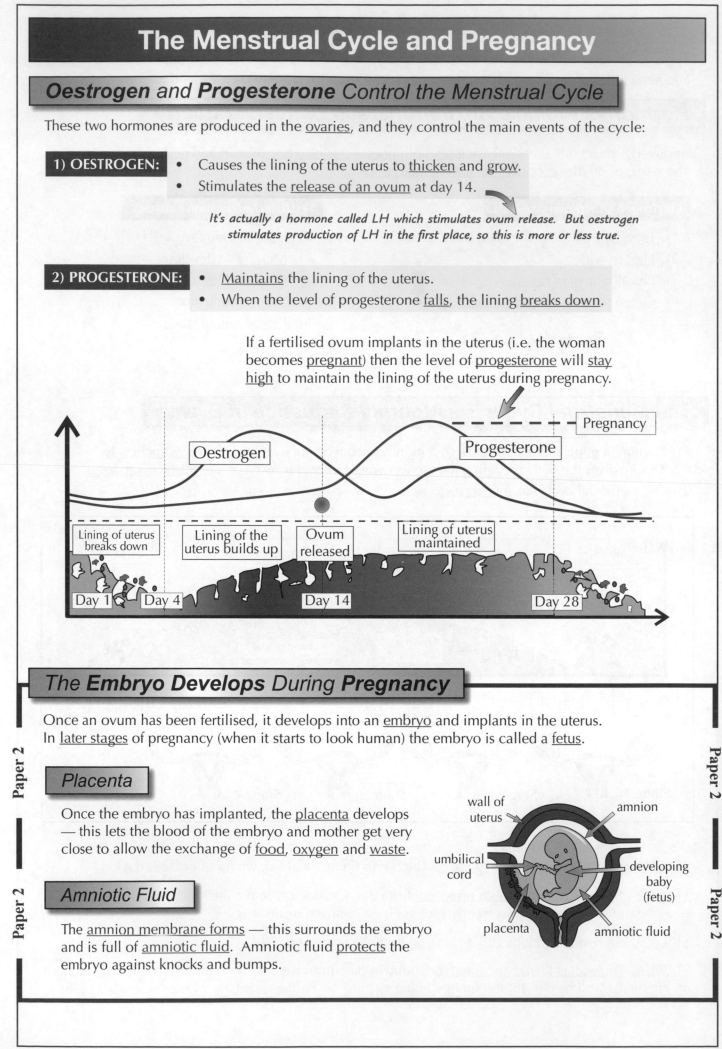

The Embryo Develops During Pregnancy

Once an ovum has been fertilised, it develops into an <u>embryo</u> and implants in the uterus. In <u>later stages</u> of pregnancy (when it starts to look human) the embryo is called a <u>fetus</u>.

Placenta

Once the embryo has implanted, the <u>placenta</u> develops — this lets the blood of the embryo and mother get very close to allow the exchange of <u>food</u>, <u>oxygen</u> and <u>waste</u>.

Amniotic Fluid

The <u>amnion membrane forms</u> — this surrounds the embryo and is full of <u>amniotic fluid</u>. Amniotic fluid <u>protects</u> the embryo against knocks and bumps.

Warm-Up and Exam Questions

There's only one way to do well in the exam — learn the facts and then practise lots of exam questions to see what it'll be like on the big day. We couldn't have made it easier for you — so do it.

Warm-Up Questions

1) What is the function of the testes?
2) What is the function of the vas deferens?
3) What is the name of the male sex hormone?
4) What secondary sexual characteristics does oestrogen produce in women?
5) What is the function of the placenta in pregnancy?

Exam Questions

1   Copy and complete the table to show the functions of different structures in the female reproductive system.

Structure	Function
Ovary	
	Carries the ovum (egg) from the ovary to the uterus.
Uterus	

(3 marks)

2   The diagram shows the levels of oestrogen and progesterone over a 28 day menstrual cycle.

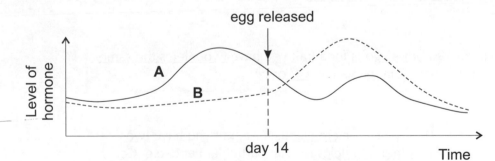

a)   State which curve, **A** or **B**, represents oestrogen. Explain your answer.

(1 mark)

b)   During which part of the cycle is the lining of the uterus thickest?
Explain your answer.

(2 marks)

c)   The level of both hormones decreases in the second half of the cycle.
Suggest how the level of progesterone would be different if the egg was fertilised.
Explain your answer.

(2 marks)

Alleles and Inheritance

This page is all about how <u>characteristics</u> (like eye colour) are <u>inherited</u>. Before you start, you might want to refresh your memory of <u>genes</u>, <u>chromosomes</u> and <u>DNA</u> on p.93-94. It'll make life a lot easier.

Alleles are *Different Versions* of the Same Gene

1) Most of the time you have <u>two copies</u> of each gene (i.e. <u>two alleles</u>, see p.94) — one from each parent.

2) If the alleles are different, you have <u>instructions</u> for <u>two different versions</u> of a characteristic (e.g. blue eyes or brown eyes) but you only <u>show one version</u> of the two (e.g. brown eyes).

3) The version of the characteristic that appears is caused by the <u>dominant allele</u>. The other allele is said to be <u>recessive</u>.

4) The characteristic caused by the recessive allele only appears if <u>both alleles</u> are recessive.

Paper 2

5) Some characteristics are caused by <u>codominant alleles</u>. Neither allele is recessive, so you <u>show characteristics</u> from <u>both alleles</u> (e.g. not blood group A or B, but blood group <u>AB</u>).

In *Genetic Diagrams*, *Letters* are Used to Represent *Genes*

Genetic diagrams can be used to show how <u>alleles</u> are <u>inherited</u>. They're covered in more detail over the next few pages.

1) <u>Dominant alleles</u> are always shown in a genetic diagram with a <u>capital letter</u> (e.g. 'C') and <u>recessive alleles</u> with a <u>small letter</u> (e.g. 'c').

2) If you're <u>homozygous</u> for a trait you have <u>two alleles the same</u> for that particular gene, e.g. <u>CC</u> or <u>cc</u>.

3) If you're <u>heterozygous</u> for a trait you have <u>two different alleles</u> for that particular gene, e.g. <u>Cc</u>.

4) Your <u>genotype</u> is the <u>alleles</u> that you have. Your <u>phenotype</u> is the <u>characteristics</u> the alleles produce.

Genetic diagrams show how alleles can be inherited

Lots of tricky, technical words to learn on this page. It's really important that you do learn them all though, so you can use them correctly and explain what they mean. Try covering up the page and scribbling down everything you can remember. Keep going till you've got it all.

Genetic Diagrams

If you haven't read the previous page, do it now. Trust me — you won't be able to make head nor tails of this lot if you haven't <u>learnt what all the words mean</u> first.

Genetic Diagrams *Show the* Possible Alleles *in the* Offspring

Imagine you're cross-breeding <u>hamsters</u>, and that some have a normal, boring disposition while others have a leaning towards crazy acrobatics. And suppose you know that the behaviour is due to <u>one gene</u>...

Let's say that the allele which causes the crazy nature is <u>recessive</u> — so use a '<u>b</u>'.
And normal (boring) behaviour is due to a <u>dominant allele</u> — call it '<u>B</u>'.

1) A <u>crazy</u> hamster <u>must</u> have the <u>genotype bb</u> (i.e. it must be homozygous for this trait).

2) However, a <u>normal hamster</u> could have <u>two</u> possible genotypes — BB (homozygous) or Bb (heterozygous), because the dominant allele (B) <u>overrules</u> the recessive one (b).

3) Here's what happens if you breed from two <u>heterozygous</u> hamsters:

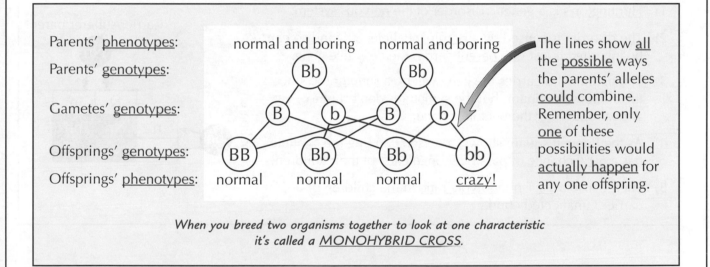

Parents' <u>phenotypes</u>: normal and boring   normal and boring

Parents' <u>genotypes</u>: Bb   Bb

Gametes' <u>genotypes</u>: B   b   B   b

Offsprings' <u>genotypes</u>: BB   Bb   Bb   bb

Offsprings' <u>phenotypes</u>: normal   normal   normal   <u>crazy!</u>

The lines show <u>all</u> the <u>possible</u> ways the parents' alleles <u>could</u> combine. Remember, only <u>one</u> of these possibilities would <u>actually happen</u> for any one offspring.

When you breed two organisms together to look at one characteristic it's called a <u>MONOHYBRID CROSS</u>.

Results *of the* Heterozygous Cross

There's a <u>75% chance</u> of having a normal, boring hamster, and a <u>25% chance</u> of a crazy one.
To put that another way... you'd expect a <u>3 : 1 ratio</u> of normal : crazy hamsters.
This ratio is called a <u>phenotypic ratio</u> (because it's a ratio of different phenotypes).

Breeding Two Homozygous *Hamsters*

If you breed <u>two homozygous</u> hamsters there's only <u>one possible offspring</u> you can end up with.

For example, breeding <u>BB</u> and <u>bb</u> hamsters can only give offspring with a <u>Bb genotype</u> — and they'd all have a <u>normal phenotype</u>.

More Genetic Diagrams

Just when you thought it was safe... <u>More genetic diagrams</u>. Mwa ha haaa. Ahem. Actually they're really not that bad. And I've given you lots of <u>lovely examples</u> to help you out.

There's **Another Way** to **Draw Genetic Diagrams**

You can also draw a type of genetic diagram called a <u>Punnett square</u>. They're dead easy to do. You start by drawing a <u>grid</u> like this.

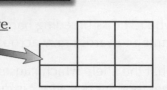

Then you <u>fill it in</u> like this:

1) Put the <u>possible gametes</u> from <u>one</u> parent down the side, and those from the <u>other</u> parent along the top.

2) In each middle square, <u>fill in</u> the letters from the top and side that <u>line up</u> with that square. The <u>pairs of letters</u> in the middle show the possible combinations of the gametes.

Example:

1) <u>Huntington's</u> is a genetic disorder of the <u>nervous system</u>.

2) The disorder is caused by a <u>dominant allele</u>, 'N', and so can be inherited if just <u>one parent</u> carries the defective gene.

3) The parent who carries the gene will be a <u>sufferer</u> too since the allele is dominant, but the <u>symptoms</u> don't start to appear until <u>after</u> the person is about 40.

4) As the Punnett square shows, a person carrying the N allele has a <u>50% chance</u> of passing it on to each of their children.

5) There's also a <u>1 : 1 phenotypic ratio</u> in the children of carrier : unaffected child.

Carrier/sufferer parent

	N	n
n	Nn	nn
n	Nn	nn

Normal parent — nn

You Can Draw **Genetic Diagrams** for **Codominant Inheritance**

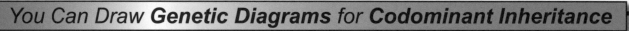

For the Paper 2 exam, you might need to work out the outcome of a monohybrid cross involving <u>codominant alleles</u> (see page 110).

Don't worry, it's pretty straightforward — you can use a <u>genetic diagram</u> like the ones above to help you.

Here's an <u>example</u>:

Codominant Inheritance of Blood Groups

1) Your <u>blood type</u> is determined by <u>two codominant alleles</u> (<u>A</u> and <u>B</u>) and one recessive one (O).

2) Blood can be <u>type A</u> (AA or AO genotype), <u>type B</u> (BB or BO genotype), <u>type AB</u> (AB genotype) or <u>type O</u> (OO genotype).

3) As the Punnett square shows, for two people with <u>type AB</u> blood there's a <u>50% chance</u> their children will be type AB, a <u>25% chance</u> they'll be type A and a <u>25% chance</u> they'll be type B.

'O' is a recessive allele, but it's usually written as a capital letter. There's an exception to every rule...

Parent 1 — AB

	A	B
A	AA	AB
B	AB	BB

Parent 2 — AB

Paper 2

Paper 2

Paper 2

Paper 2

Family Pedigrees

Once you've got your head around genetic diagrams (see pages 111-112), family pedigrees are really quite straightforward. Which is probably something of a relief.

You Need to Understand Family Pedigrees

Knowing how inheritance works helps you to interpret a family pedigree (a family tree of genetic disorders).

Here's a worked example using cystic fibrosis — a genetic disorder of the cell membranes.

Example: Inheritance of Cystic Fibrosis

1) The allele which causes cystic fibrosis is a recessive allele, 'f', carried by about 1 person in 30.

2) Because it's recessive, people with only one copy of the allele won't have the disorder — they're known as carriers.

3) For a child to have a chance of inheriting the disorder, both parents must be either carriers or sufferers.

4) As the diagram shows, there's a 1 in 4 chance of a child having the disorder if both parents are carriers.

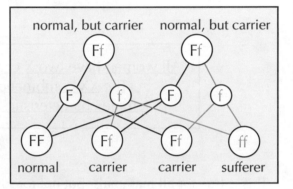

Example: Family Pedigree Showing Inheritance of Cystic Fibrosis

Below is a family pedigree for a family that includes cystic fibrosis sufferers.

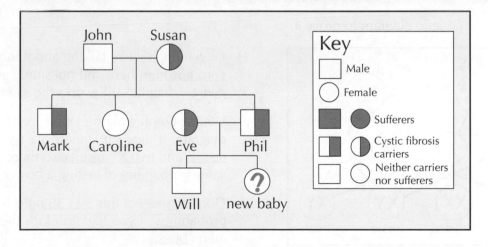

1) The allele for cystic fibrosis isn't dominant because plenty of the family carry the allele but aren't sufferers.

2) There is a 25% chance that the new baby will be a sufferer and a 50% chance that it will be a carrier because both of its parents are carriers but not sufferers.

3) The case of the new baby is just the same as in the genetic diagram above — so the baby could be normal (FF), a carrier (Ff) or a sufferer (ff).

Sex Determination

Now for a couple of <u>very important</u> little chromosomes...

Your Chromosomes Control Whether You're Male or Female

There are <u>23 matched pairs</u> of <u>chromosomes</u> in every human body cell. The <u>23rd pair</u> is labelled <u>XX</u> or <u>XY</u>. They're the two chromosomes that decide whether you turn out <u>male</u> or <u>female</u>.

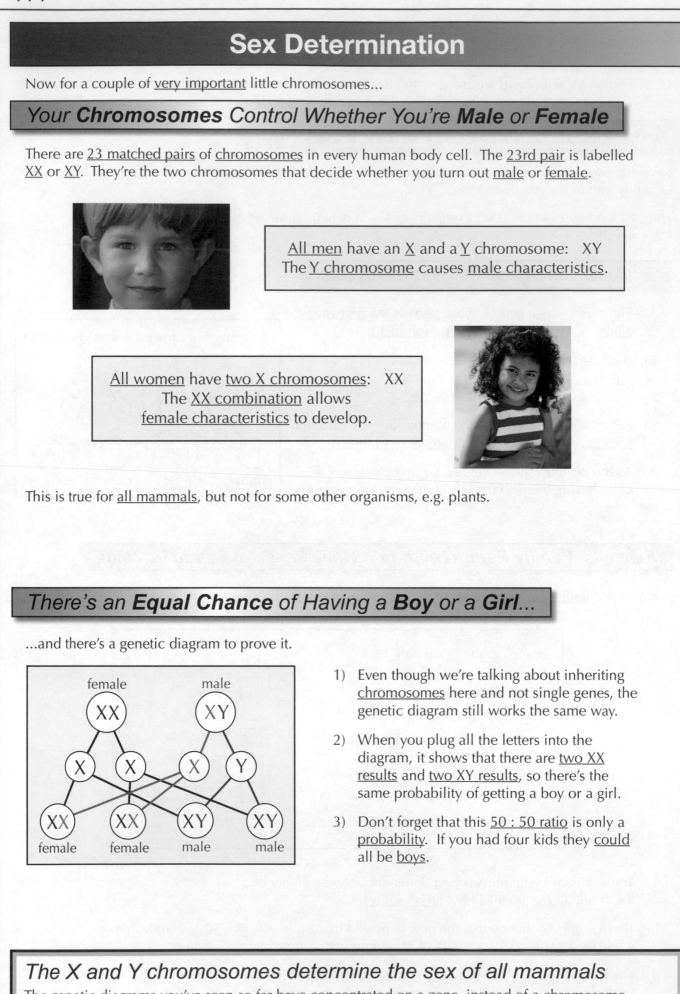

> <u>All men</u> have an <u>X</u> and a <u>Y</u> chromosome: XY
> The <u>Y chromosome</u> causes <u>male characteristics</u>.

> <u>All women</u> have <u>two X chromosomes</u>:   XX
> The <u>XX combination</u> allows
> <u>female characteristics</u> to develop.

This is true for <u>all mammals</u>, but not for some other organisms, e.g. plants.

There's an Equal Chance of Having a Boy or a Girl...

...and there's a genetic diagram to prove it.

1) Even though we're talking about inheriting <u>chromosomes</u> here and not single genes, the genetic diagram still works the same way.

2) When you plug all the letters into the diagram, it shows that there are <u>two XX results</u> and <u>two XY results</u>, so there's the same probability of getting a boy or a girl.

3) Don't forget that this <u>50 : 50 ratio</u> is only a <u>probability</u>. If you had four kids they <u>could</u> all be <u>boys</u>.

The X and Y chromosomes determine the sex of all mammals

The genetic diagrams you've seen so far have concentrated on a <u>gene</u>, instead of a <u>chromosome</u>, but the principle's the same. Sex determination is a nice easy topic to end all this genetics business on — which is double the reason to make sure you know it all inside out.

Warm-Up and Exam Questions

By doing these questions, you'll soon find out what you know and what you don't.
Once you've finished, take the time to go back over the bits you've struggled with.

Warm-Up Questions

1) What are alleles?
2) What does genotype mean?
3) In a genetic diagram, what are capital letters used to represent?
4) Which chromosome causes male characteristics?

Exam Questions

1   Wilma carries a recessive allele, **b**, for red hair and a dominant allele, **B**, for brown hair.

   a)   What is Wilma's phenotype?

   (1 mark)

   b)   Wilma's genotype is **Bb**.
        What is the term used to describe this genotype?

   (1 mark)

2   Fruit flies usually have red eyes. However, there are a small number of
    white-eyed fruit flies. Having white eyes is a recessive characteristic.

    Two fruit flies with red eyes have the heterozygous genotype for this characteristic.
    They are crossed to produce offspring.

   a)   Draw a genetic diagram to show the genotypes of the parent flies, the genotypes of
        the parents' gametes and the genotypes and phenotypes of the possible offspring.

        Use **R** to represent the dominant allele and **r** to represent the recessive allele.

   (4 marks)

   b)   State the probability that one of the fruit flies' offspring will have white eyes.

   (1 mark)

3   Albinism is a condition characterised by the lack of pigment in the hair and skin.
    It is caused by the recessive allele **a**. The dominant allele **A** results in normal pigmentation.

   a)   State the possible genotypes of a rabbit that shows no symptoms of albinism.

   (1 mark)

   A rabbit with albinism mated with a rabbit that showed no symptoms of the condition.
   They produced 12 offspring, 7 of which had albinism.

   b)   Calculate the percentage of offspring with albinism. Show your working.

   (2 marks)

   c)   i)   Deduce the genotypes of the parent rabbits. Use a genetic diagram
             to show the parents' genotypes, the genotypes of their gametes,
             and the possible genotypes and phenotypes of the offspring.

   (4 marks)

       ii)   From your genetic diagram, what percentage of
             offspring are likely to have albinism?

   (1 mark)

Exam Questions

3   c)   iii)   Explain why the percentage of offspring with albinism you calculated in part b) is not the same as that suggested by the genetic diagram.

(1 mark)

4   Polydactyly is a genetic disorder transmitted by the dominant allele **D**. The corresponding recessive allele is **d**. The family pedigree of a family with a history of polydactyly is shown.

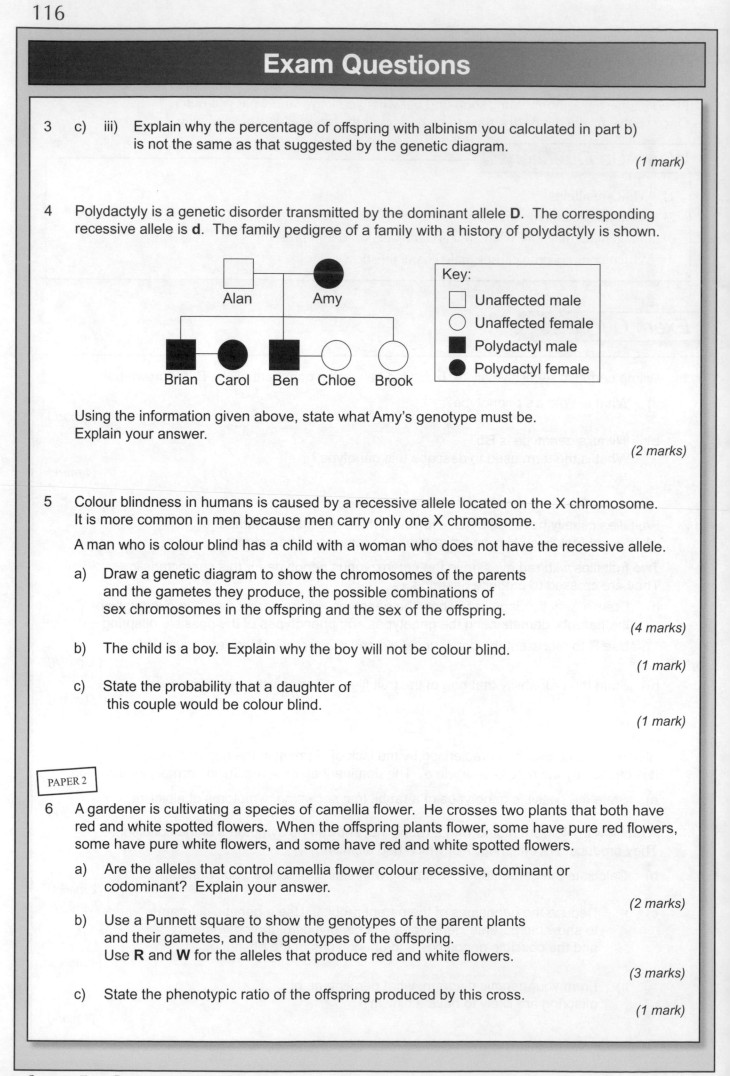

Using the information given above, state what Amy's genotype must be.
Explain your answer.

(2 marks)

5   Colour blindness in humans is caused by a recessive allele located on the X chromosome.
It is more common in men because men carry only one X chromosome.

A man who is colour blind has a child with a woman who does not have the recessive allele.

a)   Draw a genetic diagram to show the chromosomes of the parents
and the gametes they produce, the possible combinations of
sex chromosomes in the offspring and the sex of the offspring.

(4 marks)

b)   The child is a boy. Explain why the boy will not be colour blind.

(1 mark)

c)   State the probability that a daughter of
this couple would be colour blind.

(1 mark)

PAPER 2

6   A gardener is cultivating a species of camellia flower. He crosses two plants that both have red and white spotted flowers. When the offspring plants flower, some have pure red flowers, some have pure white flowers, and some have red and white spotted flowers.

a)   Are the alleles that control camellia flower colour recessive, dominant or
codominant? Explain your answer.

(2 marks)

b)   Use a Punnett square to show the genotypes of the parent plants
and their gametes, and the genotypes of the offspring.
Use **R** and **W** for the alleles that produce red and white flowers.

(3 marks)

c)   State the phenotypic ratio of the offspring produced by this cross.

(1 mark)

Variation

All variation means is how animals or plants of the same species <u>look or behave slightly differently</u> <u>from each other</u>. There are two kinds of variation — <u>genetic</u> and <u>environmental</u>.

Genetic Variation is Caused by... Genes (Surprise)

Sexual reproduction produces genetic variation in other species too, e.g. <u>plants</u>.

1) All <u>animals</u> (including humans) are bound to be <u>slightly different</u> from each other because their <u>genes</u> are slightly different.

2) You might remember from p.94 that genes determine how your body turns out — they control your <u>inherited traits</u>, e.g. <u>eye colour</u>. We all end up with a <u>slightly different</u> set of genes. The <u>exceptions</u> to this rule are <u>identical twins</u>, because their genes are <u>exactly the same</u>.

Most Variation in Animals is Due to Genes AND Environment

1) Most variation in animals is caused by a <u>mixture</u> of genetic and environmental factors.

2) Almost every single aspect of a human (or other animal) is <u>affected by</u> <u>our environment</u> in some way, however small. In fact it's a lot <u>easier</u> to list the factors which <u>aren't</u> affected in any way by environment:

If you're not sure what "environment" means, think of it as "upbringing" instead.

- <u>Eye colour</u>,
- <u>Hair colour</u> in most animals (in humans, vanity plays a big part),
- <u>Inherited disorders</u> like haemophilia, cystic fibrosis, etc.,
- <u>Blood group</u>.

3) <u>Environment</u> can have a large effect on human growth even <u>before</u> someone's born. For example, a baby's <u>weight</u> at birth can be affected by the mother's <u>diet</u>.

4) And having a <u>poor diet</u> whilst you're growing up can <u>stunt your growth</u> — another environmental variation.

5) For some characteristics, it's <u>hard to say</u> which factor is more important — genes or environment...

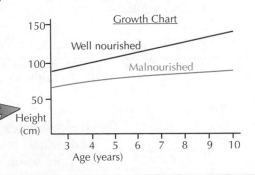

- <u>Health</u> — Some people are more likely to get certain <u>diseases</u> (e.g. <u>cancer</u> and <u>heart disease</u>) because of their genes. But <u>lifestyle</u> also affects the risk, e.g. if you smoke or only eat junk food.
- <u>Intelligence</u> — One theory is that although your <u>maximum possible IQ</u> might be determined by your <u>genes</u>, whether you get to it depends on your <u>environment</u>, e.g. your <u>upbringing</u> and <u>school</u> life.
- <u>Sporting ability</u> — Again, genes probably determine your <u>potential</u>, but training is important too.

Environmental Variation in Plants is Much Greater

Plants are strongly affected by:
1) sunlight, 2) moisture level, 3) temperature, 4) the mineral content of the soil.

For example, plants may grow <u>twice as big</u> or <u>twice as fast</u> due to <u>fairly modest</u> changes in environment such as the amount of <u>sunlight</u> or <u>rainfall</u> they're getting, or how <u>warm</u> it is or what the <u>soil</u> is like.

Think about it — if you give your pot plant some plant food (full of lovely minerals), then your plant grows loads faster. Farmers and gardeners use <u>mineral fertilisers</u> to improve crop yields.

Evolution and Natural Selection

The <u>theory of evolution</u> states that one of your (probably very distant) ancestors was a <u>blob</u> in a swamp somewhere. Something like that, anyway. It's probably best to read on for more details...

Make Sure You Know the *Theory of Evolution*

> **THEORY OF EVOLUTION:**
> **Life began as simple organisms from which more complex organisms evolved (rather than just popping into existence).**

1) The whole <u>process</u> of evolution usually takes place gradually over <u>millions of years</u>.

2) It's still going on today, e.g. some <u>bacteria</u> are evolving to become <u>resistant to antibiotics</u> (see page 120).

Natural Selection *Means the "Survival of the Fittest"*

<u>Natural selection</u> is one of the key <u>processes</u> that causes <u>evolution</u>. It works like this:

1) Living things show <u>variation</u> — they're <u>not</u> all the same.

(OK, it's fairly simple so far.)

Genetic variation is caused by sexual reproduction (see p.96) and mutations in genes (see p.120).

2) The <u>resources</u> living things need to survive are <u>limited</u>. Individuals must <u>compete</u> for these resources to <u>survive</u> — only some of the individuals will survive.

3) Some of the <u>varieties</u> of a particular species will have a <u>better chance</u> of survival. Those varieties will then have an increased chance of <u>breeding</u> and passing on their <u>genes</u>.

4) This means that a <u>greater</u> proportion of individuals in the next generation will have the better <u>alleles</u>, and so the <u>characteristics</u>, that help <u>survival</u>.

5) Over many generations, the species becomes better and better able to <u>survive</u>. The 'best' features are <u>naturally selected</u> and the species becomes more and more <u>adapted</u> to its environment.

I wonder what exams evolved from...

Natural selection's all about the organisms with the best characteristics surviving to pass on their genes so that the whole species ends up adapted to its environment. It doesn't happen overnight though.

Evolution and Natural Selection

Here's an **Example** of Natural Selection

1) Once upon a time maybe all rabbits had <u>short ears</u> and managed OK.

2) Then one day out popped a rabbit with <u>big ears</u> who could hear better and was always the first to dive for cover at the sound of a predator.

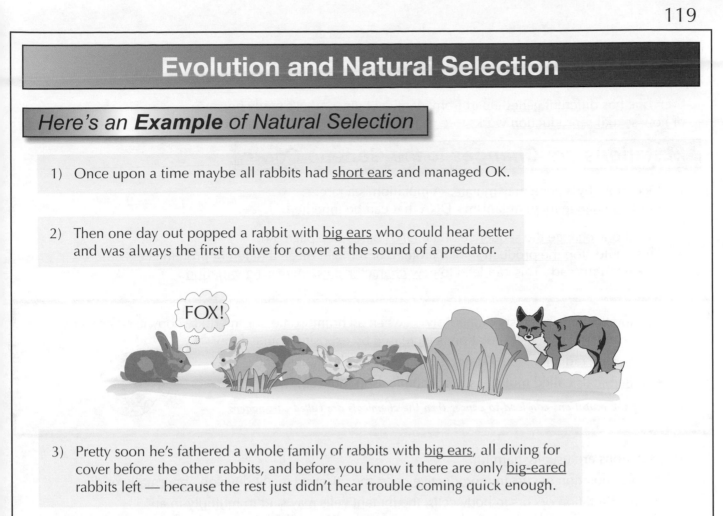

FOX!

3) Pretty soon he's fathered a whole family of rabbits with <u>big ears</u>, all diving for cover before the other rabbits, and before you know it there are only <u>big-eared</u> rabbits left — because the rest just didn't hear trouble coming quick enough.

This is how populations <u>adapt</u> to survive better in their environment (an organism doesn't actually change when it's alive — changes only occur from generation to generation).

Over many generations the <u>characteristic</u> that <u>increases survival</u> becomes <u>more common</u> in the population. If members of a species are separated somehow, and evolve in different ways to adapt to different conditions, then over time you can end up with two totally <u>different species</u>.

The **Best Genes** for a **Particular Environment** Tend to Survive

1) The individuals who are <u>less suited</u> to an environment are <u>less likely</u> to survive than those that are better suited, and so have <u>less chance</u> to pass their <u>alleles</u> on.

2) Gradually, over time, this results in a population which is extremely <u>well suited</u> to the environment in which it lives.

3) Remember — <u>variations</u> that are caused by the <u>environment</u> itself (e.g. accidentally losing a finger) <u>aren't</u> involved in natural selection. Variations in a species can have either <u>environmental</u> or <u>genetic causes</u>, but only the <u>genetic</u> ones are passed on to the next generation and influence the <u>evolution</u> of the species.

Natural selection — the fittest pass on their characteristics

It's no good being really great at surviving if for some reason you don't breed and <u>pass on your genes</u>. Also remember that it's only <u>genetic traits</u> that get passed on. So if you have funny ears, but have plastic surgery to make them nicer, your kids can still inherit your old ears, not your new prettier ones.

Mutations and Antibiotic Resistance

Everyone has different <u>genes</u> (apart from identical twins). That's partly because
of how <u>sexual reproduction</u> works (see page 96) and partly due to <u>mutation</u>.

Mutations are Changes to the Genetic Code

1) <u>Occasionally</u> a gene may <u>mutate</u>. A mutation is a <u>rare</u>,
   <u>random change</u> in an organism's <u>DNA</u> that can be <u>inherited</u>.

2) Mutations <u>change the sequence</u> of the <u>DNA bases</u> (see page 94).
   This could <u>stop the production</u> of a <u>protein</u>, or it might mean a <u>different</u> protein is
   produced instead. This can lead to <u>new characteristics</u>, <u>increasing variation</u>.

3) Mutations can happen <u>spontaneously</u> — when a chromosome doesn't quite copy itself properly.
   However, the chance of mutation is <u>increased</u> by exposing yourself to:
   - <u>ionising radiation</u>, e.g. X-rays, gamma rays or ultraviolet light,
   - <u>chemicals</u> called <u>mutagens</u>, e.g. chemicals in tobacco.

   If the mutations can lead to cancer then the chemicals are called <u>carcinogens</u>.

4) Mutations are <u>usually harmful</u>.
   - If a mutation occurs in <u>reproductive cells</u>, the offspring might develop <u>abnormally</u> or <u>die</u>.
   - If a mutation occurs in body cells, the mutant cells may start to <u>multiply</u> in an
     <u>uncontrolled</u> way and <u>invade</u> other parts of the body (which is <u>cancer</u>).

5) <u>Some</u> mutations have <u>no effect</u> at all, for example, if they occur in an <u>unimportant</u> part of the DNA
   — these mutations are said to be <u>neutral</u>.

6) <u>Very occasionally</u>, mutations are <u>beneficial</u> and give an organism a <u>survival advantage</u>, so it can live
   on in conditions where the others die. This is <u>natural selection</u> at work (see the previous two pages).
   For example, a mutation in a bacterium might make it <u>resistant to antibiotics</u>. If this mutant gene is
   passed on, you might get a <u>resistant</u> "<u>strain</u>" of bacteria, which antibiotics can't kill — see below...

Bacteria can Evolve and Become Antibiotic-Resistant

1) Like all organisms, bacteria sometimes develop <u>random mutations</u> in their DNA.
   These can lead to <u>changes</u> in the bacteria's characteristics.
   Sometimes, they mean that a bacterium is <u>less affected</u> by a particular <u>antibiotic</u>.

2) For the bacterium, this ability to resist antibiotics is a big <u>advantage</u>.
   It's better able to survive, even in a host who's being treated to get rid of
   the infection, and so it lives for longer and <u>reproduces</u> many more times.

3) This leads to the <u>gene</u> for resistance being <u>passed on</u> to lots of offspring
   — it's just <u>natural selection</u>. This is how it spreads and becomes
   <u>more common</u> in a population of bacteria over time.

*If you're prescribed
antibiotics, it's important
to finish the whole course
— this helps to prevent the
spread of antibiotic resistance.
Doctors only prescribing
antibiotics when they're really
needed helps too.*

4) This is a problem for people who become <u>infected</u> with these bacteria,
   because you <u>can't</u> easily get rid of them with antibiotics. Sometimes drug
   companies can come up with a <u>new</u> antibiotic that's effective, but '<u>superbugs</u>'
   that are resistant to most known antibiotics (e.g. MRSA) are becoming more common.

Paper 2

Paper 2

Warm-Up and Exam Questions

You need to test your knowledge with a few warm-up questions, followed by some exam questions...

Warm-Up Questions

1) Give four environmental conditions that strongly affect plant characteristics.
2) Outline the theory of evolution.
3) Name three types of ionising radiation. What effect can ionising radiation have on DNA?
4) Give an example of where chemical mutagens can be found.

Exam Questions

1   Helen and Stephanie are identical twins.

   a)   Helen has brown hair and Stephanie has blonde hair.
      Are these likely to be the natural hair colours of both girls? Explain your answer.

(2 marks)

   b)   Helen weighs 7 kg more than Stephanie.
      Explain whether this is due to genes, environmental factors or both.

(2 marks)

   c)   Stephanie has a birthmark on her shoulder. Helen doesn't.
      State whether birthmarks are caused by genes and explain your answer.

(1 mark)

2   Genetic variation in a population arises partly due to mutations.

   a)   What is meant by the term **mutation**?

(2 marks)

   b)   Explain how mutations can increase variation in a species.

(3 marks)

   c)   Some mutations are neutral, having no effect on an
      organism, but most do have an impact.
      i)   Suggest how some mutations may be beneficial.

(2 marks)

      ii) Suggest why a mutation in a reproductive cell could be harmful.

(1 mark)

3   The photograph shows an adult buff tip moth.
   The buff tip moth's appearance mimics a
   broken stick, making it well camouflaged.

   Describe and explain how the moth
   might have evolved to look like this.
       (5 marks)

Exam Questions

4   Suggest explanations for the following observations.

a)   In 1986, an explosion at the Chernobyl Nuclear Power Plant released radioactive material into the surrounding area. This material decayed, giving off gamma rays. After the explosion, the rate of thyroid cancer amongst children in the surrounding area increased dramatically.

(3 marks)

b)   If fruit flies with normal wings are given high doses of X-rays, they are apparently unharmed. However, when they breed, they produce a completely new variety of fruit fly with short wings.

(3 marks)

5   *Staphylococcus aureus* (SA) is a common bacterium that is found on the skin and mucous membranes. It can enter the body through open wounds and may cause mild infections in healthy people, but more serious illness in people with weakened immune systems. Some strains of SA have developed resistance to the antibiotic methicillin, and are known as Methicillin-resistant *Staphylococcus aureus* (MRSA).

a)   Name the process that leads to the spread of antibiotic resistance in bacteria.

(1 mark)

b)   The table below shows the different stages that led to *Staphylococcus aureus* becoming resistant to methicillin. The stages are shown in the wrong order. Write out the letters **A-D** to show the stages in the correct order.

	Stage
A	The gene for methicillin resistance became more common in the population over time, eventually giving a large proportion of the population resistance.
B	Individual bacteria with the mutated genes were more likely to survive and reproduce in a host being treated with methicillin.
C	Random mutations in the DNA of *Staphylococcus aureus* led to it being less affected by methicillin.
D	The gene for methicillin resistance was passed on to lots of offspring, who also survived and reproduced.

(4 marks)

c)   Suggest why MRSA is a more serious problem in hospitals than in wider society.

(2 marks)

d)   Explain why antibiotic resistance in bacteria is a concern for humans.

(1 mark)

e)   Suggest why the National Health Service (NHS) is trying to reduce the use of antibiotics.

(3 marks)

Revision Summary for Section 7

There's a lot to remember in this section, with quite a variety of topics — but the 'R' word pretty much sums it all up. (Reproduction.) So now all you've got to do is the other 'R' word. (Revise.) But don't worry — I've made another load of questions to help you. Work your way through them and then, if you get any wrong, go back and learn those bits again. Can't say fairer than that.

1) What is a gene?

2) Name the four different bases found in DNA. How do they pair up?

3) a) Name the type of cell division used in asexual reproduction.
b) Apart from asexual reproduction, what else is this type of cell division used for?

4) Explain why sexual reproduction results in offspring that are genetically different from either parent.

5) Name the type of cell division that creates gametes. Where does it take place in humans?

6) Name the male and female reproductive parts of a flower.

7) What is pollination?

8) Give three differences between plants that are pollinated by insects and ones that are wind-pollinated.

9) What is fertilisation? How does the pollen get from the stigma to the ovary?

10) Give an example of a plant that reproduces asexually and briefly describe how it happens.

11) Describe how to make plant clones from cuttings.

12) Where are sperm made? Where are ova made?

13) What secondary sexual characteristics does testosterone trigger in males?

14) Sketch a timeline of the 28-day menstrual cycle. Label the four stages of the cycle and show when the ovum is released.

15) What roles do oestrogen and progesterone play in the menstrual cycle?

16) What is the function of the amniotic fluid in pregnancy?

17) What does it mean if you are homozygous for a particular trait?

18) What are codominant alleles?

19)* Draw a genetic diagram for a cross between a man who has blue eyes (bb) and a woman who has green eyes (Bb). The gene for blue eyes (b) is recessive. What is the probability of the couple having a blue-eyed child?

20) Which two chromosomes determine whether you are male or female?

21) Draw a genetic diagram showing that there's an equal chance of a baby being a boy or a girl.

22) List four features of animals which aren't affected at all by their environment, and three which are.

23) Explain what is meant by natural selection.

24) What is a 'superbug'?

* Answer on p.210

Ecosystems

You Need to Learn Some **Definitions** to get you Started

> Habitat   — The place where an organism lives, e.g. a rocky shore or a field.
> Population — All the organisms of one species in a habitat.
> Community   — All the different species in a habitat.
> Ecosystem   — All the organisms living in a particular area and all the non-living
>   (abiotic) conditions, e.g. temperature, climate, soil-type.

You Can Use a **Quadrat** to Estimate **Population Sizes**

A quadrat is a square frame enclosing a known area, e.g. 1 m².
You just place it on the ground, and look at what's inside it. To estimate population size in an area:

1) Place a 1 m² quadrat on the ground at a random point within the area you're investigating.

2) Count all the organisms within the quadrat.

3) Multiply the number of organisms by the total area (in m²) of the habitat.

You can then do this again in another area and compare the population sizes.

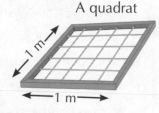

A quadrat

*Samples should be random to avoid bias, e.g. if you were investigating
a field you could pick random sample sites by dividing the field into a
grid and using a random number generator to select coordinates.*

Two Important Points About This Kind of Counting Method...

1) The sample may not be representative of the population, i.e. what you find in your particular
   sample might be different from what you'd have found if you'd looked at other bits of the habitat.

2) The sample size affects the accuracy of the estimate — the bigger your sample,
   the more accurate your estimate of the total population is likely to be. So it's
   better to use the quadrat at several points, get an average value for the number
   of organisms in a 1 m² quadrat, then multiply that by the total area.

You Can Use **Quadrats** to Investigate **Distribution** too

You can use quadrats to help find out how organisms (like plants) are distributed across
their habitat — e.g. how species change from a hedge towards the middle of a field.
The quadrats are laid out along a line called a transect.

Here's what to do:

1) Mark out a line in the area you
   want to study e.g. from the hedge
   to the middle of the field.

2) Then collect data at
   regular intervals along
   the line using quadrats.

tape measure

quadrat

*Transects can be used in any
ecosystem, not just fields.
For example, along a beach.*

*A point quadrat is another sort of quadrat that's used sometimes for studying plant populations.
It looks kind of like a test-tube rack. You poke a metal pin down each hole in the rack and record
what species it touches, then move the rack along a bit. This makes it very precise, but also very faffy.*

Food Chains and Food Webs

A <u>trophic level</u> is a <u>feeding</u> level. It comes from the Greek word <u>trophe</u> meaning 'nourishment'.

*Food Chains Show **What's Eaten by What** in an Ecosystem*

1) <u>Food chains</u> always start with a <u>producer</u>, e.g. a plant.
   Producers <u>make</u> (produce) <u>their own food</u> using energy from the Sun.

2) Producers are eaten by <u>primary consumers</u>.
   Primary consumers are then eaten by <u>secondary consumers</u>
   and secondary consumers are eaten by <u>tertiary consumers</u>.

3) All these organisms eventually die and get eaten by <u>decomposers</u>,
   e.g. bacteria. Decomposers <u>break down</u> (decompose) <u>dead material</u> and <u>waste</u>.

4) Each <u>stage</u> (e.g. producers, primary consumers) is called a <u>trophic level</u>.

*Consumers are organisms
that eat other organisms.
'Primary' means 'first', so
primary consumers are the first
consumers in a food chain.
Secondary consumers are second
and tertiary consumers are third.*

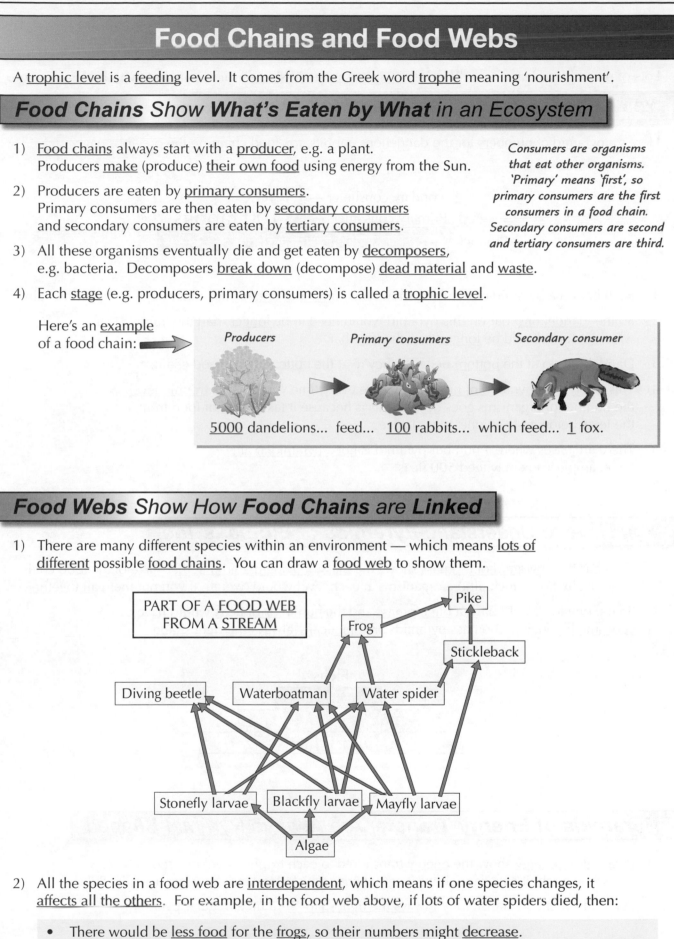

Here's an <u>example</u>
of a food chain:

Producers   **Primary consumers**   **Secondary consumer**

<u>5000</u> dandelions... feed...   <u>100</u> rabbits... which feed...   <u>1</u> fox.

*Food Webs Show How **Food Chains** are **Linked***

1) There are many different species within an environment — which means <u>lots of
   different</u> possible <u>food chains</u>. You can draw a <u>food web</u> to show them.

PART OF A <u>FOOD WEB</u>
FROM A <u>STREAM</u>

Pike

Frog

Stickleback

Diving beetle   Waterboatman   Water spider

Stonefly larvae   Blackfly larvae   Mayfly larvae

Algae

2) All the species in a food web are <u>interdependent</u>, which means if one species changes, it
   <u>affects all the others</u>. For example, in the food web above, if lots of water spiders died, then:

- There would be <u>less food</u> for the <u>frogs</u>, so their numbers might <u>decrease</u>.

- The number of <u>mayfly larvae</u> might <u>increase</u> since the water spiders wouldn't be eating them.

- The <u>diving beetles</u> wouldn't be <u>competing</u> with the water
  spiders for food, so their numbers might <u>increase</u>.

Pyramids of Number, Biomass and Energy

Lots of pyramids to learn here. They're <u>not always pyramid-shaped</u> mind you, but that's biology for you.

You Need to Understand **Pyramids of Numbers**

Here's a <u>pyramid of numbers</u> for the dandelions, rabbits, fox food chain on the previous page.

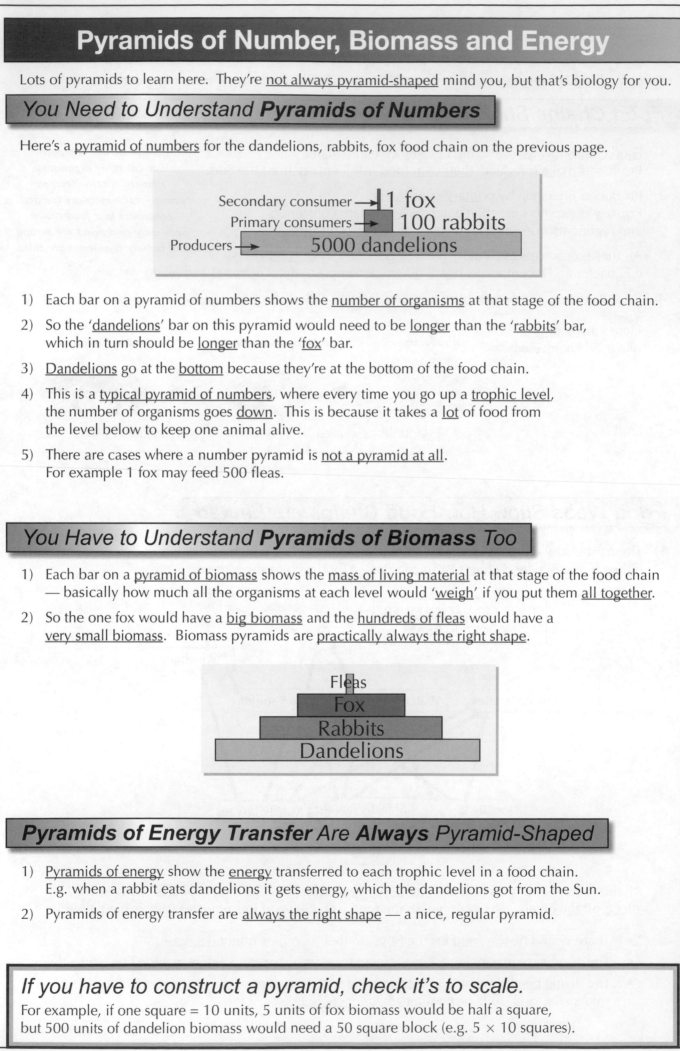

Secondary consumer → 1 fox
Primary consumers → 100 rabbits
Producers → 5000 dandelions

1) Each bar on a pyramid of numbers shows the <u>number of organisms</u> at that stage of the food chain.

2) So the '<u>dandelions</u>' bar on this pyramid would need to be <u>longer</u> than the '<u>rabbits</u>' bar, which in turn should be <u>longer</u> than the '<u>fox</u>' bar.

3) <u>Dandelions</u> go at the <u>bottom</u> because they're at the bottom of the food chain.

4) This is a <u>typical pyramid of numbers</u>, where every time you go up a <u>trophic level</u>, the number of organisms goes <u>down</u>. This is because it takes a <u>lot</u> of food from the level below to keep one animal alive.

5) There are cases where a number pyramid is <u>not a pyramid at all</u>. For example 1 fox may feed 500 fleas.

You Have to Understand **Pyramids of Biomass** Too

1) Each bar on a <u>pyramid of biomass</u> shows the <u>mass of living material</u> at that stage of the food chain — basically how much all the organisms at each level would '<u>weigh</u>' if you put them <u>all together</u>.

2) So the one fox would have a <u>big biomass</u> and the <u>hundreds of fleas</u> would have a <u>very small biomass</u>. Biomass pyramids are <u>practically always the right shape</u>.

Fleas
Fox
Rabbits
Dandelions

Pyramids of Energy Transfer Are **Always** Pyramid-Shaped

1) <u>Pyramids of energy</u> show the <u>energy</u> transferred to each trophic level in a food chain. E.g. when a rabbit eats dandelions it gets energy, which the dandelions got from the Sun.

2) Pyramids of energy transfer are <u>always the right shape</u> — a nice, regular pyramid.

If you have to construct a pyramid, check it's to scale.

For example, if one square = 10 units, 5 units of fox biomass would be half a square, but 500 units of dandelion biomass would need a 50 square block (e.g. 5 × 10 squares).

Energy Transfer

Some organisms get their <u>energy</u> from the Sun and some get it from other organisms.

Energy is Transferred Along a Food Chain

1) Energy from the <u>Sun</u> is the source of energy for nearly <u>all</u> life on Earth.

2) <u>Plants</u> use light energy from the Sun to make <u>food</u> during photosynthesis. This energy then works its way through the food chain as animals eat the plants and each other.

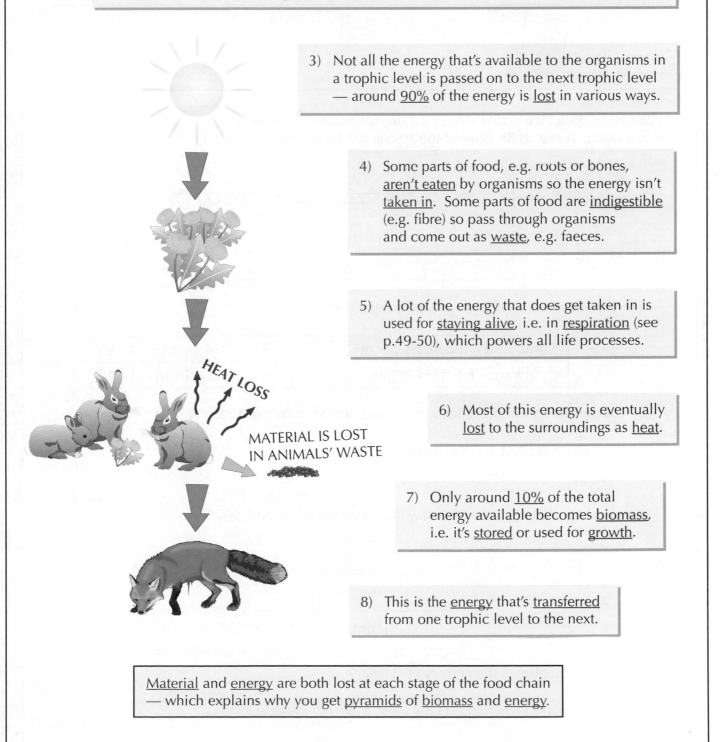

3) Not all the energy that's available to the organisms in a trophic level is passed on to the next trophic level — around <u>90%</u> of the energy is <u>lost</u> in various ways.

4) Some parts of food, e.g. roots or bones, <u>aren't eaten</u> by organisms so the energy isn't <u>taken in</u>. Some parts of food are <u>indigestible</u> (e.g. fibre) so pass through organisms and come out as <u>waste</u>, e.g. faeces.

5) A lot of the energy that does get taken in is used for <u>staying alive</u>, i.e. in <u>respiration</u> (see p.49-50), which powers all life processes.

HEAT LOSS

MATERIAL IS LOST IN ANIMALS' WASTE

6) Most of this energy is eventually <u>lost</u> to the surroundings as <u>heat</u>.

7) Only around <u>10%</u> of the total energy available becomes <u>biomass</u>, i.e. it's <u>stored</u> or used for <u>growth</u>.

8) This is the <u>energy</u> that's <u>transferred</u> from one trophic level to the next.

<u>Material</u> and <u>energy</u> are both lost at each stage of the food chain — which explains why you get <u>pyramids</u> of <u>biomass</u> and <u>energy</u>.

Warm-Up and Exam Questions

Right, now you've got to grips with how energy and material move through a food chain, have a go at these practice questions. If there's anything you're struggling with, go back and read that bit again.

Warm-Up Questions

1) What is the correct scientific term for:
   a) all the different species in a habitat?
   b) all the organisms in a particular area and all the non-living (abiotic) conditions?
2) What is meant by the term producer? What is a consumer?
3) What is a trophic level?

Exam Questions

1 Bill investigated the distribution of dandelions across a field next to a wood. A sketch Bill drew of the area is shown below.

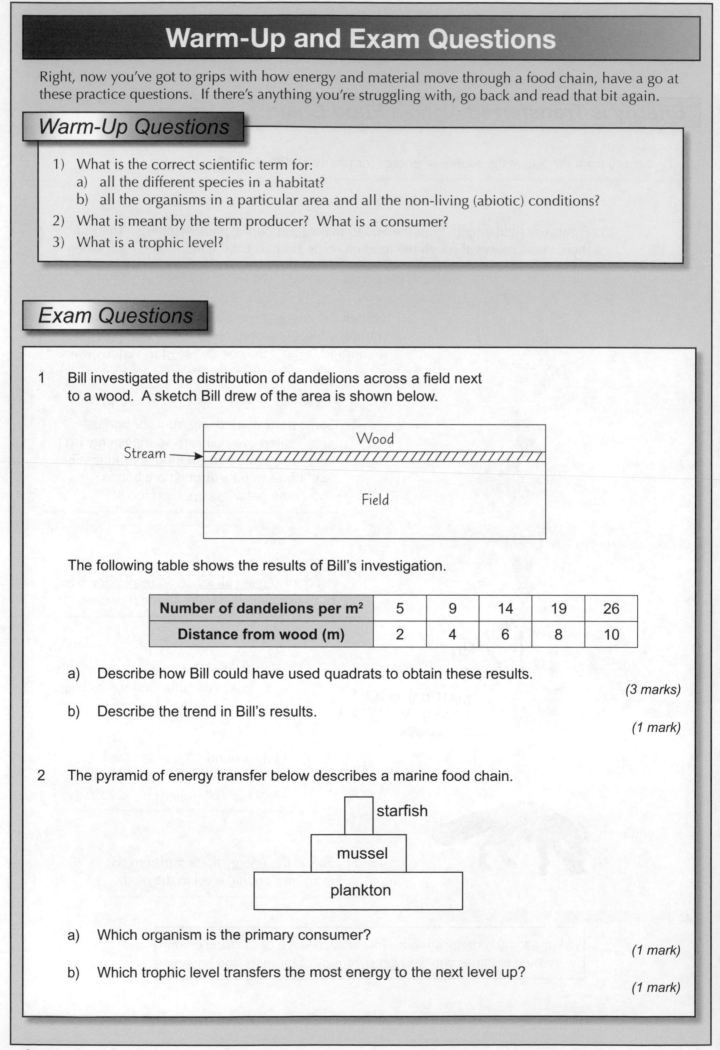

The following table shows the results of Bill's investigation.

Number of dandelions per m²	5	9	14	19	26
Distance from wood (m)	2	4	6	8	10

a) Describe how Bill could have used quadrats to obtain these results.

(3 marks)

b) Describe the trend in Bill's results.

(1 mark)

2 The pyramid of energy transfer below describes a marine food chain.

a) Which organism is the primary consumer?

(1 mark)

b) Which trophic level transfers the most energy to the next level up?

(1 mark)

Exam Questions

3 A single robin has a mass of 15 g and eats caterpillars. Each robin eats 25 caterpillars that each have a mass of 2 g. The caterpillars feed on 10 stinging nettles that together have a mass of 500 g. Study the pyramid diagrams shown then answer the questions that follow.

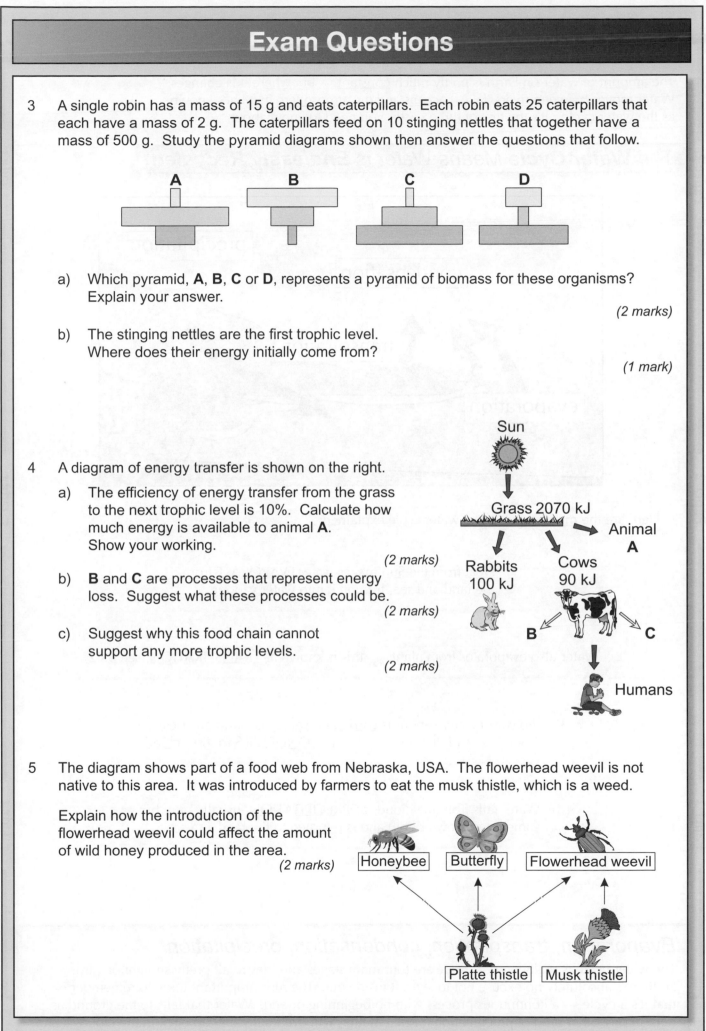

a) Which pyramid, **A**, **B**, **C** or **D**, represents a pyramid of biomass for these organisms? Explain your answer.

(2 marks)

b) The stinging nettles are the first trophic level. Where does their energy initially come from?

(1 mark)

4 A diagram of energy transfer is shown on the right.

a) The efficiency of energy transfer from the grass to the next trophic level is 10%. Calculate how much energy is available to animal **A**. Show your working.

(2 marks)

b) **B** and **C** are processes that represent energy loss. Suggest what these processes could be.

(2 marks)

c) Suggest why this food chain cannot support any more trophic levels.

(2 marks)

5 The diagram shows part of a food web from Nebraska, USA. The flowerhead weevil is not native to this area. It was introduced by farmers to eat the musk thistle, which is a weed.

Explain how the introduction of the flowerhead weevil could affect the amount of wild honey produced in the area.

(2 marks)

The Water Cycle

The <u>amount</u> of water on Earth is pretty much <u>constant</u> — but <u>where</u> it is changes.
Water moves between <u>rivers</u>, <u>lakes</u>, <u>oceans</u> and the <u>atmosphere</u> in what's known
as the <u>water cycle</u>. It's the <u>first of three</u> cycles you need to know about.

The **Water Cycle** Means Water is **Endlessly Recycled**

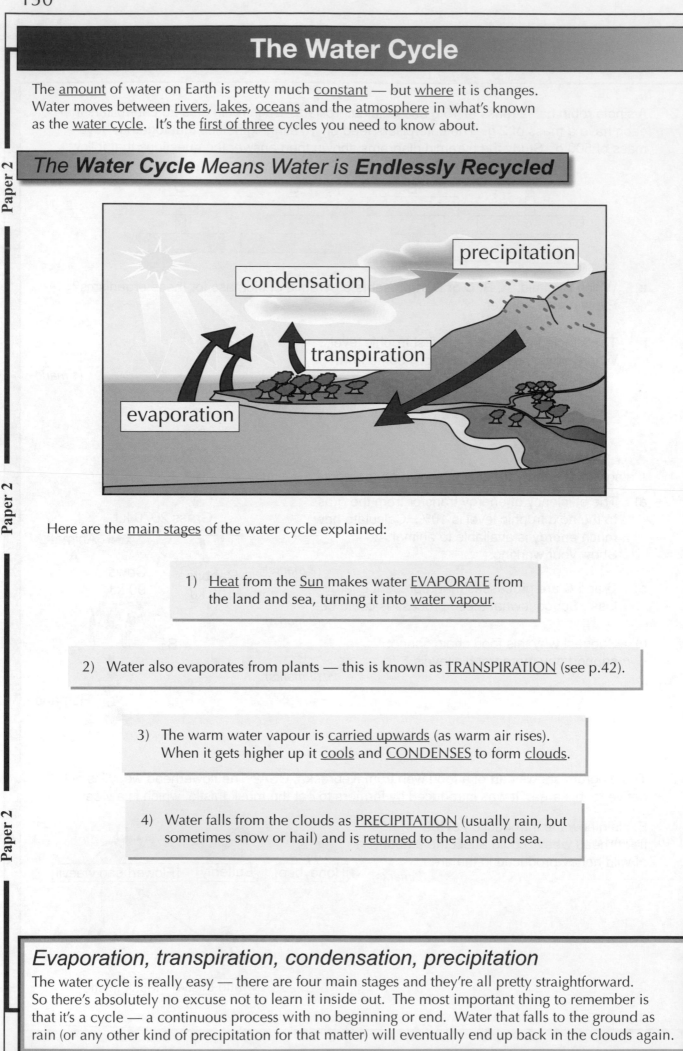

Here are the <u>main stages</u> of the water cycle explained:

1) <u>Heat</u> from the <u>Sun</u> makes water <u>EVAPORATE</u> from
    the land and sea, turning it into <u>water vapour</u>.

2) Water also evaporates from plants — this is known as <u>TRANSPIRATION</u> (see p.42).

3) The warm water vapour is <u>carried upwards</u> (as warm air rises).
    When it gets higher up it <u>cools</u> and <u>CONDENSES</u> to form <u>clouds</u>.

4) Water falls from the clouds as <u>PRECIPITATION</u> (usually rain, but
    sometimes snow or hail) and is <u>returned</u> to the land and sea.

Evaporation, transpiration, condensation, precipitation

The water cycle is really easy — there are four main stages and they're all pretty straightforward.
So there's absolutely no excuse not to learn it inside out. The most important thing to remember is
that it's a cycle — a continuous process with no beginning or end. Water that falls to the ground as
rain (or any other kind of precipitation for that matter) will eventually end up back in the clouds again.

The Carbon Cycle

All the <u>nutrients</u> in our environment are constantly being <u>recycled</u> — there's a nice balance between what <u>goes in</u> and what <u>goes out</u> again. This page is all about the recycling of <u>carbon</u>.

The **Carbon Cycle** Shows How **Carbon** is **Recycled**

<u>Carbon</u> is an important element in the materials that living things are made from.
But there's only a <u>fixed amount</u> of carbon in the world. This means it's constantly <u>recycled</u>:

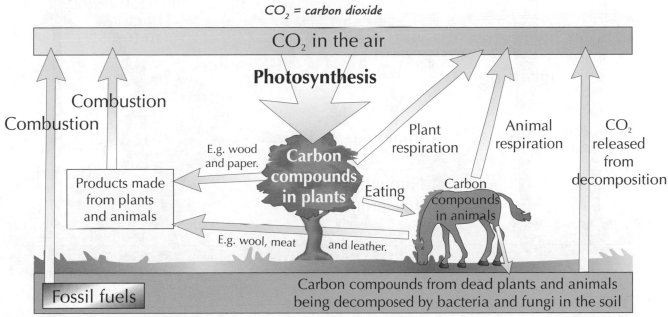

Fossil fuels are made of decayed plant and animal matter.

This diagram isn't half as bad as it looks. <u>Learn</u> these important points:

1) There's only <u>one arrow</u> going <u>down</u>. The whole thing is 'powered' by <u>photosynthesis</u>. Green <u>plants</u> use the carbon from CO_2 in the air to make <u>carbohydrates</u>, <u>fats</u> and <u>proteins</u>.

2) <u>Eating</u> passes the carbon compounds in the plant along to <u>animals</u> in a food chain or web.

3) Both plant and animal <u>respiration</u> while the organisms are alive <u>releases CO_2</u> back into the <u>air</u>.

4) Plants and animals eventually <u>die</u> and <u>decompose</u>, or are killed and turned into <u>useful products</u>.

5) When plants and animals decompose they're broken down by bacteria and fungi. These decomposers <u>release CO_2</u> back into the air by <u>respiration</u>, as they break down the material.

6) Some useful plant and animal <u>products</u>, e.g. wood and fossil fuels, are <u>burned</u> (<u>combustion</u>). This also releases <u>CO_2</u> back into the air.

Lots of processes release CO_2 — only photosynthesis takes it in

Carbon is a very <u>important element</u> for living things. Carbon molecules are found in plants, animals, your petrol tank and on your burnt toast. They get cycled round and the concentration of them in the atmosphere fluctuates up and down. Make sure you've learnt it all before you move on.

The Nitrogen Cycle

Nitrogen, just like carbon, is constantly being <u>recycled</u>. So the nitrogen in your proteins might once have been in the <u>air</u>. And before that it might have been in a <u>plant</u>. Or even in some <u>horse wee</u>. Nice.

Nitrogen is Also Recycled in the Nitrogen Cycle

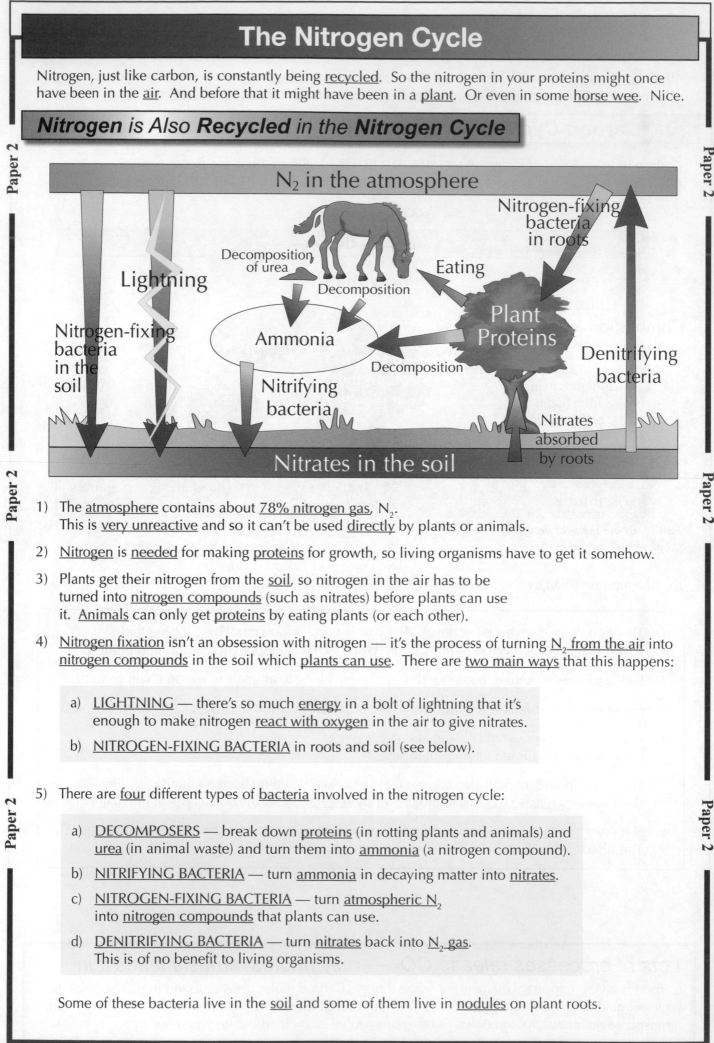

1) The <u>atmosphere</u> contains about <u>78% nitrogen gas</u>, N_2.
   This is <u>very unreactive</u> and so it can't be used <u>directly</u> by plants or animals.

2) <u>Nitrogen</u> is <u>needed</u> for making <u>proteins</u> for growth, so living organisms have to get it somehow.

3) Plants get their nitrogen from the <u>soil</u>, so nitrogen in the air has to be
   turned into <u>nitrogen compounds</u> (such as nitrates) before plants can use
   it. <u>Animals</u> can only get <u>proteins</u> by eating plants (or each other).

4) <u>Nitrogen fixation</u> isn't an obsession with nitrogen — it's the process of turning <u>N_2 from the air</u> into
   <u>nitrogen compounds</u> in the soil which <u>plants can use</u>. There are <u>two main ways</u> that this happens:

   a) <u>LIGHTNING</u> — there's so much <u>energy</u> in a bolt of lightning that it's
      enough to make nitrogen <u>react with oxygen</u> in the air to give nitrates.

   b) <u>NITROGEN-FIXING BACTERIA</u> in roots and soil (see below).

5) There are <u>four</u> different types of <u>bacteria</u> involved in the nitrogen cycle:

   a) <u>DECOMPOSERS</u> — break down <u>proteins</u> (in rotting plants and animals) and
      <u>urea</u> (in animal waste) and turn them into <u>ammonia</u> (a nitrogen compound).

   b) <u>NITRIFYING BACTERIA</u> — turn <u>ammonia</u> in decaying matter into <u>nitrates</u>.

   c) <u>NITROGEN-FIXING BACTERIA</u> — turn <u>atmospheric N_2</u>
      into <u>nitrogen compounds</u> that plants can use.

   d) <u>DENITRIFYING BACTERIA</u> — turn <u>nitrates</u> back into <u>N_2 gas</u>.
      This is of no benefit to living organisms.

   Some of these bacteria live in the <u>soil</u> and some of them live in <u>nodules</u> on plant roots.

Air Pollution

Air pollutants can cause lots of problems when they're released into the atmosphere.

Carbon Monoxide is Poisonous

1) When fossil fuels are burnt without enough air supply they produce the gas carbon monoxide (CO).

2) It's a poisonous gas. If it combines with red blood cells, it prevents them from carrying oxygen.

3) Carbon monoxide's mostly released in car emissions.
   Most modern cars are fitted with catalytic converters that turn the carbon monoxide into carbon dioxide, decreasing the amount of CO that's released into the atmosphere.

Acid Rain is Caused by Sulfur Dioxide

1) Burning fossil fuels releases harmful gases like CO_2
   (a greenhouse gas, see next page) and sulfur dioxide (SO_2).

2) The sulfur dioxide comes from sulfur impurities in the fossil fuels.

3) When this gas mixes with rain clouds it forms dilute sulfuric acid.

4) This then falls as acid rain.

5) Internal combustion engines in cars and power stations are the main causes of acid rain.

Acid rain is also caused by nitrogen oxides that are produced by burning fossil fuels.

sulfur dioxide → → → Clean Cloud → Acid Cloud → Acid Rain

Acid Rain Kills Fish and Trees

1) Acid rain can cause a lake to become more acidic.
   This has a severe effect on the lake's ecosystem.
   Many organisms are sensitive to changes in pH
   and can't survive in more acidic conditions.
   Many plants and animals die.

2) Acid rain can kill trees. The acid damages leaves
   and releases toxic substances from the soil,
   making it hard for the trees to take up nutrients.

Learn all the facts on this page

Exam questions on this topic might ask you to describe the effects of air pollution, mini-essay style. Or they may give you a graph or table to interpret — in which case you'll have to apply your knowledge.

The Greenhouse Effect

The <u>greenhouse effect</u> is always in the news. We need it, since it makes Earth a suitable temperature for living on. But unfortunately it's starting to trap more heat than is necessary.

Greenhouse Gases Trap Heat from the Sun

1) The <u>temperature</u> of the Earth is a <u>balance</u> between the heat it gets from the Sun and the heat it radiates back out into space.

2) Gases in the <u>atmosphere</u> absorb most of the heat that would normally be radiated out into space, and re-radiate it in all directions (including back towards the Earth).

This is what happens in a greenhouse. The Sun shines in, and the glass helps keeps some of the heat in.

3) If this didn't happen, then at night there'd be nothing to keep any heat <u>in</u>, and we'd quickly get <u>very cold</u> indeed.

4) There are several different gases in the atmosphere that help keep the <u>heat in</u>. They're called "<u>greenhouse gases</u>" (oddly enough) and they include <u>water vapour</u>, <u>carbon dioxide</u> and <u>methane</u>.

Global Warming — the Earth is Heating Up

1) <u>Human beings</u> are <u>increasing</u> the amount of <u>carbon dioxide</u> in the atmosphere (see next page). We're also increasing levels of other gases that can act as greenhouse gases, e.g. <u>CFCs</u> and <u>nitrous oxide</u> (again, see next page). This has <u>enhanced</u> the <u>greenhouse effect</u>.

2) As a result of all this, the Earth is <u>heating up</u> — this is <u>global warming</u>.

3) Global warming is a type of <u>climate change</u> and causes other types of climate change, e.g. changing rainfall patterns.

4) Climate change could lead to things like <u>changing crop growth</u> patterns or <u>flooding</u> due to the <u>polar ice caps melting</u>.

We need the greenhouse effect, but it's starting to go too far

There's a <u>consensus</u> among scientists that global warming is happening and that <u>human activity</u> has caused most of the recent warming. But, they don't know exactly what the effects will be.

1

The Greenhouse Effect

Humans are increasing the levels of greenhouse gases in the atmosphere. Here's how...

Human Activity Produces Lots of Greenhouse Gases

Carbon Dioxide

1) <u>Humans</u> release <u>carbon dioxide</u> into the atmosphere all the time as part of our <u>everyday lives</u> — in <u>car exhausts</u>, <u>industrial processes</u>, as we <u>burn fossil fuels</u> etc.

2) People around the world are also <u>cutting down</u> large areas of forest (<u>deforestation</u>) for <u>timber</u> and to clear land for <u>farming</u> — and this activity affects the <u>level of carbon dioxide</u> in the <u>atmosphere</u> (see page 137).

Methane

1) <u>Methane gas</u> is also produced <u>naturally</u> from various sources, e.g. <u>rotting plants</u> in <u>marshland</u>.

2) However, two 'man-made' sources of methane are <u>on the increase</u>: <u>rice growing</u> and <u>cattle rearing</u> — it's the cows' "pumping" that's the problem, believe it or not.

Nitrous Oxide

1) <u>Nitrous oxide</u> is released naturally by <u>bacteria</u> in <u>soils</u> and the <u>ocean</u>.

2) A lot more is released from soils after <u>fertiliser</u> is used.

3) It's also released from <u>vehicle engines</u> and industry.

CFCs

1) <u>CFCs</u> are <u>man-made</u> chemicals that were once used in <u>aerosol sprays</u> (e.g. deodorant) and <u>fridges</u>. They're really <u>powerful</u> greenhouse gases.

2) Most countries have agreed <u>not to produce them</u> any more because they also damage the <u>ozone layer</u>, which prevents UV radiation from reaching the Earth.

3) But some CFCs still remain and get released, e.g. by <u>leaks</u> from old fridges.

Water Pollution

I'm sorry to bring so much <u>gloom</u> in such a short space, but here's another environmental problem for you to learn about — <u>river pollution</u> by fertiliser or sewage.

Fertilisers can Leach into *Water* and Cause *Eutrophication*

You might think <u>fertiliser</u> would be a good thing for the environment because it makes plants grow faster. Unfortunately it causes <u>big problems</u> when it ends up in <u>lakes</u> and <u>rivers</u> — here's how...

1) <u>Nitrates</u> and <u>phosphates</u> are put onto fields as <u>mineral fertilisers</u>.

2) If <u>too much fertiliser</u> is applied and it <u>rains</u> afterwards, nitrates are easily <u>leached</u> (washed through the soil) into rivers and lakes.

3) The result is <u>eutrophication</u>, which can cause serious damage to rivers and lakes:

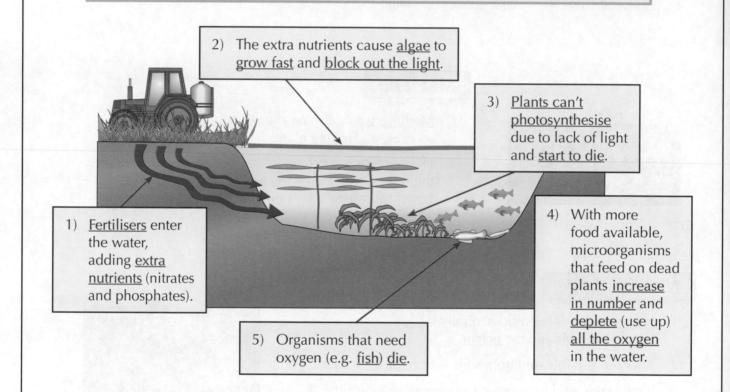

2) The extra nutrients cause <u>algae</u> to <u>grow fast</u> and <u>block out the light</u>.

3) <u>Plants can't photosynthesise</u> due to lack of light and <u>start to die</u>.

1) <u>Fertilisers</u> enter the water, adding <u>extra nutrients</u> (nitrates and phosphates).

4) With more food available, microorganisms that feed on dead plants <u>increase in number</u> and <u>deplete</u> (use up) <u>all the oxygen</u> in the water.

5) Organisms that need oxygen (e.g. <u>fish</u>) <u>die</u>.

Sewage can Also Cause *Eutrophication*

1) Another cause of <u>eutrophication</u> is pollution by <u>sewage</u>.

2) Sewage contains lots of <u>phosphates</u> from <u>detergents</u>, e.g. washing powder. It also contains <u>nitrates</u> from urine and faeces.

3) These extra nutrients cause eutrophication in the <u>same way that fertilisers do</u>.

Paper 2

Paper 2

Lots of tricky words on this page...

...'nitrates', 'phosphates', 'eutrophication', 'leached'. You might not use them much in everyday conversation, but if you use them <u>correctly</u> in the <u>exam</u>, it'll really <u>impress</u> the <u>examiners</u>.

Deforestation

Deforestation Affects The Soil, Water Cycle and Carbon Cycle

Deforestation is bad. Chop down all the trees, and the animals and insects that lived there will disappear too. But there are some other nasty effects that you need to know about...

Soil Erosion

1) Tree roots hold the soil together.

2) When trees are removed, soil can be washed away by the rain (eroded) leaving infertile ground.

Leaching

1) Trees take up nutrients from the soil before they can be washed away (leached) by rain, but return them to the soil when leaves die.

2) When trees are removed nutrients get leached away, but don't get replaced, leaving infertile soil.

Disturbing the Water Cycle

1) Trees stop rainwater reaching rivers too quickly.

2) When they're cut down, rainwater can run straight into rivers — this can lead to flooding.

3) Transpiration from trees releases some of the rainwater back into the atmosphere (see page 130).

4) When they're cut down this can make the local climate drier.

Disturbing the Balance of Carbon Dioxide and Oxygen

1) Forests take up CO_2 by photosynthesis, store it in wood, and slowly release it when they decompose (microorganisms feeding on bits of dead wood release CO_2 as a waste product of respiration).

2) When trees are cut down and burnt, the stored carbon is released at once as CO_2. This contributes to global warming (see p.134).

3) Fewer trees in the forest also means that less photosynthesis takes place, releasing less oxygen. This causes the oxygen level in the atmosphere to drop.

Warm-Up and Exam Questions

It's finally the end of the section, but before you go on to the next one a few questions need answering.

Warm-Up Questions

1) Methane is a greenhouse gas.
   Explain why the level of methane in the atmosphere is increasing.
2) CFCs are also greenhouse gases. Give two man-made products that used to contain CFCs.
3) How can deforestation lead to flooding?

Exam Questions

1   Carbon is constantly being recycled. The diagram below
     shows some of the processes occurring in the carbon cycle.

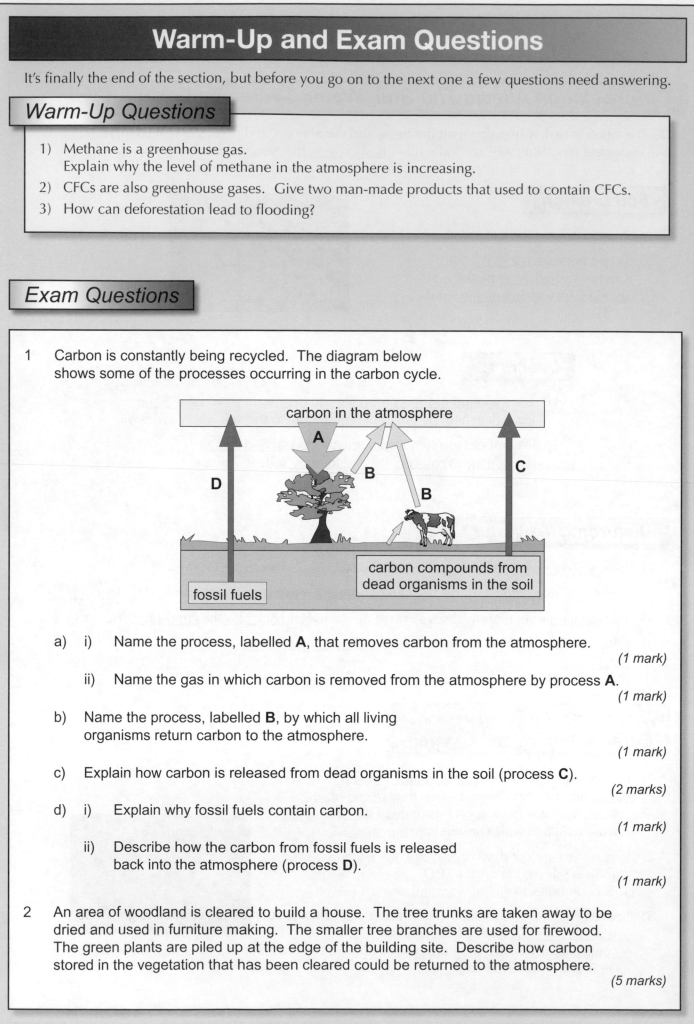

a)   i)   Name the process, labelled **A**, that removes carbon from the atmosphere.

(1 mark)

     ii)   Name the gas in which carbon is removed from the atmosphere by process **A**.

(1 mark)

b)   Name the process, labelled **B**, by which all living
     organisms return carbon to the atmosphere.

(1 mark)

c)   Explain how carbon is released from dead organisms in the soil (process **C**).

(2 marks)

d)   i)   Explain why fossil fuels contain carbon.

(1 mark)

     ii)   Describe how the carbon from fossil fuels is released
           back into the atmosphere (process **D**).

(1 mark)

2   An area of woodland is cleared to build a house. The tree trunks are taken away to be
     dried and used in furniture making. The smaller tree branches are used for firewood.
     The green plants are piled up at the edge of the building site. Describe how carbon
     stored in the vegetation that has been cleared could be returned to the atmosphere.

(5 marks)

Exam Questions

3   A student is investigating the local air quality. He collects data on the concentration of sulfur dioxide in the air at different sites in his town on the same day. His data is shown in the table.

Site	Sulfur dioxide concentration (micrograms/m³)
1	9.8
2	9.4
3	7.1

    a)   What is the mean sulfur dioxide concentration across the three sites?

(2 marks)

    b)   Describe and explain the environmental impacts of sulfur dioxide air pollution.

(3 marks)

4   The Earth is kept warm by greenhouse gases.

    a)   Explain the role of greenhouse gases in keeping the Earth warm.

(2 marks)

    b)   Give **one** way in which conditions on Earth would be different if there were no greenhouse gases.

(1 mark)

    c)   Explain the relationship between greenhouses gases and global warming.

(3 marks)

    d)   Give **one** possible consequence of global warming and explain how it could affect humans.

(2 marks)

PAPER 2

5   The water cycle describes the constant movement of water molecules on the Earth.

    a)   Water is released into the atmosphere by plants. Name this process.

(1 mark)

    b)   Name **two** types of precipitation.

(2 marks)

    c)   Describe the shortest route a water molecule could take through the water cycle to get from an ocean to a garden pond.

(4 marks)

PAPER 2

6   Eutrophication is a process that occurs in lakes or rivers in response to the addition of excess nitrates from sources such as sewage. It results in oxygen depletion of the water, and the death of aerobic organisms such as fish. *P. denitrificans* is a species of denitrifying bacteria that can live in aerobic or anaerobic conditions.

    a)   Explain why *P. denitrificans* would be a suitable organism to use to treat eutrophication in a lake.

(3 marks)

    b)   *P. denitrificans* can be found in waterlogged soils, such as those used to grow rice. A rice farmer wants to increase the yield of his crops by adding a nitrate-based fertiliser. Suggest why the presence of *P. denitrificans* in his soil may make the fertiliser less effective.

(2 marks)

Exam Questions

7 A river flows through some farmland. Data showing the concentration of nitrates in the river and the average number of fish per cubic metre of water between 2002 and 2010 are shown below.

	2002	2004	2006	2008	2010
Nitrate concentration (mg per litre)	22	33	48	63	74
Average number of fish per m³	23	21	10	1	0

a) Describe the relationship between the nitrate concentration and the average number of fish per cubic metre between 2002 and 2010.

(1 mark)

b) Suggest an explanation for the trend in the nitrate concentration over this time period.

(1 mark)

c) Name the process illustrated by the data in the table.

(1 mark)

PAPER 2

8 An investigation was carried out into the number of microorganisms along a stream. A sewage outflow pipe was located mid-way along the study site. The results are shown to the right.

Describe and explain the change in number of microorganisms downstream from the outflow pipe.

(4 marks)

9 Read the passage below about deforestation, then answer the questions that follow.

Forests cover around 30% of the Earth's surface, but the destruction of tropical forests is taking place at a rate of around 13 million hectares per year. Tropical forests are home to more than half of animal and plant species, so this deforestation has a devastating effect on biodiversity. It is also thought to contribute to global warming by disturbing the balance of
5 carbon dioxide in the atmosphere.

Studying areas that have been cleared of trees in the past provides insight into other effects of deforestation. The Huangtu Plateau is a large area in north central China characterised by a fine, loose soil called loess. In the past, the plateau was forested and highly fertile, but human activity over the past two thousand years has greatly decreased the tree cover. The removal
10 of trees has been linked to increased soil erosion and increasingly infertile land. Deforestation in this area also appears to be linked to an increasing number of natural disasters, including floods.

a) Explain how deforestation contributes to global warming (lines 4 and 5).

(4 marks)

b) Explain how the removal of trees could cause increased soil erosion (line 10).

(2 marks)

c) Describe **one** way, other than soil erosion, in which deforestation results in infertile land (line 10).

(2 marks)

Revision Summary for Section 8

Here goes, folks — another beautiful page of revision questions to keep you at your desk studying hard until your parents have gone out and you can finally nip downstairs to watch TV.

1) Define the following:
   a) a habitat
   b) a population
   c) an ecosystem

2) How could you estimate a population size in a habitat using a quadrat?
   Give two reasons why your results might not be 100% accurate.

3) How could you investigate the distribution of organisms within an area using quadrats?

4) What's a secondary consumer?

5) Give an example of a decomposer.

6) What does a food web show?

7) Explain why pyramids of number are not always pyramid-shaped.

8) What is the source of all the energy in a typical food chain?

9) Approximately how much energy is passed on to the next trophic level?

10) Give two reasons why energy is lost between trophic levels.

11) Draw a sketch of the water cycle. Include evaporation, transpiration, condensation and precipitation.
    What do those words mean?

12) How does carbon enter the carbon cycle from the air?

13) Give two ways that carbon can enter the air from dead plants and animals.

14) What role do decomposers play in the nitrogen cycle?

15) What role do nitrogen-fixing bacteria play in the nitrogen cycle?

16) Name a gas that causes acid rain. How is it produced?

17) How does acid rain affect lakes and trees?

18) How does the greenhouse effect work?

19) What is the effect of increasing the concentration of greenhouse gases in the atmosphere?

20) Name four greenhouse gases that humans make. How are they produced?

21) Explain how fertilisers can cause eutrophication.

22) Describe four effects of deforestation.

Increasing Crop Yields

Growing plants outdoors can be <u>very difficult</u>, especially on a <u>large scale</u> — it's almost impossible to control the weather and other conditions. But there's a way around that...

The Rate of **Photosynthesis** Affects **Crop Yield**

1) A plant's <u>rate of photosynthesis</u> is affected by the amount of <u>light</u>, the amount of <u>carbon dioxide</u> (CO_2) and the <u>temperature</u> (see pages 33 and 34).

2) Since plants have to photosynthesise in order to make food for themselves and <u>grow</u>, these three factors need to be <u>carefully controlled</u> in order to <u>maximise crop yield</u>.

You Can **Create** the **Ideal Conditions** for **Photosynthesis**

Photosynthesis can be helped along by artificially creating the ideal conditions in <u>glasshouses</u> (big greenhouses to you and me) or <u>polytunnels</u> (big tube-like structures made from polythene).

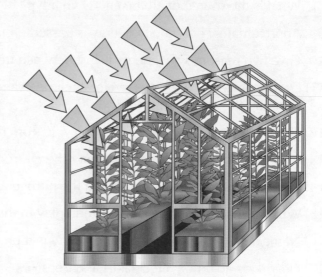

1) Keeping plants <u>enclosed</u> in a glasshouse makes it easier to keep them free from <u>pests</u> and <u>diseases</u>.

2) Commercial farmers often supply <u>artificial light</u> after the Sun goes down to give their plants <u>more</u> time to <u>photosynthesise</u>.

3) Glasshouses <u>trap</u> the Sun's <u>heat</u> to keep the plants <u>warm</u>. In winter, a farmer might also use a <u>heater</u> to help keep the temperature at the ideal level.

4) Farmers can also <u>increase</u> the level of <u>carbon dioxide</u> in glasshouses, e.g. by using a <u>paraffin heater</u> to heat the place. As the paraffin burns, it makes carbon dioxide as a <u>by-product</u>.

By <u>increasing</u> the <u>temperature</u> and <u>CO_2 concentration</u>, as well as the amount of <u>light</u> available, a farmer can <u>increase</u> the rate of <u>photosynthesis</u> for his or her plants. This means the plants will grow faster and bigger — and <u>crop yields</u> will be <u>higher</u>.

You can use glasshouses to control the growing environment

Farmers use glasshouses to make sure crops get the right amount of carbon dioxide, light and heat. They can alter the conditions using paraffin heaters, artificial light and ventilation. This ensures nothing becomes a limiting factor for photosynthesis, which means a good crop is produced.

Increasing Crop Yields

As well as growing plants in glasshouses, there are other ways of increasing <u>crop yields</u>. <u>Fertilisers</u> are handy for giving plants the nutrients they need and <u>pesticides</u> can stop pesky pests from eating crops.

Fertilisers *Are Used to Ensure the* **Crops** *Have Enough* **Nutrients**

1) Plants need <u>certain elements</u>, e.g. <u>nitrogen</u>, <u>potassium</u> and <u>phosphorus</u>, so they can make important compounds like proteins.

2) If plants don't get enough of these elements, their <u>growth</u> and <u>life processes</u> are affected.

3) Sometimes these elements are <u>missing</u> from the soil because they've been used up by a <u>previous crop</u>.

4) Farmers use fertilisers to <u>replace</u> these missing elements or provide <u>more</u> of them. This helps to increase the <u>crop yield</u>.

Pest Control Stops Pests *Eating Crops*

1) <u>Pests</u> include microorganisms, insects and mammals (e.g. rats). Pests that feed on crops are <u>killed</u> using various methods of <u>pest control</u>. This means fewer plants are damaged or destroyed, <u>increasing crop yield</u>.

2) <u>Pesticides</u> are a form of <u>chemical pest control</u>. They're often <u>poisonous</u> to <u>humans</u>, so they must be used carefully to keep the amount of pesticide in <u>food</u> below a <u>safe level</u>. Some pesticides also <u>harm other wildlife</u>.

3) <u>Biological control</u> is an <u>alternative</u> to using pesticides. It means using <u>other organisms</u> to reduce the numbers of pests, either by <u>encouraging wild organisms</u> or <u>adding new ones</u>.

4) The helpful organisms could be <u>predators</u> (e.g. ladybirds eat aphids), <u>parasites</u> (e.g. some flies lay their eggs on slugs, eventually killing them), or <u>disease-causing</u> (e.g. bacteria that affect caterpillars).

5) Biological control can have a <u>longer-lasting</u> effect than spraying pesticides, and be <u>less harmful</u> to <u>wildlife</u>. But introducing new organisms can cause <u>problems</u> — e.g. <u>cane toads</u> were introduced to Australia to eat beetles, but they are now a major <u>pest</u> themselves because they poison the native species that eat them.

Reducing pest numbers can increase crop yield

It's very important for commercial farmers to stop pests eating their crops and there are two main ways they can do this — with <u>pesticides</u> or <u>biological control</u>. Each method has its advantages and disadvantages — the farmer has to think about all of these when deciding which to use.

Bacteria and Making Yoghurt

Lots of microorganisms are used to produce food, including <u>bacteria</u>. You need to know how <u>yoghurt</u> is produced, and that microorganisms can be grown in giant <u>fermenters</u> for use in industry.

Bacteria **Ferment Milk** to Produce **Yoghurt**

<u>Fermentation</u> is when <u>microorganisms</u> break sugars down to release energy — usually by <u>anaerobic respiration</u>. Yoghurt is basically <u>fermented milk</u>. Here's how it's made...

1) The <u>equipment</u> is <u>sterilised</u> to kill off any unwanted microorganisms.

2) The milk is <u>pasteurised</u> (heated up to 72 °C for 15 seconds) — again to kill any harmful microorganisms. Then the milk's <u>cooled</u>.

3) *Lactobacillus* bacteria are added, and the mixture is <u>incubated</u> (heated to about 40 °C) in a vessel called a <u>fermenter</u> (see next page).

4) The bacteria ferment the <u>lactose sugar</u> in the milk to form <u>lactic acid</u>.

5) Lactic acid causes the milk to <u>clot</u>, and <u>solidify</u> into <u>yoghurt</u>.

6) Finally, <u>flavours</u> (e.g. fruit) and <u>colours</u> are sometimes added and the yoghurt is <u>packaged</u>.

Microorganisms are Grown in **Fermenters**

1) <u>Microorganisms</u> (like bacteria) can be used to make really <u>useful stuff</u>, e.g. penicillin or insulin (see p.152).

2) <u>In industry</u>, microorganisms are grown in large containers called <u>fermenters</u>. The fermenter is full of liquid '<u>culture medium</u>' in which microorganisms can grow and reproduce.

3) The conditions inside the fermentation vessels are kept at the <u>optimum</u> (best) levels <u>for growth</u> — this means the <u>yield</u> of <u>products</u> from the microorganisms can be <u>as big as possible</u>.

Lactobacillus *bacteria ferment lactose to form lactic acid*

Microorganisms are <u>really useful</u> — you can use them to make all sorts of stuff that other organisms can't. For starters, without microorganisms you couldn't make yoghurt. And that would be sad. But remember you can't just use any old bacteria for making yoghurt — first you have to kill off any harmful microorganisms in the milk and then you can add the useful ones, like *Lactobacillus*.

Growing Bacteria

In industry, if you want to grow lots of microorganisms, it's best to use a <u>fermenter</u>. Inside a fermenter you can make sure the <u>conditions</u> are just right, so you can get as much product as possible.

Fermenters Can Provide *Optimum Conditions* for *Microorganisms*

Here's a bit about how fermenters work:

The <u>pH</u> is monitored and kept at the <u>optimum level</u> for the microorganisms' <u>enzymes</u> to work <u>efficiently</u>. This keeps the <u>rate of reaction</u> and product yield as high as possible.

<u>Nutrients</u> needed by the microorganisms for <u>growth</u> are provided in the liquid <u>culture medium</u>.

Microorganisms are kept in <u>contact</u> with <u>fresh medium</u> by <u>paddles</u> that <u>circulate</u> (or <u>agitate</u>) the medium around the vessel. This <u>increases</u> the product yield because microorganisms can <u>always access</u> the <u>nutrients</u> needed for <u>growth</u>.

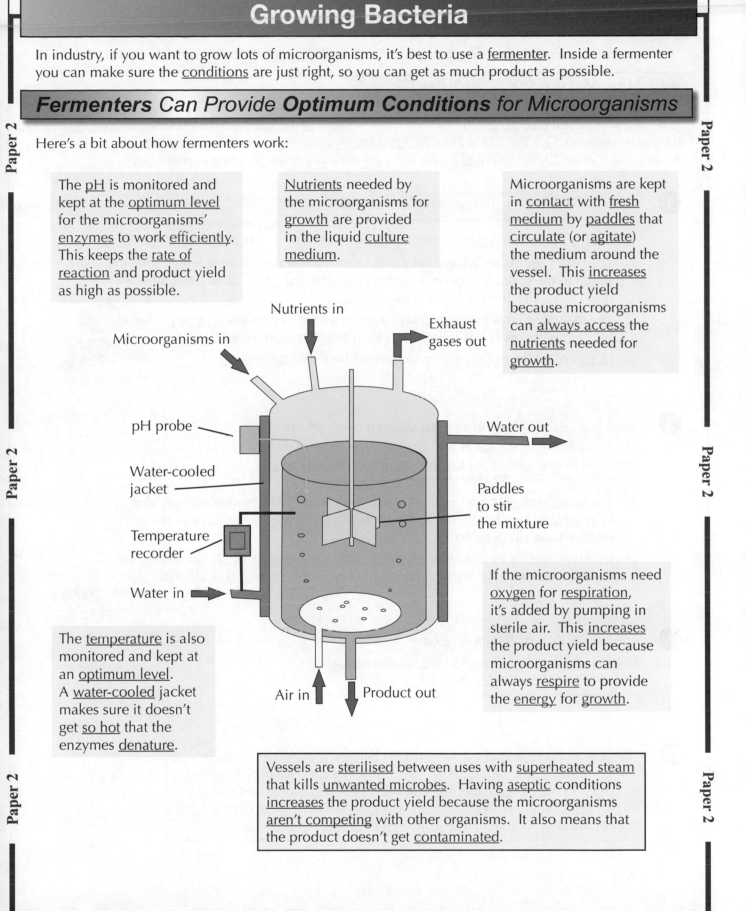

The <u>temperature</u> is also monitored and kept at an <u>optimum level</u>. A <u>water-cooled</u> jacket makes sure it doesn't get <u>so hot</u> that the enzymes <u>denature</u>.

If the microorganisms need <u>oxygen</u> for <u>respiration</u>, it's added by pumping in sterile air. This <u>increases</u> the product yield because microorganisms can always <u>respire</u> to provide the <u>energy</u> for <u>growth</u>.

Vessels are <u>sterilised</u> between uses with <u>superheated steam</u> that kills <u>unwanted microbes</u>. Having <u>aseptic</u> conditions <u>increases</u> the product yield because the microorganisms <u>aren't competing</u> with other organisms. It also means that the product doesn't get <u>contaminated</u>.

Optimum conditions for microorganisms = high yield of product

Microorganisms will happily grow in a <u>fermenter</u> even when it's cold and <u>blowing a gale</u> outside. That's because inside a fermenter you can control all the conditions so they're perfect. The more microorganisms that grow, the more product you can make, so it's important to keep them happy.

Yeast and Making Beer

Yeast is used to <u>ferment sugar</u> into <u>alcohol</u> when making beer.

We Use Yeast for Brewing Beer

Yeast is a very useful <u>microorganism</u>. When yeast respires <u>aerobically</u> (in the presence of <u>oxygen</u>) it turns sugar into <u>CO_2</u>. But when there <u>isn't enough oxygen</u>, yeast respires <u>anaerobically</u>, turning sugar into <u>CO_2</u> and <u>alcohol</u> — we use anaerobically respiring yeast to make <u>beer</u>.

 1 Firstly you need to get the <u>sugar out</u> of the grain:

Germination is when a seed starts to grow into a new plant.

1) Beer is made from <u>grain</u> — usually <u>barley</u>.

2) The barley grains are allowed to <u>germinate</u> for a few days, during which time the <u>starch</u> in the grains is broken down into <u>sugar</u> by <u>enzymes</u>. Then the grains are <u>dried</u> in a kiln. This process is called <u>malting</u>.

3) The malted grain is <u>mashed up</u> and water is added to produce a <u>sugary solution</u> with lots of bits in it. This is then sieved to remove the bits.

4) <u>Hops</u> are added to the mixture to give the beer its <u>bitter flavour</u>.

 2 <u>Yeast</u> is <u>added</u> and the mixture is <u>incubated</u> (warmed up).

The yeast <u>ferments</u> the <u>sugar</u> into <u>alcohol</u>. The fermenting vessels are designed to stop <u>unwanted microorganisms</u> and <u>air getting in</u>.

1) The <u>rising concentration of alcohol (ethanol)</u> in the fermentation mixture due to <u>anaerobic respiration</u> eventually starts to <u>kill</u> the <u>yeast</u>. As the yeast dies, fermentation <u>slows</u> down.

2) Different species of yeast can <u>tolerate different levels of alcohol</u>. Some species can be used to produce strong beer with a <u>high concentration</u> of alcohol.

 3 The beer is <u>drawn off</u> through a tap.

Sometimes chemicals called <u>clarifying agents</u> are added to <u>remove particles</u> and make it <u>clearer</u>.

4 The <u>beer</u> is then <u>pasteurised</u> — <u>heated</u> to <u>kill any yeast</u> left in the beer and completely stop fermentation. Beer tastes better if it's unpasteurised and aged in the <u>right conditions</u>. But big breweries pasteurise it because there's a <u>risk</u> that unpasteurised beer will <u>spoil</u> if it's not stored in the right conditions after it's sold. Finally the <u>beer</u> is <u>casked</u> ready for sale.

Anaerobic respiration in yeast produces alcohol

It's important that no air can get into the fermenting vessels so that the yeast respire anaerobically. It's during anaerobic respiration that the yeast converts sugar into alcohol. A handy trick. Now learn it.

Yeast

The <u>rate of respiration</u> of yeast changes depending on the conditions it's in.

The **Respiration Rate** of **Yeast** Depends on Its **Conditions**

You can do experiments to investigate how the <u>rate of CO_2 production</u> by yeast changes under <u>different conditions</u>. Here's how to measure the effect of <u>changing temperature</u>:

1) Mix together some <u>sugar</u>, <u>yeast</u> and <u>distilled water</u>, then add the mixture to a <u>test tube</u>.

2) Attach a <u>bung</u> with a tube leading to a second test tube of <u>water</u>.

3) Place the tube containing the yeast mixture in a <u>water bath</u> at a <u>certain temperature</u>.

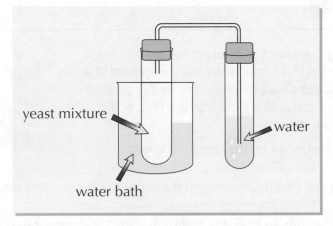

yeast mixture

water

water bath

4) Leave the tube to warm up a bit and then <u>count how many bubbles</u> are produced in a given <u>period of time</u> (e.g. one minute). Use this to calculate the <u>rate</u> of CO_2 production (which gives an indication of <u>respiration rate</u>).

5) Repeat the experiment with the water bath set at <u>different temperatures</u>.

6) Respiration is controlled by <u>enzymes</u> — so as temperature <u>increases</u>, so should the rate of respiration (up until the optimum temperature, see page 9 for more).

You Can Also Test Other **Variables**

1) The example looks at how temperature affects the rate, but the basic idea would be the same whatever variable you were investigating.

2) For example, you could vary the <u>concentration of sugar</u> (but keep the temperature of the water bath the same).

3) You could also alter the experiment to give <u>more accurate</u> results by replacing the second tube with a <u>gas syringe</u> — you'd measure the <u>volume</u> of gas produced instead.

The more bubbles produced, the faster the rate of respiration

Remember, yeast is a <u>living organism</u>. Its respiration is carried out by <u>enzymes</u>, which are affected by things like <u>temperature</u> and <u>pH</u>. So if you change these conditions, CO_2 production will change too.

Warm-Up and Exam Questions

Now's your chance to practice some incredibly life-like exam questions, but do the warm-up first — you don't want to end up straining something.

Warm-Up Questions

1) Why do farmers use pest control?
2) Name the bacteria used to produce yoghurt from milk.
3) Give two conditions which need to be kept at an optimum level inside a fermenter.
4) Why do brewers want their yeast to respire anaerobically, not aerobically?

Exam Questions

1   Chloe is investigating the effect of different factors on yeast growth. The diagram on the right shows the equipment she has set up so far. As the yeast respires, the gas produced will travel through the tube and bubble into the lime water, which will gradually turn cloudy.

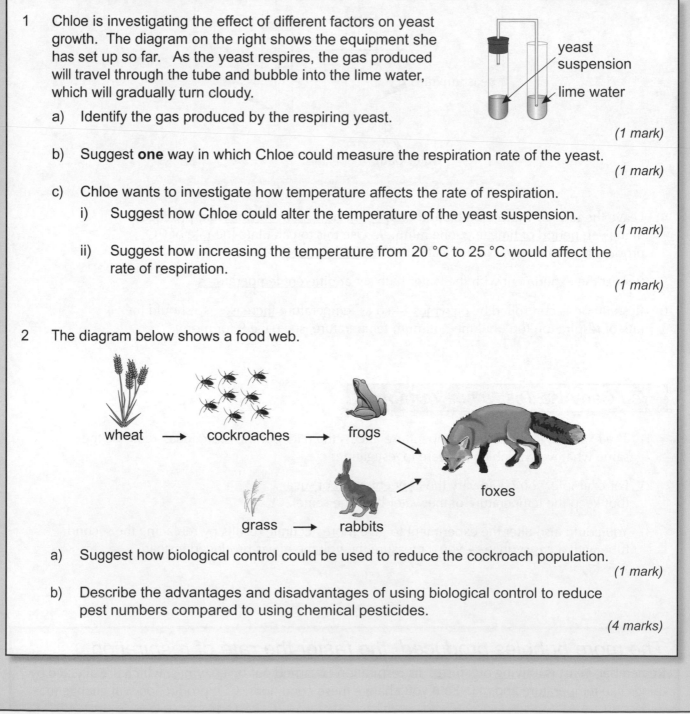

yeast suspension

lime water

a)   Identify the gas produced by the respiring yeast.

(1 mark)

b)   Suggest **one** way in which Chloe could measure the respiration rate of the yeast.

(1 mark)

c)   Chloe wants to investigate how temperature affects the rate of respiration.

i)   Suggest how Chloe could alter the temperature of the yeast suspension.

(1 mark)

ii)   Suggest how increasing the temperature from 20 °C to 25 °C would affect the rate of respiration.

(1 mark)

2   The diagram below shows a food web.

wheat   →   cockroaches   →   frogs

foxes

grass   →   rabbits

a)   Suggest how biological control could be used to reduce the cockroach population.

(1 mark)

b)   Describe the advantages and disadvantages of using biological control to reduce pest numbers compared to using chemical pesticides.

(4 marks)

Exam Questions

3   A farmer has three polythene tunnels which she uses to grow strawberries. She uses a different fertiliser (A, B or C) in each tunnel and records the strawberry yield for 5 years. Her results are shown in the table below.

Fertiliser	Strawberry yield each year (kg)				
	2008	2009	2010	2011	2012
A	592	615	580	632	599
B	600	601	566	604	587
C	575	630	599	661	612

   a)   Suggest why the farmer grows her strawberries in polythene tunnels. Explain your answer.

(3 marks)

   b)   i)   Which fertiliser, A-C, had the best effect on strawberry yield overall? Explain your answer.

(2 marks)

         ii)   Explain how fertilisers increase crop yield.

(3 marks)

4   Glasshouses make it easier for farmers to control the environment around plants. Some farmers use paraffin heaters inside their glasshouses. The word equation for the burning of paraffin is: paraffin + oxygen → carbon dioxide + water (+ heat). Explain the benefit to farmers of using paraffin heaters inside their glasshouses.

(4 marks)

PAPER 2

5   A fermenter is a large container used to grow microorganisms.

   a)   Copy and complete the passage below about fermenters, using suitable words.

      Conditions inside a fermenter are carefully monitored and controlled. For example, the .... and pH are kept at .... levels so that the microorganisms' enzymes can work efficiently. .... stir the mixture so that the microorganisms can always have access to ...., which are needed for growth.

(4 marks)

   b)   Explain why aseptic conditions are needed inside a fermenter.

(2 marks)

   c)   The diagram on the right shows a fermenter.

         i)   Explain the purpose of the air supply.

(1 mark)

         ii)   Name the part of the diagram labelled **A** and describe its purpose.

(2 marks)

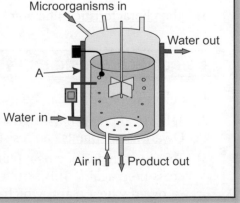

Selective Breeding

'Selective breeding' sounds like it has the potential to be a tricky topic, but it's actually dead simple. You take the best plants or animals and breed them together to get the best possible offspring. That's it.

Selective Breeding is Mating the Best Organisms Together

Organisms are selectively bred to develop the best features, which are things like:

- Maximum yield of meat, milk, grain etc.
- Good health and disease resistance.
- In animals, other qualities like temperament, speed, fertility, good mothering skills, etc.
- In plants, other qualities like attractive flowers, nice smell, etc.

This is the basic process involved in selective breeding:

1) From your existing stock select the ones which have the best characteristics.

2) Breed them with each other.

3) Select the best of the offspring, and breed them together.

4) Continue this process over several generations, and the desirable trait gets stronger and stronger. In farming, this will give the farmer gradually better and better yields.

Selective breeding is also known as artificial selection.

Selective Breeding is Very Useful

Selective breeding can increase the productivity of cows

1) Cows can be selectively bred to produce offspring with, e.g. a high meat yield.

2) First, the animals with characteristics that will increase meat yield (e.g. the largest cows and bulls) are selected and bred together.

3) Next, the offspring with the best characteristics (e.g. the largest) are selected and bred together.

4) If this is continued over several generations, cows with very large meat yields can be produced.

Selective breeding can increase the number of offspring in sheep

1) Farmers can selectively breed sheep to increase the number of lambs born.

2) Female sheep (ewes) who produce large numbers of offspring are bred with rams whose mothers had large numbers of offspring.

3) The characteristic of having large numbers of offspring is passed on to the next generation.

Selective breeding can increase crop yield

1) Selective breeding can be used to combine two different desirable characteristics.

2) Tall wheat plants have a good grain yield but are easily damaged by wind and rain. Dwarf wheat plants can resist wind and rain but have a lower grain yield.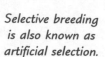

3) These two types of wheat plant were cross-bred, and the best resulting wheat plants were cross-bred again. This resulted in a new variety of wheat combining the good characteristics — dwarf wheat plants which could resist bad weather and had a high grain yield.

Fish Farming

We're catching so many wild fish that, if we're not careful, there won't be many left.
A possible solution to this problem is <u>fish farms</u> — big <u>enclosures</u> or <u>tanks</u> where fish are raised for food.
<u>Fish farms</u> rear fish in a controlled way that's designed to produce <u>as many fish as possible</u>.

Fish Can Be Farmed In Cages In The Sea

<u>Salmon farming</u> in Scotland is a good example of this:

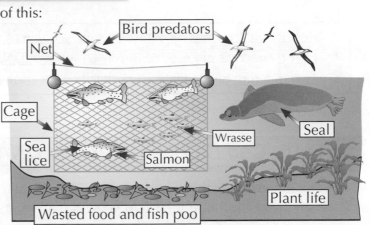

1) The fish are kept in <u>cages</u> in the <u>sea</u> to <u>stop them using as much energy</u> swimming about.

2) The cage also <u>protects</u> them from <u>interspecific predation</u> (being eaten by other animals like birds or seals).

3) They're fed a <u>diet</u> of food pellets that's <u>carefully controlled</u> to <u>maximise</u> the amount of energy they get. The better <u>quality</u> the food is, the <u>quicker</u> and <u>bigger</u> the fish will grow. (Which is good for us as fish is a great <u>source of protein</u>.)

4) Young fish are reared in <u>special tanks</u> to ensure as many survive as possible.

5) It's important to keep younger fish <u>separate</u> from <u>bigger fish</u>, and to provide <u>regular food</u> — this makes sure that the big fish <u>don't eat the little ones</u>. This is <u>intraspecific predation</u> — where organisms eat individuals of the same species.

6) Fish kept in cages are more prone to <u>disease</u> and <u>parasites</u>. One pest is <u>sea lice</u>, which can be treated with <u>pesticides</u> which kill them. To <u>avoid pollution</u> from chemical pesticides, <u>biological pest control</u> (see p. 143) can be used instead, e.g. a small fish called a <u>wrasse</u> eats the lice off the backs of the salmon.

7) The fish can be <u>selectively bred</u> (see previous page) to produce <u>less aggressive</u>, <u>faster-growing</u> fish.

Fish Can Be Farmed In Tanks Too

Freshwater fish, e.g. <u>carp</u>, can be farmed in <u>ponds</u> or <u>indoors</u> in tanks where conditions can be <u>controlled</u>. This is especially useful for controlling the <u>water quality</u>.

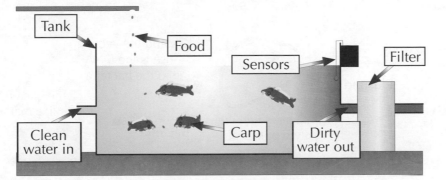

1) The <u>water</u> can be <u>monitored</u> to check the <u>temperature</u>, <u>pH</u> and <u>oxygen level</u> is OK.

2) It's easy to control <u>how much food</u> is supplied and give <u>exactly the right sort</u> of food.

3) The water can be <u>removed</u> and <u>filtered</u> to get rid of <u>waste food</u> and <u>fish poo</u>. This keeps the water <u>clean</u> for the fish and avoids <u>pollution</u> wherever the water ends up.

Genetic Engineering

The idea of genetic engineering is to move <u>useful genes</u> from one organism's chromosomes into the cells of another. This sounds tricky, but people have found <u>enzymes</u> and <u>vectors</u> (carriers) that can do it.

Enzymes Can Be Used To Cut Up DNA...

...or Join DNA Pieces Together

1) <u>Restriction enzymes</u> recognise <u>specific sequences</u> of DNA and <u>cut the DNA</u> at these points.

2) <u>Ligase</u> enzymes are used to join <u>two pieces of DNA</u> together.

3) <u>Two different bits</u> of DNA stuck together are known as <u>recombinant DNA</u>.

Vectors Can Be Used To Insert DNA Into Other Organisms

A <u>vector</u> is something that's used to <u>transfer DNA</u> into a <u>cell</u>.
There are two sorts that you need to know about — <u>plasmids</u> and <u>viruses</u>:

- Plasmids are <u>small</u>, <u>circular</u> molecules of DNA that can be <u>transferred</u> between <u>bacteria</u>.
- Viruses <u>insert</u> DNA into the organisms they <u>infect</u>.

Here's how genetic engineering works:

1) The <u>DNA</u> you want to <u>insert</u> (e.g. the gene for human insulin) is cut out with a <u>restriction enzyme</u>. The <u>vector DNA</u> is then cut open using the <u>same</u> restriction enzyme.

2) The vector DNA and the DNA you're inserting are <u>mixed together</u> with <u>ligase enzymes</u>.

3) The ligases <u>join</u> the two pieces of DNA together to produce <u>recombinant DNA</u>.

4) The recombinant DNA (i.e. the vector containing new DNA) is <u>inserted</u> into other cells, e.g. bacteria.

5) These cells can now <u>use the gene you inserted</u> to <u>make the protein</u> you want.
   E.g. <u>bacteria</u> containing the gene for <u>human insulin</u> can be grown in huge numbers in a fermenter (see page 145) to produce <u>insulin</u> for people with <u>diabetes</u>.

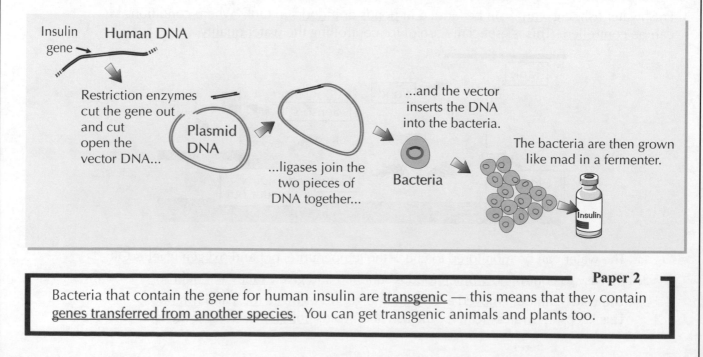

Insulin gene — Human DNA

Restriction enzymes cut the gene out and cut open the vector DNA...

Plasmid DNA

...ligases join the two pieces of DNA together...

Bacteria

...and the vector inserts the DNA into the bacteria.

The bacteria are then grown like mad in a fermenter.

Insulin

Paper 2

Bacteria that contain the gene for human insulin are <u>transgenic</u> — this means that they contain <u>genes transferred from another species</u>. You can get transgenic animals and plants too.

Genetic Engineering and Cloning Plants

You can use genetic engineering to produce plants with desirable characteristics, or you can use cloning to grow more of plants that already have desirable characteristics. Either way you can grow more food...

Genetically Modified Plants Can Improve Food Production

1) Crops can be genetically modified to increase food production in lots of different ways — one is to make them resistant to insects, another is to make them resistant to herbicides (chemicals that kill plants).

2) Making crops insect-resistant means farmers don't have to spray as many pesticides (see page 143) — so wildlife that doesn't eat the crop isn't harmed. It also increases crop yield, making more food.

3) Making crops herbicide-resistant means farmers can spray their crops to kill weeds, without affecting the crop itself. This can also increase crop yield.

4) There are concerns about growing genetically modified crops though. One is that transplanted genes may get out into the environment. For example, a herbicide resistance gene may be picked up by weeds, creating a new 'superweed' variety. Another concern is that genetically modified crops could adversely affect food chains — or even human health.

5) Some people are against genetic engineering altogether — they worry that changing an organism's genes might create unforeseen problems — which could then get passed on to future generations.

Micropropagation is Used to Clone Plants

Clones are genetically identical organisms. They can be made artificially, which is great if you have just one organism with really useful properties — cloning it gives you lots more.

Plants can be cloned from existing plants using a technique called micropropagation (tissue culture):

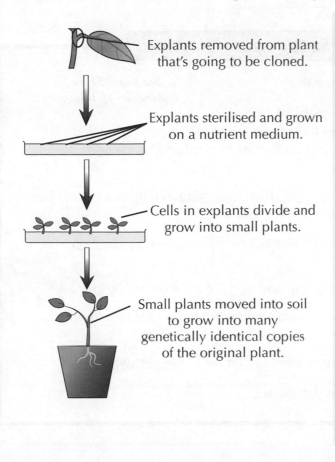

Explants removed from plant that's going to be cloned.

Explants sterilised and grown on a nutrient medium.

Cells in explants divide and grow into small plants.

Small plants moved into soil to grow into many genetically identical copies of the original plant.

1) A plant with desirable characteristics (e.g. large fruit or pretty flowers) is selected to be cloned. Small pieces (called explants) are taken from the tips of the stems and the side shoots of this plant.

2) The explants are sterilised to kill any microorganisms.

3) The explants are then grown *in vitro* — this means that they're placed in a petri dish containing a nutrient medium. The medium has all the nutrients the explants need to grow. It also contains growth hormones.

4) Cells in the explants divide and grow into a small plant. If large quantities of plants are required (e.g. to sell), further explants can be taken from these small plants, and so on until enough small plants are produced.

5) The small plants are taken out of the medium, planted in soil and put into glasshouses — they'll develop into plants that are genetically identical to the original plant — so they share the same characteristics.

Cloning Animals

It's not just plants that can be cloned — animals can be cloned too. So if you have a particular favourite sheep, it's possible to create another one just like it. Keep reading to find out how...

Cloning a Mammal is Done by Transplanting a Cell Nucleus

The first mammal to be successfully cloned from an adult cell was a sheep called "Dolly" in 1996. This is the method that was used to produce Dolly:

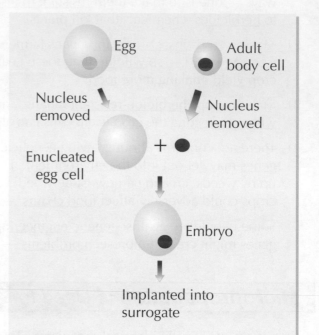

1) The nucleus of a sheep's egg cell was removed, creating an enucleated cell (i.e. a cell without a nucleus).

2) A diploid nucleus (with a full set of paired chromosomes — see page 93) was inserted in its place. This was a nucleus from a mature udder cell of a different sheep.

3) The cell was stimulated (by an electric shock) so that it started dividing by mitosis, as if it was a normal fertilised egg.

4) The dividing cell was implanted into the uterus of another sheep to develop until it was ready to be born.

5) The result was Dolly, a clone of the sheep that the udder cell came from.

Other animals can also be cloned using this method.

There Are Advantages and Disadvantages to Cloning

There are many possible uses for cloned transgenic animals:

See page 152 for an explanation of 'transgenic'.

1) Animals that can produce medicines in their milk could be cloned. Researchers have managed to transfer human genes that produce useful proteins into sheep and cows, for example human antibodies used in therapy for illnesses like arthritis, some types of cancer and multiple sclerosis.

2) Animals (probably pigs) that have organs suitable for organ transplantation into humans could be developed by genetic engineering and then cloned in the same way.

3) The main benefits of cloning are that the useful genetic characteristics are always passed on — this doesn't always happen with breeding.

4) Farmers also don't have to wait until the breeding season, and infertile animals can be cloned.

5) But there are risks too. There's evidence that cloned animals might not be as healthy as normal ones. Embryos formed by cloning from adult cells often don't develop normally.

6) Cloning is also a new science and it might have consequences that we're not yet aware of.

7) At the moment it's also difficult, time-consuming and expensive.

Warm-Up and Exam Questions

Would you believe it, these are the last warm-up and exam questions in the book — not including the practice papers that is. Forget about them for now though and enjoy working your way through these.

Warm-Up Questions

1) How is selective breeding done?
2) True or False? Both plants and animals can be selectively bred.
3) In genetic engineering, what is a vector?
4) What type of enzymes would you use to recognise and cut specific DNA sequences?
5) Name one useful product that humans have genetically modified bacteria to produce.
6) What is a clone?

Exam Questions

1   The characteristics of two varieties of wheat plants are shown in the table below.

Variety	Grain yield	Resistance to bad weather
Tall stems	High	Low
Dwarf stems	Low	High

Describe how selective breeding could be used to create a wheat plant with a high grain yield and high resistance to bad weather.

(3 marks)

2   The picture shows a worker treating the water at a fish farm.

a)   i)   Suggest what must be removed from the water to maintain the water quality.

(1 mark)

ii)   Name **one** other factor that needs to be monitored to make sure the water quality is maintained.

(1 mark)

b)   Suggest why the fish tanks are covered over.

(1 mark)

c)   Explain what intraspecific predation is and give **one** way in which it can be avoided on a fish farm.

(2 marks)

d)   Name the process a fish farmer could use to produce fish with more desirable characteristics.

(1 mark)

e)   Fish can be farmed in cages in the sea or in indoor tanks. Describe an investigation to find out which of these methods results in the highest growth rate of fish.

(6 marks)

Exam Questions

3 Genetic engineering can be used to produce large amounts of human insulin.
   The table below lists the first three steps involved in the process.

   a) Copy and complete the table by writing the type of the enzymes involved in each step.

Step	Description	Enzymes involved
1	Human insulin gene is cut from human DNA.	
2	A plasmid from a bacterial cell is cut open.	
3	The human insulin gene is joined with the plasmid to produce recombinant DNA.	

(3 marks)

   b) State the vector involved in the production of human insulin.

(1 mark)

   c) Describe how large amounts of human insulin are made from the recombinant DNA produced in step 3.

(3 marks)

PAPER 2

4 Some animals could be genetically engineered to have organs suitable
   for transplantation into humans.

   a) Give **one** reason why these animals would then be cloned,
       rather than being left to reproduce naturally.

(1 mark)

   b) Suggest **one** possible risk involved with cloning animals.

(1 mark)

   c) Suggest **one** other possible use of cloned transgenic animals
       that could help to treat human diseases.

(1 mark)

5 The graph below shows the milk yield for a population of cows over three generations.

   a) Do you think that selective
       breeding is likely to have
       been used with these
       cows? Explain your
       answer.
       (1 mark)

   b) Calculate the increase
       in the average milk
       yield per year per cow
       between generation 1 and
       generation 3.
       (2 marks)

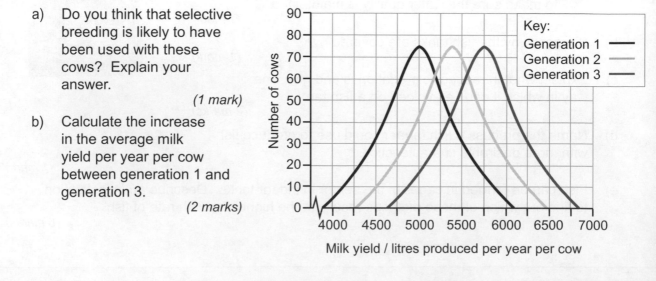

Exam Questions

PAPER 2

6 The image on the right shows a tomato grown on a transgenic plant. State the main way in which the genes of the tomato shown will differ from those found in a tomato grown on a non-transgenic plant.
(1 mark)

7 Dolly the sheep was cloned from an adult cell.

a) Copy and complete the passage below describing how Dolly was cloned.

The nucleus was removed from a sheep's .... cell to create an enucleated cell. A diploid .... was removed from an adult cell of a different sheep and inserted into the enucleated cell.
(2 marks)

b) i) Plants can also be cloned.
Describe how plants are cloned using micropropagation.
(4 marks)

ii) Explain why micropropagation is beneficial for commercial farmers.
(1 mark)

8 Read the article below about GM crops and answer the questions that follow.

Recently some farmers took part in crop trials to see what effects growing herbicide-resistant GM crops might have on wildlife. They used four kinds of crops in the trials. In each case, the farmer split one of their normal fields in half. They then grew a 'normal'
5 crop in one half and its GM equivalent in the other. With the GM crops, the farmers followed instructions about how much of which herbicides to use, and when to apply them. They applied herbicides to the 'normal' crop as they usually would. As the crops grew, the researchers monitored the populations of insects, slugs, spiders and
10 other wildlife in each environment.

The researchers found that with three kinds of crops, growing normal crops was better for wildlife — they found more butterflies and bees on the normal crops. With the fourth crop, the opposite seemed to be true — there were slightly more butterflies and bees around the GM crops.

a) Some people are worried that growing GM crops will reduce the variety of wildlife in the environment. Do you think the results of the trial support this concern? Explain your answer.
(1 mark)

b) Other than the effect on the variety of wildlife, give **two** reasons why people may be concerned about the production of GM crops.
(2 marks)

c) Crops can also be genetically modified to be pest-resistant. Suggest how growing pest-resistant crops in the UK could benefit farmers.
(1 mark)

158

Revision Summary for Section 9

And that's another section finished. Award yourself a gold star, relax, get a cup of tea, and take a leisurely glance through these beautiful revision summary questions. Once you've glanced at them, you'll have to answer them. And then you'll have to check your answers and go back and revise any bits you got wrong. And then do the questions again. In fact, it's not a matter of relaxing at all. More a matter of knuckling down to lots of hard work. Oops. Sorry.

1) a) How can farmers create the ideal conditions for photosynthesis inside a glasshouse?
   b) How does this help them to improve crop yield?
2) Why do farmers use artificial fertilisers?
3) Describe how biological control reduces pest numbers.
4) Describe the process of making yoghurt. Don't forget to name the bacteria involved.
5) Draw and label a diagram of a fermenter.
6) List the conditions that have to be controlled in a fermenter.
7) Describe the main stages in brewing beer.
8) Describe an experiment to measure carbon dioxide production by yeast during anaerobic respiration.
9) What is selective breeding?
10) Give three examples of the use of selective breeding.
11) Describe how fish farms reduce the following:
    a) disease,
    b) interspecific predation.
12) Describe the function of:
    a) a restriction enzyme,
    b) a ligase.
13) Give two examples of vectors used in genetic engineering.
14) Give an account of the important stages of genetically engineering a bacterium
    to produce the human insulin gene.
15) What is a transgenic organism?
16) Describe one way plants can be genetically modified to help improve food production.
17) Give an advantage of producing cloned plants.
18) What are explants? How are they used in micropropagation?
19) Describe the process of cloning an animal from an adult cell (e.g. cloning a sheep).
20) Describe the advantages and disadvantages of cloning transgenic animals.

SECTION 9 — USE OF BIOLOGICAL RESOURCES

Experimental Know-How

<u>Scientists</u> need to know how to <u>plan</u> and <u>carry out scientific experiments</u>. Unfortunately, the examiners think <u>you</u> should be able to do the same. But don't worry — that's what this section's all about.

You Might Get Asked Questions on *Reliability* and *Validity*

1) <u>RELIABLE results</u> come from <u>experiments</u> that give the <u>same data</u>:

> - each time the experiment is <u>repeated</u> (by you),
> - each time the experiment is <u>reproduced</u> by <u>other scientists</u>.

2) <u>VALID results</u> are both <u>reliable</u> AND come from <u>experiments</u> that were designed to be a <u>fair test</u>.

In the exam, you could be asked to suggest ways to <u>improve</u> the <u>reliability</u> or <u>validity</u> of some <u>experimental results</u>. If so, there are a couple of things to think about:

1) *Controlling Variables* Improves *Validity*

1) A variable is something that has the potential to <u>change</u>, e.g. temperature.
    In a lab experiment you usually <u>change one variable</u> and <u>measure</u> how it affects <u>another variable</u>.

> EXAMPLE: you might change <u>only</u> the temperature of an enzyme-controlled reaction and measure how it affects the rate of reaction.

2) To make it a <u>fair test</u>, <u>everything else</u> that could affect the results should <u>stay the same</u> — otherwise you can't tell if the thing you're changing is causing the results or not.

> EXAMPLE continued: you need to keep the pH the same, otherwise you won't know if any change in the rate of reaction is caused by the change in temperature, or the change in pH.

3) The variable you CHANGE is called the INDEPENDENT variable.
4) The variable you MEASURE is called the DEPENDENT variable.
5) The variables that you KEEP THE SAME are called CONTROL variables.

> EXAMPLE continued:
> Independent variable = temperature   Dependent variable = rate of reaction
> Control variables = pH, volume of reactants, concentration of reactants etc.

6) Because you can't always control all the variables, you often need to use a CONTROL EXPERIMENT — an experiment that's kept under the <u>same conditions</u> as the rest of the investigation, but doesn't have anything done to it. This is so that you can see what happens when you don't change anything at all.

2) *Carrying Out Repeats* Improves *Reliability*

To improve reliability you need to <u>repeat</u> any measurements you make and calculate the <u>mean</u> (average). You need to repeat each measurement at least <u>three times</u>.

Getting reliable and valid results is very important

An exam question might <u>describe an experiment</u>, then ask <u>you to suggest</u> what variables need to be controlled. For example, you know that <u>enzymes</u> are affected by <u>temperature</u> and <u>pH</u>, so these variables need to be kept constant (providing you're not investigating one of them). You might also need to say <u>how</u> you'd control the variables, e.g. temperature could be controlled using a <u>water bath</u>.

Experimental Know-How

You Might Have to Suggest Ways to Make an Experiment Safer

1) It's important that experiments are safe. If you're asked to suggest ways to make an experiment safer, you'll first need to identify what the <u>potential hazards</u> might be. Hazards include things like:

- <u>Microorganisms</u>, e.g. some bacteria can make you ill.
- <u>Chemicals</u>, e.g. sulfuric acid can burn your skin and alcohols catch fire easily.
- <u>Fire</u>, e.g. an unattended Bunsen burner is a fire hazard.
- <u>Electricity</u>, e.g. faulty electrical equipment could give you a shock.

2) Then you'll need to suggest ways of <u>reducing</u> the <u>risks</u> involved with the hazard, e.g.

- If you're working with <u>sulfuric acid</u>, always wear gloves and safety goggles. This will reduce the risk of the acid coming into contact with your skin and eyes.
- If you're using a <u>Bunsen burner</u>, stand it on a heat proof mat. This will reduce the risk of starting a fire.

You Could be Asked About Accuracy...

1) It's important that results are <u>ACCURATE</u>. Really accurate results are those that are <u>really close</u> to the <u>true answer</u>.

2) The accuracy of your results usually depends on your <u>method</u>.

E.g. say you wanted to measure the <u>rate</u> of an <u>enzyme-controlled reaction</u> that releases a <u>gas</u> as a product. The rate of the reaction would be the <u>amount of gas produced per unit time</u>. You could <u>estimate</u> how much gas is produced by <u>counting</u> the number of <u>bubbles</u> that are released. But the bubbles could be <u>different sizes</u>, and if they're produced really quickly you might <u>miss some</u> when counting. It would be more accurate to <u>collect the gas</u> (e.g. in a gas cylinder) and <u>measure</u> its <u>volume</u>.

3) To make sure your results are as <u>accurate</u> as possible, you also need to make sure you're measuring the <u>right thing</u> and that you <u>don't miss anything</u> that should be included in the measurements.

E.g. if you want to know the <u>length</u> of a <u>potato chip</u>, you need to <u>start measuring</u> from '<u>0 cm</u>' on the ruler, <u>not</u> the <u>very end</u> of the ruler (or your measurement will be a few mm too short).

...And Precision

1) Results also need to be <u>PRECISE</u>. Precise results are those taken using <u>sensitive instruments</u> that measure in <u>small increments</u>, e.g. using a ruler with a millimetre scale gives more precise data than using a ruler with a scale in centimetres.

2) By recording your results to a <u>greater number</u> of <u>decimal places</u>, you'll increase their precision, e.g.

In some exam questions, you'll be told how precise to be in your answer. So if you're told to give an answer to 2 decimal places, make sure you do or you could lose marks.

Repeat	Data set 1	Data set 2
1	12	11.98
2	14	14.00
3	13	13.01

The results in data set 2 are more precise than those in data set 1.

Safety first — goggles on before you read this book...

Sometimes you'll be asked to <u>describe</u> how you'd carry out your <u>own experiment</u> in the exam. All this stuff about reliability and what not will apply then too. So make sure you learn it and write it down.

Drawing Graphs and Interpreting Results

If you're presented with some results from an experiment you've got to know <u>what to do with them</u>.

You Should Be Able to Identify **Anomalous Results**

1) Most results vary a bit, but any that are <u>totally different</u> are called <u>anomalous results</u>.

2) They're <u>caused</u> by <u>human errors</u>, e.g. by a mistake made when measuring or by not setting up a piece of equipment properly.

3) You could be asked to <u>identify</u> an anomalous result in the exam and suggest what <u>caused</u> it — just look for a result that <u>doesn't fit in</u> with the rest (e.g. it's <u>too high</u> or <u>too low</u>) then try to figure out what could have <u>gone wrong</u> with the experiment to have caused it.

4) If you're calculating an <u>average</u>, you can <u>ignore</u> any anomalous results.

You Need to Be Able to **Draw Graphs**...

In the exam, you might be asked to draw a <u>graph</u> or <u>bar chart</u> from a set of results. If you're not told which one to go for, here's how you decide:

1) If the independent variable is <u>categoric</u> (comes in distinct categories, e.g. blood types, metals) you should use a <u>bar chart</u> to display the data.

2) If the independent variable is <u>continuous</u> (can take any value within a range, e.g. length, volume, time) you should use a <u>line graph</u> to display the data.

Here are a few useful tips for <u>drawing line graphs</u>:

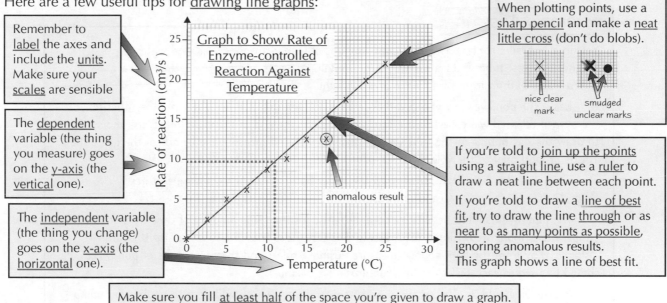

Remember to <u>label</u> the axes and include the <u>units</u>. Make sure your <u>scales</u> are sensible

The <u>dependent</u> variable (the thing you measure) goes on the <u>y-axis</u> (the <u>vertical</u> one).

The <u>independent</u> variable (the thing you change) goes on the <u>x-axis</u> (the <u>horizontal</u> one).

When plotting points, use a <u>sharp pencil</u> and make a <u>neat little cross</u> (don't do blobs).

nice clear mark

smudged unclear marks

anomalous result

If you're told to <u>join up the points</u> using a <u>straight line</u>, use a <u>ruler</u> to draw a neat line between each point.

If you're told to draw a <u>line of best fit</u>, try to draw the line <u>through</u> or as <u>near</u> to <u>as many points as possible</u>, ignoring anomalous results. This graph shows a line of best fit.

Make sure you fill <u>at least half</u> of the space you're given to draw a graph.

...And **Interpret** Them

1) A graph is used to show the <u>relationship</u> between two variables — you need to be able to look at a graph and <u>describe</u> this relationship. For example, the graph above shows that <u>as temperature increases, so does rate of reaction</u>.

2) You also need to be able to <u>read information</u> off a graph. In this example, if you wanted to know what the rate of reaction was at <u>11 °C</u>, you'd draw a <u>vertical line up</u> from the x-axis at 11 °C and a <u>horizontal line across</u> to the y-axis. This would tell you that the rate of reaction at 11 °C was around <u>9.7 cm³/s</u>

You might have to describe the results in a table too...

...or pick out an anomalous result from one. You'll also be expected to do <u>basic maths</u>, like <u>calculating</u> a <u>mean</u> (add everything together and divide by the total number of values) or a <u>percentage</u>.

Planning Experiments and Evaluating Conclusions

In the exam, you could be asked to <u>plan</u> or <u>describe</u> how you'd <u>carry out</u> an experiment. The experiment might be one you've already come across or you might be asked to come up with an <u>experiment of your own</u> to test something. You might also be asked to say what you think of someone else's <u>conclusion</u>.

You Need to Be Able to Plan a **Good Experiment**

Here are some <u>general tips</u> on what to include when planning an experiment:

1) Say <u>what</u> you're <u>measuring</u> (i.e. what the <u>dependent variable</u> is going to be).

2) Say <u>what</u> you're <u>changing</u> (i.e. what the <u>independent variable</u> is going to be) and describe <u>how</u> you're going to change it.

3) Describe the <u>method</u> and the <u>apparatus</u> you'd use (e.g. to measure the variables).

4) Describe what <u>variables</u> you're keeping <u>constant</u> — and <u>how</u> you're going to do it.

5) Say that you need to <u>repeat</u> the experiment at least three times, to make the results <u>more reliable</u>.

6) Say whether you're using a <u>control</u> or not.

Here's an <u>idea</u> of the sort of thing you might be asked in the exam and what you might write as an answer.

Exam-style Question:

1   Describe an investigation to find out what effect temperature has on the rate of photosynthesis in Canadian pondweed.   (6)

Example Answer:

Set up a test tube containing a measured amount of Canadian pondweed and water. Connect the test tube up to a capillary tube containing water and a syringe, then place it in a water bath in front of a source of white light.

Leave the pondweed to photosynthesise for a set amount of time. As it photosynthesises, the oxygen released will collect in the capillary tube. At the end of the experiment, use the syringe to draw the gas bubble in the tube up alongside a ruler and measure the length of the gas bubble. This is proportional to the volume of O_2 produced.

Carry out the experiment again with the water bath set to different temperatures (e.g. 10 °C, 20 °C, 30 °C and 40 °C).

The pondweed should be left to photosynthesise for the same amount of time at each temperature (monitored using a stopwatch). The test tubes should also be set up the same distance away from the light source (measured using a ruler) and the same mass of pondweed should be used in each test tube (measured using a balance).

A control should also be set up at each temperature. This should be a test tube containing water and boiled pondweed (so that it can't photosynthesise).

Repeat the experiment three times at each temperature and use the results to find an average rate of photosynthesis at each temperature. This will make the results more reliable.

You Could Be Asked to **Evaluate** a **Conclusion**

In the exam, you could be given an experimental <u>conclusion</u> and asked to <u>evaluate</u> it. This just means saying whether or not you think <u>evidence</u> from the experiment <u>supports</u> the conclusion — and <u>why</u>.

Plan your way to exam success...

The number of marks available for a question like this will vary, but it'll usually be around five or six. <u>Think</u> about what you're going to say <u>beforehand</u>. You don't want to <u>forget</u> something <u>important</u>.

Practice Papers

Once you've been through all the questions in this book, you should feel pretty confident about the exams. As final preparation, here is a set of **practice papers** to really get you set for the real thing. These papers are designed to give you the best possible preparation for your exams.

Candidate Surname	Candidate Forename(s)

Centre Number	Candidate Number

Certificate International GCSE

Biology
Paper 1B

Practice Paper
Time allowed: 2 hours

You must have:
- A ruler.
- A calculator.

Total marks:

Instructions to candidates
- Use **black** ink to write your answers.
- Write your name and other details in the spaces provided above.
- Answer **all** questions in the spaces provided.
- In calculations, show clearly how you worked out your answers.

Information for candidates
- The marks available are given in brackets at the end of each question.
- There are 120 marks available for this paper.

Advice for candidates
- Read all the questions carefully.
- Write your answers as clearly and neatly as possible.
- Keep in mind how much time you have left.

Answer **all** questions

1   Mitosis and meiosis are both types of cell division.

(a)   Complete the table by putting a tick (✓) or a cross (✗) in each box to show whether the description matches mitosis or meiosis. The first one has been done for you.

Description	Mitosis	Meiosis
occurs during growth and repair	✓	✗
produces gametes		
produces cells that are genetically identical		
occurs during asexual reproduction		
produces four new cells		

[4]

The diagram below shows the human male and female reproductive systems.

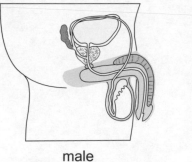

male
reproductive system

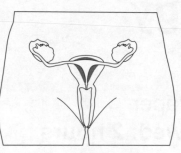

female
reproductive system

(b)   Cells in the reproductive systems undergo cell division to produce gametes. Gametes contain half the usual number of chromosomes.

(i)   What word describes cells that contain half the usual number of chromosomes?

....

[1]

(ii)   In humans, how many chromosomes does one gamete contain?

....

[1]

(iii) Name the structures in the human male reproductive system where gametes are produced.

....
[1]

(c)   An embryo develops in the female reproductive system.
      Describe how a human embryo is formed.

....

....

....
[3]

[Total 10 marks]

Turn over ▶

2 Some pondweed was used to investigate how the amount of light available affects the rate of photosynthesis.

The apparatus that was used for this experiment is shown below.

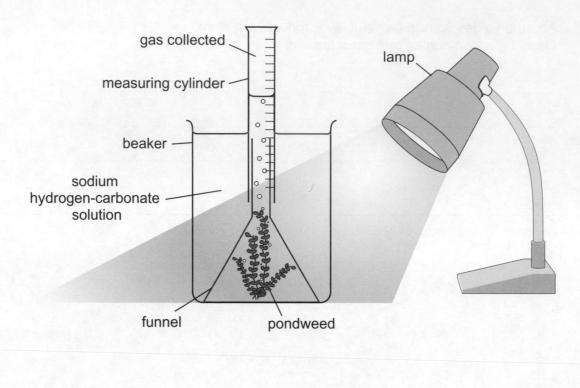

(a) What gas is being collected in the measuring cylinder?

....

[1]

(b) What would happen to the volume of gas collected if the investigation was repeated with the lamp turned off? Give a reason for your answer.

....

....

....

[3]

(c) Sodium hydrogen-carbonate dissolves in water and releases carbon dioxide.
Suggest why sodium hydrogen-carbonate was added to the water in this experiment.

....

....

....

[2]

(d)   Explain how temperature affects the rate of photosynthesis, and suggest how temperature could be controlled in the experiment.

....

....

....

....

....

....

[3]

(e)   After the experiment was conducted, a leaf from the pondweed was tested for starch.

   (i) Which of the following is **not** a stage in testing a leaf for starch?

        Place a cross (✗) in the appropriate box to indicate your answer.

        ☐ Boil the leaf to remove the chlorophyll.

        ☐ Dry the leaf in an oven to remove water.

        ☐ Heat the leaf with ethanol to soften it.

        ☐ Add a few drops of iodine solution.

[1]

   (ii) Would you expect the test to produce a positive result? Explain your answer.

        ....

        ....

[1]

[Total 11 marks]

Turn over ▶

3   The diagram below shows nutrients being absorbed from the gut into the blood.

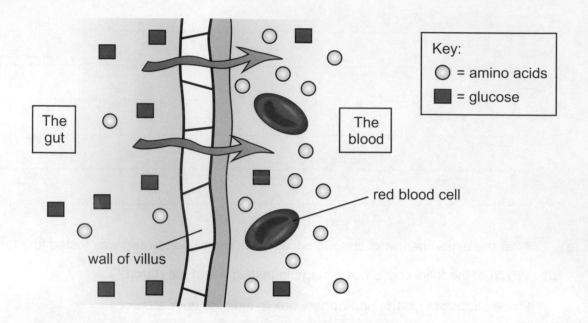

(a)   Describe how villi are adapted to absorb the products of digestion.

....

....

....

....

....

[3]

(b)   The diagram shows glucose being absorbed into the blood by diffusion.
Describe how the amino acids are absorbed into the blood.

....

....

....

[2]

(c)   The diagram shows red blood cells in the blood.

(i) State the function of red blood cells.

....

[1]

(ii) Explain how red blood cells are adapted to their function.

....

....

....

....

....

[3]

[Total 9 marks]

Turn over ▶

4   A student grew three plants in a windowsill tray. This is shown in Diagram 1.

He then put the plants in a cardboard box with a cut-out hole. This is shown in Diagram 2.

Diagram 3 shows the same plants after three days in the cardboard box.

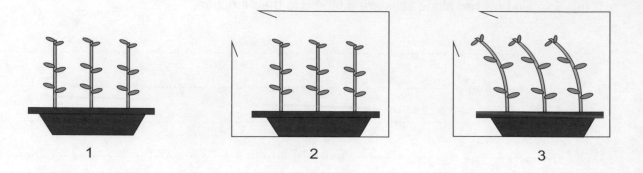

1   2   3

(a)   Explain what caused the plants' response.

....

....

....

....

....

....

[4]

(b)   Name the response shown by the plants in this experiment.

....

[1]

[Total 5 marks]

5   Cystic fibrosis is a genetic disorder caused by a recessive allele.

A couple have a baby boy. The doctor tells them that the baby has inherited cystic fibrosis.
Neither parent shows signs of the disorder.

(a) (i)   In the space below, construct a diagram to show how the baby inherited cystic fibrosis.

Your diagram should show the genotypes of both parents, the genotypes of their gametes,
and all the possible genotypes of their offspring.

Use **F** to represent the dominant allele and **f** to represent the recessive allele.

[3]

(ii)   Is the baby homozygous or heterozygous for this condition?
Explain your answer.

....

....

[1]

(b)   The doctor tells the parents that if they have another child,
the fetus can be tested to see if it will have cystic fibrosis.

State the probability that the couple's next baby will have cystic fibrosis.

....

[1]

[Total 5 marks]

Turn over ▶

6   The peppered moth is an insect that lives on the trunks of trees in Britain.
The moths are prey for birds such as thrushes.

The peppered moth exists in two varieties:

1. A light-coloured variety — they are
   better camouflaged on tree trunks in
   unpolluted areas.

2. A dark-coloured variety — they are
   better camouflaged on sooty
   tree trunks in badly polluted areas.

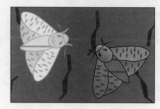

The dark variety of the moth was first recorded in the north of England in 1848.
It became increasingly common in polluted areas until the 1960s, when the number
of soot-covered trees declined because of the introduction of new laws.

(a)   Using the idea of natural selection, explain why the dark variety of moth became more
common in soot-polluted areas.

....

....

....

....

....

[4]

The following bar charts show the percentages of dark- and light-coloured peppered moths in two different towns.

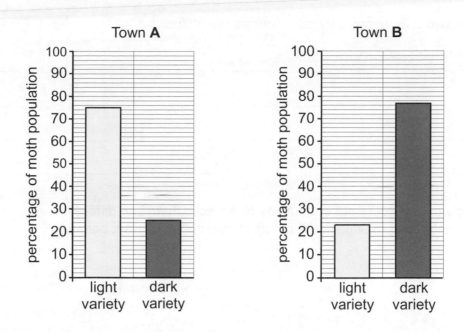

(b) State which town, **A** or **B**, is the most polluted. Give a reason for your answer.

....

....

[1]

(c) Calculate the difference in percentage between the dark-coloured moth population in Town **A** and Town **B**. Show your working.

Answer ....%

[2]

[7 marks]

Turn over ▶

174

7 Jenny carried out an experiment to investigate osmosis.

(a) Give **two** differences between osmosis and diffusion.

1. ....

   ....

2. ....

   ....

[2]

Jenny cut cylinders out of potatoes and placed them into different concentrations of sugar solution, as shown in the diagram below.

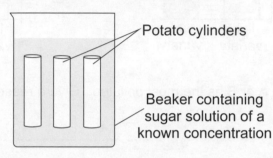

She measured the mass of the cylinders of potato before and after they had been placed in different concentrations of sugar solution for 20 minutes.
Her results are shown below.

Concentration of sugar solution (M)	Change in mass (g)			Mean change in mass (g)
	Potato cylinder 1	Potato cylinder 2	Potato cylinder 3	
0.0	+ 0.67	+ 0.65	+ 0.69	+ 0.67
0.2	+ 0.30	+ 0.31	+ 0.33	+ 0.31
0.4	+ 0.02	− 0.02	+ 0.01	0
0.6	− 0.27	− 0.31	− 0.25	− 0.28
0.8	− 0.48	− 0.5	− 0.47	− 0.48
1.0	− 0.71	−0.65	−0.72	−0.69
1.2	− 0.78	−0.81	−0.82	

(b) Calculate the mean change in mass in a 1.2 M sugar solution.
Show your working.

Answer .... g

[2]

(c)   Draw a graph of the concentration of sugar solution against the mean
       change in mass on the grid below. Use straight lines to join the points.

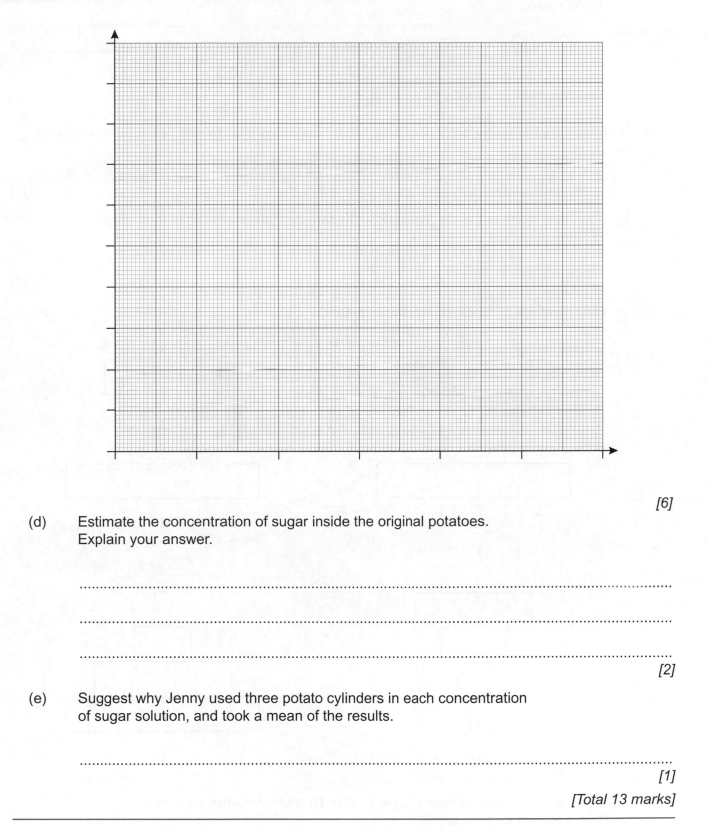

[6]

(d)   Estimate the concentration of sugar inside the original potatoes.
       Explain your answer.

       ....

       ....

       ....
[2]

(e)   Suggest why Jenny used three potato cylinders in each concentration
       of sugar solution, and took a mean of the results.

       ....
[1]
[Total 13 marks]

Turn over ▶

176

8 The diagram below shows the amount of energy contained within an area of plants. It shows how much energy from the plants is transferred to each trophic level in a food chain.

plants	→	grasshoppers	→	mice	→	snakes
11 000 J		1100 J		130 J		12 J

(a) (i) Plants are the producers in this food chain. Explain what is meant by the term **producer**.

....

[1]

(ii) State how much energy is available to the tertiary consumers in this food chain.

....

[1]

(b) Four pyramids of biomass are shown below.

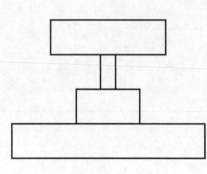

A

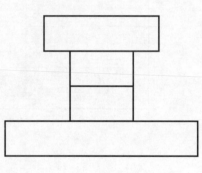

B

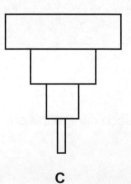

C

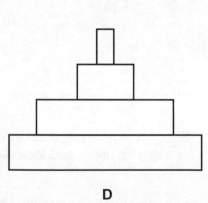

D

State which pyramid of biomass (**A**, **B**, **C** or **D**) represents this food chain.
Give a reason for your answer.

....

....

[2]

(c) Calculate the percentage of energy in the grasshoppers that is transferred to the mice.
Show your working.

Answer ....%

[2]

(d) This food chain has four trophic levels.
Most food chains have no more than five trophic levels.

Suggest why the length of food chains is limited in this way.

....

....

....

[2]

[Total 8 marks]

Turn over ▶

9 The diagram below shows an alveolus and a blood capillary.

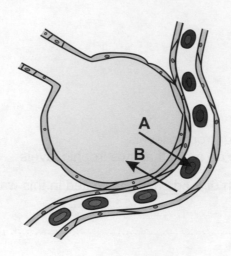

(a) The arrows on the diagram show the net movement of two gases, **A** and **B**.

Name gases **A** and **B**.

Gas **A**: ....

Gas **B**: ....

[2]

(b) Explain how alveoli are adapted for gas exchange.

....

....

....

....

[3]

(c) Ventilation allows air to enter and leave the lungs.

Complete the passage below about ventilation by writing a suitable word in each space.

To breathe out, the .... and .... relax.

This causes the volume of the thorax to ...., which ....

the pressure, so air is forced out of the lungs.

[4]

[Total 9 marks]

10 Describe an investigation to find out if lettuces grown in a polythene tunnel have a faster growth rate than those grown outside.

....

....

....

....

....

....

....

....

....

....

....

....

[Total 6 marks]

Turn over ▶

11 The kidneys play a crucial role in filtering the blood.
The diagram shows a kidney nephron and the blood vessels associated with it.

(a) Label the glomerulus and the loop of Henlé on the diagram.

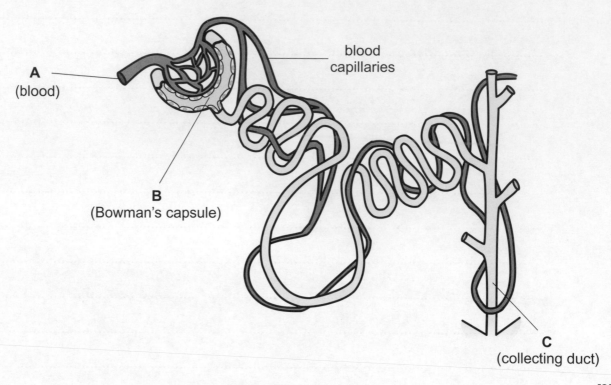

[2]

(b) Many different proteins are found in the blood at point **A** on the diagram but hardly any are found at point **B**.

Explain why there is almost no protein at point **B**.

....

....

[1]

(c) (i) The concentration of urea is greatest at point **C**. Explain why.

....

....

[1]

(ii) How would you expect the concentration of sugar at point **C** to compare to the concentration at point **B**? Explain your answer.

....

....

[2]

(d) Describe the effect of ADH on the kidney nephron.

....

....

[2]

[Total 8 marks]

Turn over ▶

12   Dan and Julie carried out an experiment to investigate the effects of different minerals on plant growth. Their teacher gave them three pea plants of the same species, all of a similar height. The method they used is described below.

---

1. Measure the height of the three pea plants.
2. Add a solution containing minerals to three beakers as follows:
   Beaker A: solution high in magnesium and nitrates.
   Beaker B: solution high in magnesium and low in nitrates.
   Beaker C: solution low in magnesium and high in nitrates.
3. Place a pea plant in each of the beakers, A, B and C.
4. Leave the plants to grow for one week.
5. Measure the height of each of the plants at the end of the week.

The results of Dan and Julie's experiment are shown below.

Beaker	Height at start (cm)	Height at end (cm)	Change in height (cm)
A	4	9	5
B	5	7	2
C	4	8	4

(a)   Explain why the growth in beaker B was poor.

....

....

....

                    [3]

(b)   Describe how you would expect the pea plant in beaker C, which was low in magnesium, to look at the end of the week. Explain your answer.

....

....
                    [2]

(c)   State **two** factors that Dan and Julie would have had to keep the same in each beaker to make the experiment a fair test.

1. ....

2. ....
                    [2]

(d)   Give **one** way in which Dan and Julie could have improved the precision of their results.

....

....

[1]

(e)   What conclusion can you draw from this experiment?

....

....

[1]

[Total 9 marks]

Turn over ▶

PRACTICE PAPER 1B

13   A study collected data from a sample of male British doctors.
It compared the death rate from coronary heart disease per 1000 men
per year to the number of cigarettes smoked each day.

The results are shown in the graph below.

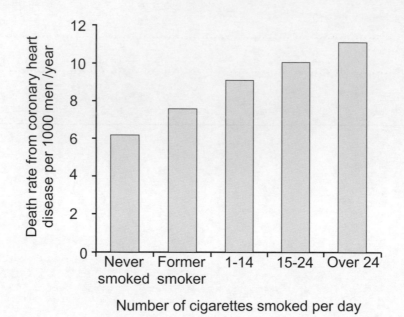

*Data used to construct the graph from R. Doll, R. Peto, J. Boreham, I Sutherland.
Mortality in relation to smoking: 50 years' observations on male British doctors.
BMJ 2004; 328:1519.*

(a) (i)   What conclusions can you draw from this graph?

....

....

....

....

[3]

(ii)   A scientist hypothesises that anyone who smokes is more likely to die from
coronary heart disease.

Suggest **one** change you could make to the study above to test this hypothesis.

....

....

[1]

(b)   Describe and explain **two** effects of smoking on the lungs.

1.   ....

     ....

     ....

2.   ....

     ....

     ....

[4]
[Total 8 marks]

14 Gary is investigating how his heart rate changes during and after exercise.
He measures his heart rate using a portable heart rate monitor. He takes
his resting heart rate before running around the school track for two minutes.
Then he rests again. His results are shown on the graph below.

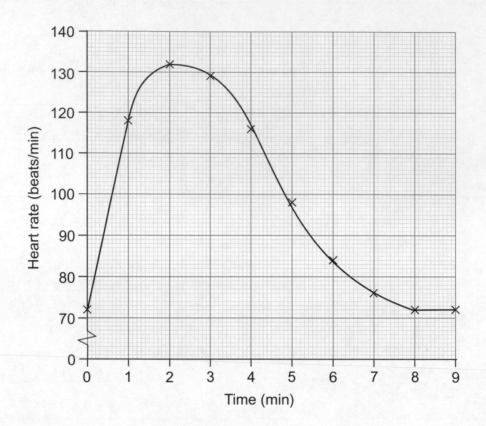

(a) (i) Give the dependent variable in Gary's experiment.

....

[1]

(ii) Give the independent variable in Gary's experiment.

....

[1]

(b) Use the graph to estimate Gary's heart rate after ninety seconds.

....

[1]

(c) Gary stopped running two minutes after taking his first heart rate measurement.
How long did it take for Gary's heart rate to return to normal after he stopped running?

....

[1]

(d)   Describe and explain how Gary's heart rate changes with exercise.

....

....

....

....

....

....

....

                                                                                                                    [5]

(e)   When Gary first starts running he respires aerobically.

   (i) Write the word equation for aerobic respiration.

....

                                                                                                                    [2]

   (ii) Give **one** advantage of aerobic respiration over anaerobic respiration.

....

....

                                                                                                                    [1]

                                                                                                    [Total 12 marks]

                                                                                            [Total for paper 120 marks]

Candidate Surname	Candidate Forename(s)

Centre Number	Candidate Number

Certificate
International GCSE

Biology
Paper 2B

Practice Paper
Time allowed: 1 hour

You must have:
* A ruler.
* A calculator.

Total marks:

Instructions to candidates
* Use **black** ink to write your answers.
* Write your name and other details in the spaces provided above.
* Answer **all** questions in the spaces provided.
* In calculations, show clearly how you worked out your answers.

Information for candidates
* The marks available are given in brackets at the end of each question.
* There are 60 marks available for this paper.

Advice for candidates
* Read all the questions carefully.
* Write your answers as clearly and neatly as possible.
* Keep in mind how much time you have left.

Answer **all** questions

1   Read the passage below, then answer the questions that follow.

Genetically modified crops — Golden Rice

Vitamin A deficiency is a major health problem across the world — particularly in developing countries in South Asia and parts of Africa. A lack of dietary vitamin A makes people more vulnerable to disease and more likely to die from infections. It's also a primary cause of preventable blindness in children, and can contribute to women dying during
5   pregnancy or shortly after childbirth.

To try and address this problem, scientists from across the world have worked together to develop a type of transgenic rice, named Golden Rice. The rice has been genetically engineered to contain a gene from a maize plant and a gene from a soil bacterium, which together allow the rice to synthesise a compound known as beta-carotene.

10   Beta-carotene is an orange pigment which occurs naturally in a range of different plants and fruits. It is also known as provitamin A. In the body it is an early component of the chemical pathway that leads to the production of vitamin A, so a larger amount of beta-carotene in the diet allows the production of a larger amount of vitamin A.

Rice is widely-eaten in many areas where vitamin A deficiency is a problem. However,
15   normal rice does not contain any beta-carotene and is therefore not a source of vitamin A. In contrast, it is estimated that an adult would only need to eat around 150 g (uncooked) of Golden Rice per day in order to obtain the estimated average daily requirement (EAR) of vitamin A.

Eating a small amount of Golden Rice is a simple solution to the problem of insufficient
20   dietary vitamin A. Farmers in the developing world can grow their own Golden Rice and protect themselves and others from the negative health impacts of vitamin A deficiency, without having to rely on dietary supplements such as vitamin tablets.

Turn over ▶

1 (a) Unlike in many developing countries (lines 1-2), vitamin A deficiency is not a major health problem in developed countries such as the UK.

Suggest **one** reason why this is the case.

....

....

[1]

(b) (i) Apart from Golden Rice, name a food that is a good source of vitamin A.

....

[1]

(ii) Give **one** function of vitamin A in the human body.

....

[1]

(c) Golden Rice is a **transgenic organism** (line 7).
Explain what this means with reference to the passage.

....

....

....

[1]

(d) Suggest why beta-carotene is also known as provitamin A (line 11).

....

....

[1]

(e) Golden Rice has been genetically modified to increase its nutrient content (line 9).
Describe **two** other ways in which organisms can be genetically modified to benefit humans.

1. ....

....

2. ....

....

[2]

(f)   There are different ways of estimating how much vitamin A a person needs in their diet.
        EAR is one. Recommended daily allowance (RDA) is another.

        The EAR for vitamin A (lines 16-17) is around 70% of the RDA. Calculate how much
        Golden Rice an adult would need to eat to obtain 100% of the RDA of vitamin A.
        Show your working.

                                                                                        .... g
                                                                                                        [2]

(g)   Suggest and explain why farmers who grow Golden Rice to supply their dietary vitamin A
        may be financially better off than if they regularly bought vitamin A tablets.

        ....

        ....

        ....
                                                                                                        [2]

(h)   With some genetically modified crop plants, farmers are not allowed to save seeds at the
        end of a growing season and replant them the following year. The project behind Golden
        Rice does allow farmers in the developing world to save seed from Golden Rice plants.

        Suggest why this is beneficial to farmers in the developing world.

        ....

        ....

        ....
                                                                                                        [2]
                                                                                          [Total 13 marks]

Turn over ▶

2   The diagram below shows the nitrogen cycle.
     The labels **A-D** represent different stages of the cycle.

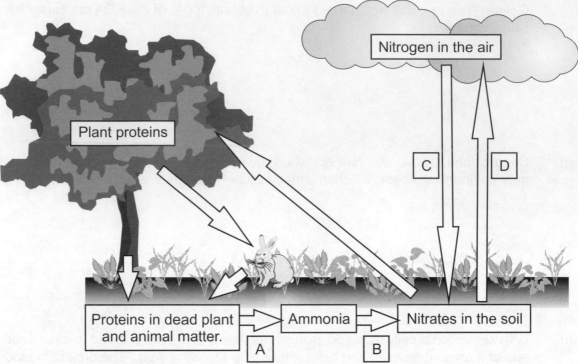

(a)   Complete the table by writing in the types of bacteria that are involved
       at each of the stages **A-D**. The first one has been done for you.

Stage	Type of Bacteria
A	Decomposers
B	
C	
D	

[3]

(b)   Decomposers also play a role in the carbon cycle.
       Explain the role of decomposers in the carbon cycle.

       ....

       ....

       ....

[2]

[Total 5 marks]

3   Environmental officers studied a river that was polluted by sewage.

They measured the amount of dissolved oxygen in the river at different points along its length. The flow of water is from point 1 towards point 15.

The graph shows their results.

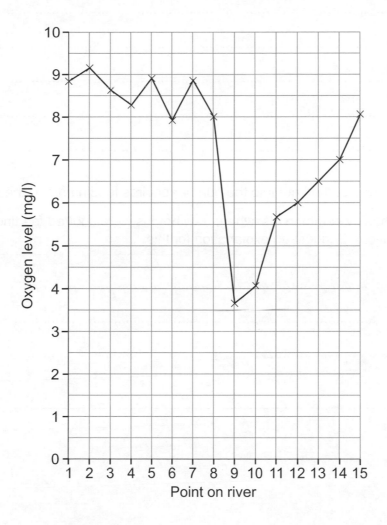

(a)   Using the information in the graph, state where the source of pollution is located.
Give a reason for your answer.

....

....

[2]

194

(b)   Explain how the pollution of water by sewage affects the oxygen level in the water.

....

....

....

....

....

....

....

[4]

(c)   A survey was carried out into the number of birds feeding along the river.

Although fairly common elsewhere, few herons were spotted feeding near the source of the pollution. Suggest an explanation for this.

....

....

....

[2]

[Total 8 marks]

4 An experiment was carried out to discover the best growth medium for the tissue culture of a certain species of plant. Four different growth media, 1 - 4, were used.

The scientists weighed ten blocks of stem tissue, each measuring 1 mm × 1 mm × 1 mm. These were placed onto growth medium 1, as shown in the diagram.

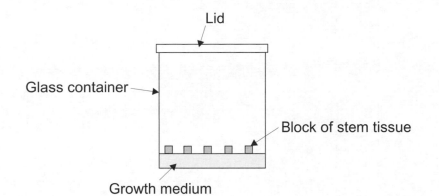

The container was then incubated at 35 °C for two days. At the end of that time, the blocks were taken out and weighed again to see how much they had grown.

This was repeated with the other three growth media.

The whole experiment was repeated again, using root tissue instead of stem tissue.

The results of the experiments are shown in the table.

Growth medium	Average % increase in mass	
	Stem tissue	Root tissue
1	120	77
2	85	62
3	65	58
4	98	102

Turn over ▶

(a)   Draw a bar chart to represent the average % increase in mass for stem and root tissue in each growth medium.

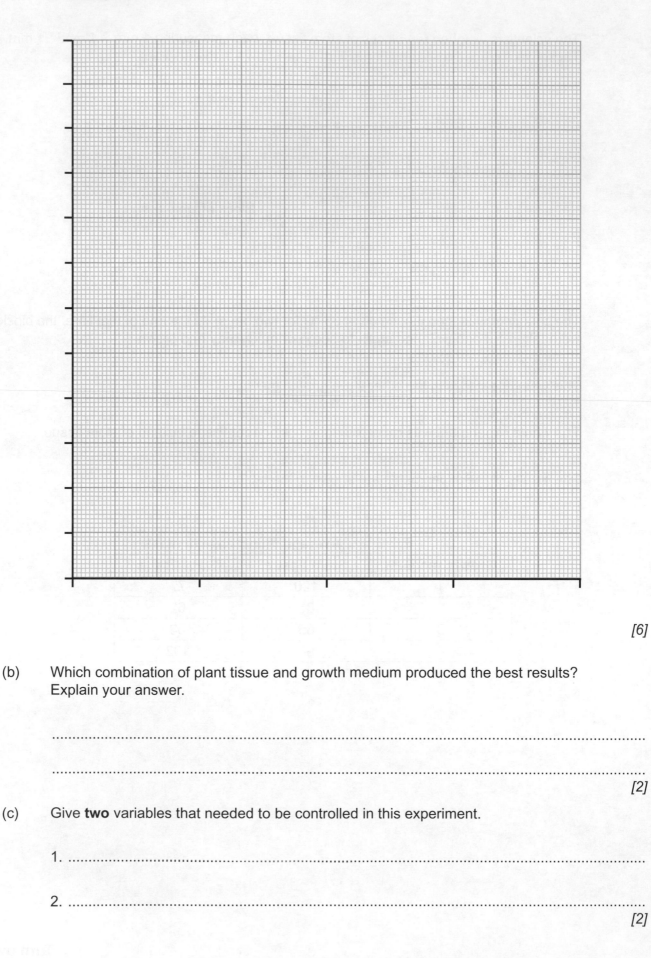

[6]

(b)   Which combination of plant tissue and growth medium produced the best results? Explain your answer.

    ....

    ....
[2]

(c)   Give **two** variables that needed to be controlled in this experiment.

    1. ....

    2. ....
[2]

(d)   Tissue culture is an example of asexual reproduction.

Give **three** differences between asexual and sexual reproduction.

1. ....

....

....

2. ....

....

....

3. ....

....

....

[3]

[Total 13 marks]

Turn over ▶

5 The diagram below shows some of the processes involved in yoghurt production.

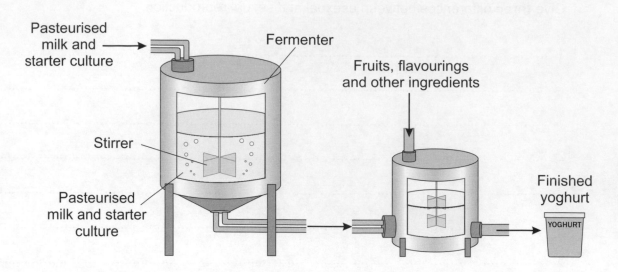

(a) The starter culture is a bacterial culture that transforms the milk into yoghurt. Suggest what type of bacteria are present in the starter culture.

....

[1]

(b) Describe the process that occurs in the fermenter.

....

....

....

[2]

(c) Before being added to the starter culture, the milk used in the fermenter is pasteurised. This means it is heated to kill any microorganisms that may be present in the milk.

Suggest and explain **one** reason why this is done.

....

....

....

[2]

The graph below shows the time it takes for the milk to be converted into yoghurt when the fermentation process is carried out at different temperatures.

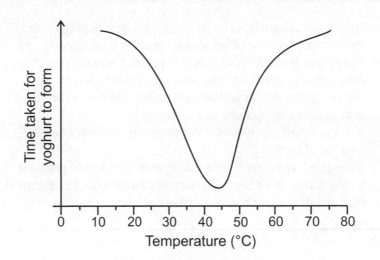

(d)   What temperature would you advise the fermentation process be carried out at? Explain your answer.

....

....

....

[2]

[Total 7 marks]

6   A student did an experiment to investigate the effect of temperature on the action of the enzyme amylase. The method used is shown below.

1. Add a set quantity of starch solution to a test tube and the same quantity of amylase solution to another.
2. Place the test tubes in a water bath at 10 °C.
3. Allow the starch and amylase solutions to reach the temperature of the water bath, then mix them together and return the mixture to the water bath.
4. Take a small sample of the mixture every minute and test for starch.
5. Stop the experiment when starch is no longer present in the sample, or after 30 minutes (whichever is sooner).
6. Repeat the experiment at different temperatures.

(a)   What happens to the starch solution during the experiment?

....
[1]

(b)   Explain why a set quantity of starch solution was used for each repeat in the experiment.

....

....
[1]

The graph below shows the student's results.

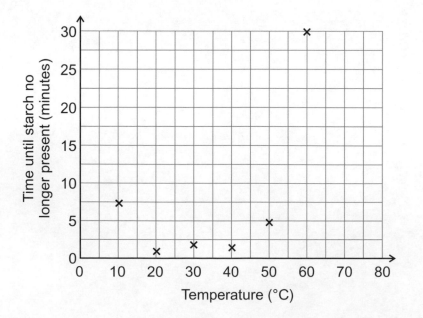

(c) Describe and explain the results between 50 °C and 60 °C.

....

....

....

....

....

[3]

(d) (i) The student thinks that one of the results shown on the graph is likely to be anomalous. Identify the anomalous result and give a reason for your answer.

....

....

[2]

(ii) Suggest what the student might have done to cause this anomalous result.

....

....

[1]

[Total 8 marks]

Turn over ▶

7   Yeast is a single-celled fungus that can be used in the manufacture of beer.

(a)   Give **two** defining characteristics of fungi.

1. ....

2. ....

[2]

(b)   Explain the role of yeast in the manufacture of beer.

....

....

[2]

The diagram below shows some apparatus used to make beer.

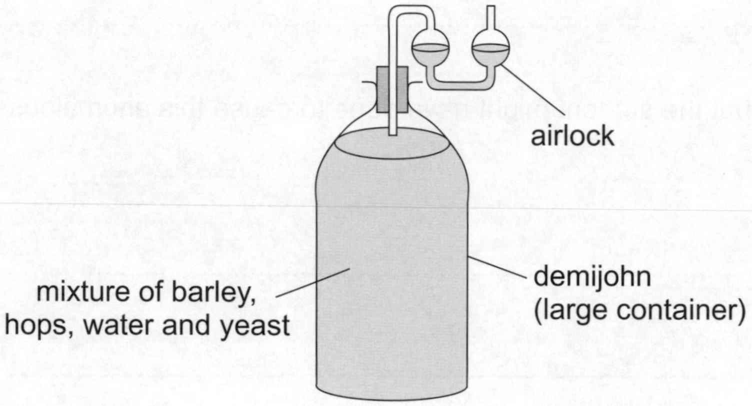

airlock

mixture of barley,
hops, water and yeast

demijohn
(large container)

(c)   One of the functions of the airlock is to prevent any air from entering the demijohn.
Explain why this is important.

....

....

[2]

[Total 6 marks]

[Total for paper 60 marks]

Pages 6-7

Warm-Up Questions

1) Similarities — any two from: e.g. both an animal cell and a plant cell have a cell membrane. / Both an animal cell and a plant cell have a nucleus. / Both an animal cell and a plant cell have cytoplasm.
   Differences — any two from: e.g. an animal cell doesn't have a vacuole, but a plant cell does. / An animal cell doesn't have a cell wall, but a plant cell does. / An animal cell doesn't contain chloroplasts, but a plant cell does.

2) It is made up of thread-like structures called hyphae, which contain lots of nuclei.

3) a) e.g. *Chlorella*
   b) e.g. *Amoeba*

4) *Plasmodium*. A protictist.

Exam Questions

1 a) It is an organelle surrounded by its own membrane *(1 mark)*. It contains genetic material *(1 mark)*.

  b) cell membrane — controls the substances that go in and out of the cell *(1 mark)*
  cytoplasm — the site of most of the chemical reactions in the cell *(1 mark)*
  vacuole — helps to support the cell *(1 mark)*
  chloroplast — site of photosynthesis *(1 mark)*

2 organelles *(1 mark)*, cells *(1 mark)*, function *(1 mark)*, organ system *(1 mark)*

3 Any three from: e.g. they feed, which means they require nutrition. / They are sensitive to chemicals in the water, allowing them to detect food. This shows they can respond to changes in their environment. / They are able to travel towards food, showing that they can move. / They release eggs/sperm, which suggests they reproduce. *(1 mark for each correct answer)*

4 a) chloroplasts *(1 mark)*
  b) sucrose *(1 mark)*, starch *(1 mark)*

5 a) Organism A is an insect because animal cells don't have a cell wall *(1 mark)*.
  b) saprotrophic nutrition *(1 mark)*
  c) Insect because it is an animal, and so has nervous coordination *(1 mark)*.

6 a) i) A, because *Lactobacillus bulgaricus* is rod-shaped *(1 mark)*.
     Pneumococcus bacteria are spherical (like the bacteria in diagram B).
     ii) It can be used to produce yoghurt from milk *(1 mark)*.
  b) A pathogen is an organism that can cause disease *(1 mark)*.
  c) By feeding off other (living or dead) organisms *(1 mark)*.
  d) Any three from: e.g. it has a cell wall. / It has a cell membrane. / It has cytoplasm. / It has plasmids. / It has a circular chromosome of DNA. / It doesn't have a nucleus. *(1 mark for each correct answer)*

7 a) The tobacco mosaic virus *(1 mark)* discolours the leaves of tobacco plants by stopping them from producing chloroplasts *(1 mark)*.
  b) E.g. the influenza virus *(1 mark)* causes 'flu' *(1 mark)*.
     The HIV virus *(1 mark)* causes AIDS *(1 mark)*.

Pages 18-20

Warm-Up Questions

1) For an enzyme to work, a substrate has to be the correct shape to fit the enzyme's active site. The substrate fits into the enzyme just like a key fits into a lock.

2) Osmosis is the net movement of water molecules across a partially permeable membrane from a region of higher water concentration to a region of lower water concentration.

3) Cells are surrounded by tissue fluid, which usually has a different concentration to the fluid inside a cell. If the tissue fluid is more dilute than the fluid inside the cell, water will move into the cell by osmosis. If the tissue fluid is more concentrated than the water inside the cell, water will move out of the cell by osmosis.

4) respiration

Exam Questions

1 a) 35 °C (accept ± 1 °C) *(1 mark)*
  b) The rate of reaction increased with increasing temperature up to 35 °C *(1 mark)*, after which point it quickly decreased *(1 mark)*.
  c) At 45 °C the enzyme's active site has changed shape/the enzyme has denatured *(1 mark)* as some of the bonds holding the enzyme together have been broken *(1 mark)*. This means the substrate no longer fits into the active site and so the reaction stops *(1 mark)*.

2 a) A biological catalyst is a substance which increases the speed of a reaction in a living organism without being changed or used up in the reaction *(1 mark)*.
  b) At low temperatures the speed of enzyme-catalysed reactions will be much slower *(1 mark)*, meaning the bacteria are less likely to reproduce *(1 mark)*.

3 a) higher, lower *(1 mark)*
  b) It will cause it to decrease *(1 mark)*.

4 a) pH 6 *(1 mark)*
     The optimum pH is the pH at which the reaction happens fastest.
  b) At very high and very low pH levels the bonds in the enzymes are broken *(1 mark)* so the shape of the active site changes/the enzyme is denatured *(1 mark)*, meaning that it can't speed up the reaction *(1 mark)*.
  c) Any two from: e.g. the temperature should be the same at each pH / the same volume of the reactant and enzyme should be used for each pH / the same method of determining when the reaction is complete should be used for each pH / everything should be measured and timed as accurately as possible using appropriate equipment *(1 mark for each correct answer, maximum 2 marks)*.

5 a) Active transport is the movement of particles against a concentration gradient/from an area of lower concentration to an area of higher concentration *(1 mark)* using energy released in respiration *(1 mark)*.
  b) Seedling A because there is more energy at higher temperatures *(1 mark)* so the potassium ions move faster, resulting in a faster rate of uptake *(1 mark)*.
  c) It would have no effect *(1 mark)*.
     Increasing a concentration gradient increases the rate of diffusion and osmosis but has no effect on the rate of active transport.

6 a) Plant cell A because this one appears turgid/swollen *(1 mark)*. When a plant has been well-watered its cells will draw in water by osmosis *(1 mark)* as the concentration of water molecules inside the cell is lower than the water concentration outside the cell *(1 mark)*.
  b) A lack of water means the plant's cells aren't turgid *(1 mark)*, which means the plant tissues have little support (and so the plant wilts/droops) *(1 mark)*.

7 a) diffusion *(1 mark)*
  b) (835 + 825 + 842 + 838) ÷ 4 = **835 s**
     (2 marks for correct answer, otherwise 1 mark for adding together 4 values and dividing by 4)
  c) As the size of the gelatine cube increases, the time taken for the cube to become yellow increases *(1 mark)*. This is because the bigger cubes have a smaller surface area to volume ratio *(1 mark)*, which decreases the rate of diffusion *(1 mark)*.

8 a) E.g. they could measure the mass of each egg before putting it in its jar and measure each egg's mass again after one day. *(1 mark for stating what will be measured, 1 mark for stating a time period over which it will be measured.)*
  b) E.g. the egg in the weak sugar solution would lose mass and the egg in water would gain mass by the end of the experiment *(1 mark for describing a result in the weak sugar solution which suggests water has moved out of the egg, 1 mark for describing a result in the water which suggests water has moved into the egg.)*

Pages 29-31

Warm-Up Questions

1) False. They all contain carbon, hydrogen and oxygen but only proteins contain nitrogen.

2) Proteins are made up of amino acids. Lipids are made up of glycerol and fatty acids.

3) Add excess Benedict's reagent to the sample and heat it without boiling. If glucose is present a coloured precipitate will form.

4) That starch is present in the sample.

Exam Questions

1 a) Vitamin A helps to improve **e.g. vision** *(1 mark)* and keep skin and hair healthy. A good source of vitamin A is **e.g. liver** *(1 mark)*. Vitamin D can be found in foods such as **e.g. eggs** *(1 mark)*. It's needed for **e.g. calcium** *(1 mark)* absorption. Your diet should also include things like **e.g. oranges** *(1 mark)* as they contain vitamin C. Calcium is needed to make **bones** *(1 mark)* and teeth. A good source of calcium is **e.g. milk/cheese** *(1 mark)*.

   b) i) E.g. to aid the movement of food through the gut *(1 mark)*

   ii) e.g. wholemeal bread *(1 mark)*

   c) We need water because just about all of our bodily functions require water *(1 mark)*.

2 a) Pregnant women need more energy than other women because they need to provide energy for their babies to develop *(1 mark)*.

   b) Teenagers need more energy than older people because they are still growing *(1 mark)*.

   c) A diet that contains all the essential nutrients plus fibre *(1 mark)* in the right proportions *(1 mark)*. / A diet that contains carbohydrates, proteins, lipids, vitamins, minerals, water and fibre *(1 mark)* in the right proportions *(1 mark)*.

3

Enzyme	Function
proteases	convert proteins into amino acids
amylase	converts starch into maltose
maltase	converts maltose into glucose
lipases	convert lipids into glycerol and fatty acids

(3 marks — 1 mark for each correct answer)

4 a)

Function	Letter of the label
Pummels the food, and produces the protease enzyme pepsin.	E
Contains salivary glands which produce amylase.	A
Where nutrients are absorbed from food.	F
Where excess water is absorbed from food.	D

(3 marks — 1 mark for each correct answer)

   b) It produces protease, amylase and lipase enzymes *(1 mark)* and releases these into the small intestine *(1 mark)*.

   c) Peristalsis is the process by which food is moved through the alimentary canal/gut *(1 mark)* to enable digestion to occur/to prevent it from becoming clogged up with food *(1 mark)*. In peristalsis, waves of circular muscle contractions squeeze balls of food through the alimentary canal/gut *(1 mark)*.

5 a) Egestion is when all the undigested parts of anything that has been ingested are formed into faeces *(1 mark)* and exit the body via the anus *(1 mark)*.

   b) Large, insoluble molecules are broken down into small, soluble molecules *(1 mark)*. This occurs mechanically (using teeth and muscles) and chemically (enzymes and bile) *(1 mark)*.

   c) assimilation *(1 mark)*

   d) ingestion *(1 mark)*

6 a) The mass of the peanut *(1 mark)*, the temperature of the water *(1 mark)*.

   b) Energy = 35 × 51 × 4.2 = 7497 J *(1 mark)*

   c) 7497 ÷ 0.7 = 10 710 J/g *(1 mark. Allow carry through of any answer from part b).)*

   d) E.g. not all of the energy released from burning the peanut is transferred to the water to heat it up *(1 mark)* because it is lost to the air/used in heating up the boiling tube instead *(1 mark)*. / Not all of the energy used to heat the water is retained by the water *(1 mark)*, because the water loses heat by conduction/convection *(1 mark)*.

   e) E.g. she could insulate the boiling tube (to reduce heat loss) *(1 mark)*.

7 a) i) bile *(1 mark)*

   ii) It is produced in the liver *(1 mark)* and acts on food in the small intestine *(1 mark)*.

   iii) The enzymes in the small intestine (where the bile/fluid acts) work best in alkaline conditions *(1 mark)*. The alkaline bile/fluid neutralises the acid from the stomach, so the enzymes can work *(1 mark)*.

   b) Bile emulsifies fat/breaks fat down into tiny droplets *(1 mark)*. This gives a larger surface area for lipases to work on and so the fat is digested more quickly *(1 mark)*. The gallstones could block the bile ducts and prevent bile from entering the small intestine *(1 mark)*. If so, any fat may be digested more slowly, possibly causing problems *(1 mark)*.

8 a) i) small intestine *(1 mark)*

   ii) E.g. they have a large surface area / they are covered in millions of microvilli *(1 mark)*. They have a single, permeable layer of surface cells *(1 mark)*. They have a good blood supply/network of capillaries *(1 mark)*.

   b) If the villi become flattened, this will reduce their surface area for the absorption of nutrients *(1 mark)*, which could mean that not enough vitamins are absorbed, leading to vitamin deficiencies *(1 mark)*.

Pages 38-39

Warm-Up Questions

1) A limiting factor is something that stops photosynthesis happening any faster.

2) If the temperature's too high (over about 45 °C), the plant's enzymes will be denatured, so the rate of photosynthesis rapidly decreases.

3) Put a plant in a sealed bell jar with some soda lime. The soda lime will absorb the carbon dioxide out of the air in the jar. Leave the jar under a light for a while and then test a leaf for starch using the iodine test. If the leaf doesn't turn blue-black it shows that carbon dioxide is needed for photosynthesis.

4) oxygen production

Exam Questions

1 a) delivers water and nutrients to every part of the leaf — E *(1 mark)*

   helps to reduce water loss by evaporation — A *(1 mark)*

   where most of the chloroplasts in the leaf are located, to maximise the amount of light they receive — B *(1 mark)*

   allows carbon dioxide to diffuse directly into the leaf — D *(1 mark)*

   b) Photosynthesis involves the conversion of light energy to chemical energy *(1 mark)*, which is stored in glucose *(1 mark)*.

   c) Word equation: carbon dioxide + water → glucose + oxygen *(1 mark for carbon dioxide + water on the left-hand side of the equation, 1 mark for glucose + oxygen on the right.)*

   Balanced symbol equation: $6CO_2 + 6H_2O \rightarrow C_6H_{12}O_6 + 6O_2$

   (1 mark for $6CO_2 + 6H_2O$ on the left-hand side of the equation, 1 mark for $C_6H_{12}O_6 + 6O_2$ on the right. Allow 1 mark if the correct symbols are used, but the equation isn't correctly balanced.)

2 a) At low light intensities, increasing the CO_2 concentration has no effect *(1 mark)*, but at higher light intensities, increasing the concentration of CO_2 increases the maximum rate of photosynthesis *(1 mark)*.

   b) The rate of photosynthesis does not continue to increase because temperature or the level of carbon dioxide becomes the limiting factor *(1 mark)*.

3 a) The chlorophyll was removed from the leaf *(1 mark)*.

   b) That starch is present in the leaf *(1 mark)*.

c) I would expect the green parts of the leaf to turn blue-black *(1 mark)* and the white part of the leaf to turn brown *(1 mark)*. This is because the green parts of the leaf contain chlorophyll and so they will be able to photosynthesise and produce starch *(1 mark)*. The white part of the leaf does not contain chlorophyll, so it will not be able to photosynthesise or produce starch *(1 mark)*.

Remember: photosynthesis produces glucose, which is stored in the leaves as starch.

4 E.g. take two plants of the same type. Grow one plant without any light for a week (e.g. in a dark cupboard). Grow the other plant in bright light for a week (e.g. in a cupboard under artificial lights). Keep both plants at the same temperature and give them the same amount of water. Keep the carbon dioxide concentration for both plants the same too. After one week, take a leaf from each plant and test it for starch using iodine solution. Record the results. Repeat the experiment at least twice.

(1 mark for stating that one plant will be grown without light and one will be grown with light, 1 mark for stating that both plants should be the same type, 1 mark for describing one control variable, e.g. temperature, 1 mark for describing a second control variable, e.g. water, 1 mark for stating what will be measured, e.g. starch production, 1 mark for stating how it will be measured, e.g. using the iodine test, 1 mark for stating that repeats should be carried out. Maximum 6 marks available.)

Pages 46-47

Warm-Up Questions

1) making amino acids and proteins

2) In unicellular organisms, substances can diffuse directly into and out of the cell (across the cell membrane). The rate of diffusion is quick because of the short distances substances have to travel. But in multicellular organisms, diffusion across the outer surface would be too slow to reach every cell in the organism's body. So multicellular organisms need transport systems to move substances to and from individual cells quickly.

3) light intensity, temperature, wind speed, humidity

Exam Questions

1 a) Osmosis *(1 mark)*. Water moves from a higher concentration in the soil to a lower concentration in the root hair cell *(1 mark)*.

b) xylem vessels *(1 mark)*

2 a) phloem *(1 mark)*

b) E.g. amino acids *(1 mark)*

3 a) The plants are lacking in magnesium and magnesium is needed to make chlorophyll (the pigment that makes plant leaves green) *(1 mark)*.

b) i) The magnesium-deficient plants had a lower total dry mass than those grown with a complete mineral supply *(1 mark)*.

ii) The magnesium-deficient plants are unable to produce chlorophyll, which is needed for photosynthesis *(1 mark)*. If photosynthesis is reduced, plant growth will also be reduced *(1 mark)* and the plants will gain less mass *(1 mark)*.

4 a) E.g. the evaporation (and diffusion) of water from a plant's surface *(1 mark)*.

b) 9 a.m. *(1 mark)*

c) Any one from: e.g. day 2 was colder, so the water evaporated/diffused more slowly. / Day 2 was less windy, so the water vapour was carried away more slowly. / Day 2 was wetter/more humid, so there was a smaller diffusion gradient, so the water diffused more slowly. / The light intensity was lower on day 2, so fewer stomata were open to allow water vapour to escape. *(1 mark for reason, 1 mark for explanation)*

d) At night the light intensity is low *(1 mark)* so the stomata close, allowing less water vapour to escape *(1 mark)*.

5 a) $10 + 11 + 9 = 30 \div 3 = \textbf{10\%}$ *(2 marks for correct answer, otherwise 1 mark for adding together 3 percentages and dividing by 3)*

b) The movement of air from the fan sweeps away water vapour, maintaining a low concentration of water outside the leaf *(1 mark)* and increasing the rate at which water is lost through diffusion *(1 mark)*. This means that the plants next to the fan would lose more water (and therefore more mass) than the plants in a still room in the same amount of time *(1 mark)*.

c) The rate of transpiration would be slower *(1 mark)* since most water loss occurs through the stomata, which are on the underside of the leaves *(1 mark)*.

d) E.g. you could put a new group of 3 basil plants in a separate room *(1 mark)* and increase the humidity in the room by misting/spraying the air with water *(1 mark)*.

If you've thought of another <u>sensible</u> way to increase or decrease the humidity around the plants, you'd still get the mark in the exam.

Revision Summary for Section 3 (page 48)

2) a) 40 units

b) temperature and light

Pages 55-56

Warm-Up Questions

1) E.g. to create large molecules from smaller ones, e.g. proteins from amino acids) / to contract muscles.

2) glucose $\rightarrow$ lactic acid (+ energy)

3) ethanol, carbon dioxide/CO_2

4) false (plants respire all the time)

Exam Questions

1 a) To release energy *(1 mark)*.

b) Any two from: e.g. aerobic respiration uses oxygen, anaerobic respiration does not. / Glucose is only partially broken down during anaerobic respiration, but is broken down fully during aerobic respiration. / Anaerobic respiration produces lactic acid, aerobic respiration does not. / Anaerobic respiration releases less energy than aerobic respiration. *(1 mark for each correct answer)*

c) $C_6H_{12}O_6 + 6O_2 \rightarrow 6CO_2 + 6H_2O$
(1 mark for using the correct formulas, 1 mark for correctly balancing the equation)

2 a) i) A: oxygen / water vapour *(1 mark)*

B: carbon dioxide *(1 mark)*

ii) diffusion *(1 mark)*

b) i) photosynthesis *(1 mark)*

ii) respiration *(1 mark)*

c) The stomata are tiny pores on the surface of the leaf *(1 mark)* that open and close to change the amount of gas that can diffuse through them into or out of the leaf cells *(1 mark)*.

d) E.g. leaves are broad *(1 mark)* so there is a large surface area for diffusion of gases *(1 mark)*. Leaves are thin *(1 mark)* so gases only have to travel/diffuse a short distance to reach cells where they're used *(1 mark)*. Air spaces in the leaf *(1 mark)* increase the surface area for gas exchange/allow gases to move easily between cells *(1 mark)*.

3 **Photosynthesis** only happens during the day, when the **light intensity** is high. During the day, plants make more **oxygen** than they use up in respiration. At night, plants only **respire**, so they take in **oxygen** and release **carbon dioxide**. *(1 mark for each correct answer)*

4 E.g. divide dried peas of the same variety into two batches. Soak one batch until the peas germinate. Boil one batch to kill the peas so they can't respire/to act as a control. Place the two batches into separate vacuum flasks with thermometers and seal the flasks with cotton wool so that air/oxygen can still enter the flasks, allowing the peas to respire aerobically. The vacuum flask/cotton wool insulates the peas against changes in the external temperature. Record the temperature of each flask at regular intervals for one week. Repeat the experiment at least three times using the same mass of peas each time. The germinating peas will respire and produce heat so the temperature of this flask should be higher than the control flask.
(1 mark for including a control (e.g. boiled peas), 1 mark for stating the organisms should be of the same type/size, 1 mark for stating that the investigation should be repeated, 1 mark for stating that the temperature should be measured, 1 mark for saying how the temperature should be measured, 1 mark for controlling one variable (e.g. external temperature / mass of organisms used), 1 mark for controlling a second variable. Maximum of 6 marks available.)

5 a) To prevent gas exchange with the surrounding air *(1 mark)*.

b) To make sure that any change in the hydrogen-carbonate indicator is due to processes occurring in the leaves *(1 mark)*.

c) Tube A: no/little change in colour of the hydrogen-carbonate indicator *(1 mark)*. Some light is available, so the rates of photosynthesis and respiration roughly balance and the CO_2 concentration in the tube remains the same/similar *(1 mark)*.

Tube B: hydrogen-carbonate indicator turns yellow *(1 mark)*. Foil blocks out all light, so the CO_2 produced by respiration is not used up in photosynthesis. This means that the CO_2 concentration in the tube increases *(1 mark)*.

Tube C: hydrogen-carbonate indicator turns purple *(1 mark)*. The rate of photosynthesis will be high because of the bright light, so the leaf takes up more CO_2 than it produces through respiration and the CO_2 concentration in the tube decreases *(1 mark)*.

To answer this question, you need to think about how the amount of light entering each tube will affect the rate of photosynthesis in the leaf — and whether there'll be a net gain or loss of CO_2 in the tube as a result. Then you need to decide how this will affect the colour of the indicator.

Page 61

Warm-Up Questions

1) Around/surrounding the lungs

2) true

3) The intercostal muscles and the diaphragm.

Exam Questions

1 a) The blood in the capillary has just returned to the lungs from the rest of the body, so contains a low concentration of oxygen *(1 mark)*. The alveolus contains air that has just been breathed in, so it has a high concentration of oxygen *(1 mark)*. So oxygen diffuses out of the alveolus and into the capillary *(1 mark)*.

b) Thin outer walls — so gases don't have to diffuse far/there's a short diffusion pathway.
Good blood supply — to maintain high concentration gradient.
Permeable outer walls — to allow gases to diffuse easily.
(1 mark for each correct answer.)

2 E.g. the person being tested should first sit still for 5 minutes. The number of breaths they take in one minute should then be recorded. These time periods should be measured with a stop watch. The same person should then run on a treadmill for 5 minutes. The number of breaths they take in one minute should then be recorded immediately. Repeats should be carried out using the same time periods, the same intensity of exercise, and at the same temperature.
(1 mark for including a control (i.e. recording the breathing rate at rest), 1 mark for stating that the same person should do the rest and exercise tests, 1 mark for stating that the breathing rate should be measured, 1 mark for saying how the breathing rate should be measured, 1 mark for stating that the investigation should be repeated, 1 mark for controlling one variable (e.g. length of rest/exercise periods / intensity of exercise / temperature at which experiment takes place), 1 mark for controlling a second variable. Maximum of 6 marks available.)

The investigation you describe here can involve exercise of any type — the important thing is that you measure its effect on breathing rate.

3 a) The percentage of male smokers has been decreasing since 1950 *(1 mark)*. The percentage of female smokers increased between 1950 and 1970, then decreased from 1970 to 2000 *(1 mark)*.

b) E.g. awareness of the health risks of smoking increased *(1 mark)*.

c) Any two from: e.g. smoking damages the walls of the alveoli *(1 mark)* reducing the area for gas exchange/leading to diseases like emphysema *(1 mark)*. / Tar damages cilia in the trachea/lungs *(1 mark)* leading to the build up of mucus/making chest infections more likely *(1 mark)*. / Tar irritates the bronchi/bronchioles *(1 mark)* leading to excess mucus production/a smoker's cough/chronic bronchitis *(1 mark)*. / Carbon monoxide reduces the oxygen carrying capacity of the blood *(1 mark)* leading to high blood pressure/increased risk of coronary heart disease/ heart attacks *(1 mark)*. / Tobacco contains carcinogens *(1 mark)* which can lead to cancers, e.g. lung cancer) *(1 mark)*.

Pages 69-71

Warm-Up Questions

1) red blood cells, white blood cells and platelets

2) antigens

3) carbon dioxide, oxygen

4) the bicuspid valve

Exam Questions

1 pulmonary artery — B
hepatic artery — F
vena cava — C
kidneys — H
aorta — E
hepatic portal vein — G
(1 mark for each correct answer)

2 a) It is biconcave *(1 mark)* which gives it a large surface area for absorbing and releasing oxygen *(1 mark)*.

b) E.g. it contains haemoglobin *(1 mark)* which reacts with oxygen so red blood cells can carry it around the body *(1 mark)*. / It has no nucleus *(1 mark)* so there is space for more haemoglobin and so more oxygen *(1 mark)*.

3 a) The cat felt threatened by the dog so its adrenal glands secreted adrenaline *(1 mark)*. Adrenaline binds to specific receptors in the heart *(1 mark)* causing the cardiac muscle to contract more frequently and with more force, so the cat's heart rate increased *(1 mark)*.

b) By increasing the oxygen supply to the tissues *(1 mark)*.

4 a) immune system *(1 mark)*

b) When *Campylobacter* bacteria enter the body, non-specific white blood cells called **phagocytes** *(1 mark)* recognise the bacteria as foreign to the body. They engulf them and then **digest** *(1 mark)* them. Other white blood cells, called **lymphocytes** *(1 mark)* produce proteins called **antibodies** *(1 mark)* that lock onto the bacteria and mark them out for destruction.

5 a) A — aorta *(1 mark)*
B — vena cava *(1 mark)*
C — left atrium *(1 mark)*

b) i) To pump blood out of the heart *(1 mark)*.

ii) The left ventricle pumps blood to the whole body *(1 mark)* so it has a very muscular wall which is thicker *(1 mark)*. The right ventricle only pumps blood to the lungs *(1 mark)* so it doesn't have as much muscle, and so it is thinner *(1 mark)*.

c) To prevent the backflow of blood *(1 mark)*.

d) Deoxygenated blood arrives at the heart through the vena cava *(1 mark)* and enters the right atrium *(1 mark)*. The blood is then pumped into the right ventricle *(1 mark)*, which contracts to pump blood to the lungs through the pulmonary artery *(1 mark)*.

6 When vaccinated, child A was given dead or inactive rubella pathogens *(1 mark)*. These would have had antigens on their surface and so would cause lymphocytes to start producing antibodies *(1 mark)*. Some of these lymphocytes remained in the blood as memory cells *(1 mark)*. When child A was exposed to the virus, the memory cells made the specific antibodies more quickly/in greater quantities, so child A didn't become ill *(1 mark)*. Child B did not have these memory cells, so when they were infected by the virus they became ill *(1 mark)*.

7 a) Arteries carry blood away from the heart *(1 mark)* and veins carry blood back to the heart *(1 mark)*.

b) E.g. the vein has a bigger lumen/thinner wall/valves *(1 mark)*. / The artery has a smaller lumen/thicker wall/no valves *(1 mark)*.

To answer this question, you needed to think about how the structure of veins and arteries differ — and how you could tell them apart by just looking at them.

c) The vein, because it has a thinner wall *(1 mark)*.

8 a) E.g. platelets *(1 mark)*

Platelets are the component of the blood that are involved in blood clotting, so if a condition means that people's blood doesn't clot properly it's likely that it's something to do with the platelets.

b) Because the blood does not clot properly, the cut will not heal quickly *(1 mark)*. As a result, the person might lose more blood from the cut *(1 mark)*. They are also at risk of infection because microorganisms could enter the cut *(1 mark)*.

9 a) Saeed *(1 mark)*

b) Because the body/muscles needs/need more energy *(1 mark)* and so respire(s) more, which requires more oxygen *(1 mark)*.

Pages 75-76
Warm-Up Questions
1) In the liver.
2) high pressure
3) bladder

Exam Questions
1 a) A — Bowman's capsule *(1 mark)*
   B — Loop of Henlé *(1 mark)*

b) As the glomerular filtrate passes along the nephron, useful substances are taken back into the blood in a process known as **selective** *(1 mark)* reabsorption. Glucose is reabsorbed back into the blood from the **proximal convoluted tubule** *(1 mark)*. **Water** *(1 mark)* is reabsorbed from the collecting duct.

c) Any two from: water / urea / salts *(1 mark for each correct answer)*

2 a) A — kidney *(1 mark)*
   B — ureter *(1 mark)*
   C — urethra *(1 mark)*

b) E.g. lungs / skin *(1 mark)*.

3 a) E.g. the maintenance of a balance between water coming into the body and water going out of the body *(1 mark)*.

b) urine *(1 mark)*

c) i) anti-diuretic hormone (ADH) *(1 mark)*
   ii) pituitary gland *(1 mark)*
   iii) It makes them more permeable *(1 mark)* so that more water can be reabsorbed back into the blood *(1 mark)*.

4 a) Bowman's capsule *(1 mark)*

b) i) As the blood flows from the renal artery into the glomerulus *(1 mark)* a high pressure builds up *(1 mark)* which squeezes/filters small molecules out of the blood into the Bowman's capsule to form the glomerular filtrate *(1 mark)*.

   ii)

Substances	Blood	Glomerular filtrate
glucose	✗	✓
urea	✗	✓
proteins	✓	✗
salts	✗	✓

(1 mark for each row completed correctly)

5 As Sian ran, she sweated, resulting in water loss and less water in her blood *(1 mark)*. Her brain detected the decreased water content of her blood *(1 mark)* and instructed the pituitary gland to release ADH (anti-diuretic hormone) into the blood *(1 mark)*. The ADH caused the kidneys to reabsorb more water *(1 mark)* resulting in less water being released in her urine, so her urine was more concentrated and appeared darker in colour *(1 mark)*.

Revision Summary for Section 5 (page 77)
11) Vessel C) is a vein. You can tell this because it has a large lumen and thin walls. A) is a capillary and is far too small to be a vein. B) is an artery — the walls are too thick to be a vein and the lumen isn't large enough.

Pages 82-83
Warm-Up Questions
1) eyes, ears, nose, tongue and skin
2) brain and spinal cord
3) electrical impulses
4) E.g. they can reduce your chances of getting injured.
5) E.g. the iris reflex (in response to bright light) / accommodation of the eye / withdrawing your hand from a painful stimulus / release of adrenaline in response to shock.

Exam Questions
1 a) E.g. so they can respond to the changes in order to avoid danger/increase their chances of survival *(1 mark)*.

b) receptors *(1 mark)*

c) Stimulus: sight of food *(1 mark)*
   Sense organ: the eye *(1 mark)*
   Effectors: muscle cells *(1 mark)*

d) hormonal system *(1 mark)*

2 a) X: sensory neurone *(1 mark)*
   Y: relay neurone *(1 mark)*
   Z: motor neurone *(1 mark)*

b) a synapse *(1 mark)*

c) The effectors are muscle cells *(1 mark)* and they respond by contracting (which causes Ffion to drop the plate) *(1 mark)*.

3 a) A: cornea *(1 mark)*
   B: pupil *(1 mark)*

b) To control the diameter of the pupil/the amount of light entering the eye *(1 mark)*.

c) i) rods *(1 mark)*, cones *(1 mark)*
   ii) the fovea *(1 mark)*

d) Information is sent using impulses *(1 mark)*, via the optic nerve *(1 mark)*.

4 a) The ciliary muscles relax *(1 mark)* allowing the suspensory ligaments to pull tight *(1 mark)*, which results in the lens becoming thinner/less rounded *(1 mark)*.

b) If the lens cannot form a rounded shape, light from nearby objects won't be bent enough to be focused on the retina *(1 mark)*. This means that people with presbyopia will be unable to focus on nearby objects *(1 mark)*.

5 a) B, because the pupil has contracted in this eye *(1 mark)* to stop too much light entering the eye *(1 mark)*.

b) i) Reflex responses happen very quickly/are automatic *(1 mark)* so the eye can adjust quickly to prevent the retina being damaged by bright light *(1 mark)*.

   ii) Light receptor cells detect the bright light *(1 mark)* and send electrical impulses along sensory neurones to the brain/central nervous system *(1 mark)*. The impulse then passes along a relay neurone *(1 mark)* to a motor neurone *(1 mark)* and then to effectors/the circular muscles in the iris, which contract, making the pupil smaller *(1 mark)*.

Pages 90-91
Warm-Up Questions
1) a) ovaries
   b) ovaries
   c) adrenal glands
2) adrenaline
3) It increases the permeability of the kidney tubules to water.
4) It's the optimum temperature for enzymes in the human body.
5) Plant hormones which control growth at the tips of shoots and roots. / Plant growth hormones.

208

Exam Questions

1 a) i) testosterone *(1 mark)*, testes *(1 mark)*

   ii) The role of insulin is to help control blood sugar level *(1 mark)*. It stimulates the liver to turn glucose into glycogen *(1 mark)*.

   b) Nervous responses are very fast and hormonal responses are slower *(1 mark)*. Nerves use electrical impulses/signals, while hormones use chemical signals *(1 mark)*. Nervous responses usually act for a short time while hormonal responses last for longer *(1 mark)*. Nerves act on a very precise area whereas hormones act on a more general area *(1 mark)*.

2 a) The maintenance of a constant internal environment *(1 mark)*.

   b) i) Through his skin as sweat *(1 mark)*. Via the lungs in his breath *(1 mark)*.

   ii) It is very concentrated *(1 mark)* because he has lost a lot of water in his sweat/breath, so loses less in his urine *(1 mark)*.

   c) E.g. it is a cooler day so he sweats less *(1 mark)*. / He drank more water before/during the ride *(1 mark)*.

3 Plant shoots grow towards **light** *(1 mark)* to maximise photosynthesis. This growth response is known as **phototropism** *(1 mark)*. Plants can also sense **gravity** *(1 mark)* so their shoots and roots grow in the right direction.

4 a) Vasoconstriction *(1 mark)*. It reduces the transfer of heat from the blood to the surroundings, so helps to keep the body warm *(1 mark)*.

   b) Sweat glands respond by producing very little sweat *(1 mark)*, because sweat transfers heat from the body to the environment when it evaporates *(1 mark)*.

5 a) Skin temperature will increase, so the sweat glands will respond by producing lots of sweat *(1 mark)*. Drinking water will help to restore the water balance in the body *(1 mark)*.

   b) The blood vessels widen/dilate / Vasodilation occurs *(1 mark)*. This allows more blood to flow near to the surface of the skin *(1 mark)* so more heat can be lost/radiated to the surroundings, cooling the body *(1 mark)*.

6 a) auxin *(1 mark)*

   b) i) A growth response away from gravity *(1 mark)*.

   ii) The shoot *(1 mark)*.

   c) The root will grow down again *(1 mark)*. Auxin will build up on the lower side of the root *(1 mark)* inhibiting growth of the lower cells, so the root will bend downwards *(1 mark)*.

Pages 98-99

Warm-Up Questions

1) in the nucleus

2) They have two copies of each chromosome.

3) 46

4) one

Exam Questions

1 Any two from: e.g. mitosis involves one division, whereas meiosis involves two divisions. / Mitosis produces two new cells, whereas meiosis produces four new cells. / Mitosis produces identical cells, whereas meiosis produces genetically different cells. / Mitosis happens in all body cells, whereas meiosis only happens in the reproductive organs. / A diploid cell that undergoes mitosis produces diploid cells, whereas a diploid cell that undergoes meiosis produces haploid cells. *(1 mark for each correct answer)*

2 During sexual reproduction two parents produce sex cells called **gametes** *(1 mark)*. These cells are **haploid** *(1 mark)*, meaning that they have half the number of chromosomes in a normal cell. In humans, sex cells contain **23** *(1 mark)* chromosomes. At fertilisation, a male sex cell fuses with a female sex cell to produce a **zygote** *(1 mark)*, which undergoes cell division by **mitosis** *(1 mark)* to produce an embryo.

3 a) DNA has two strands that are coiled together in a double helix *(1 mark)*. The two strands are linked by paired bases *(1 mark)*. There are four bases: adenine, cytosine, guanine and thymine/A, C, G and T *(1 mark)*. The bases always pair up in the same way/the base pairs are complementary, A-T and C-G *(1 mark)*.

   b) Each gene codes for a specific protein *(1 mark)*, and proteins determine inherited characteristics *(1 mark)*.

   c) There are different/alternative versions of the same gene, called alleles *(1 mark)*, that give different versions of a characteristic *(1 mark)*. The two kittens must have different versions/alleles of the gene for fur length, meaning one is long-haired and the other is short-haired *(1 mark)*.

4 a) asexual reproduction *(1 mark)*

   b) They will be identical *(1 mark)*.

   c) E.g. growth / repair of tissues *(1 mark)*

5 a) i) three *(1 mark)*

   ii) four *(1 mark)*

When a diploid cell undergoes meiosis, four haploid gametes are produced — it doesn't matter whether you're talking about human cells or mosquito cells.

   b) Meiosis produces gametes that are genetically different to each other *(1 mark)*. A male gamete and a female gamete then combine at random at fertilisation *(1 mark)*, so the offspring inherits a random mixture of chromosomes from both parents *(1 mark)*.

6 a) The amount of DNA is doubling *(1 mark)* because each new cell needs to have a complete set of chromosomes *(1 mark)*.

   b) The two new cells separate *(1 mark)*.

   c) two *(1 mark)*

Pages 104-105

Warm-Up Questions

1) anther, filament

2) a) The end part of the carpel, which pollen grains attach to.

   b) The rod-like section that supports the stigma.

3) When seeds start to grow.

4) enough water, enough oxygen, a suitable temperature

5) e.g. cuttings

Exam Questions

1 a) Pollen grains from an anther *(1 mark)* are transferred to a stigma *(1 mark)*, so that male gametes can fertilise female gametes *(1 mark)*.

   b) Sexual reproduction involving only one plant / the transfer of pollen from an anther to a stigma on the same plant *(1 mark)*.

2 a) X: Filament *(1 mark)*. It supports the anther *(1 mark)*. Y: Ovary *(1 mark)*. It contains the female gametes/eggs *(1 mark)*.

   b) Flower B because e.g. long filaments hang the anthers outside the flower *(1 mark)*, so that a lot of pollen gets blown away *(1 mark)* / the large, feathery stigmas *(1 mark)* are efficient at catching pollen drifting past in the air *(1 mark)*.

   c) Any two from: e.g. brightly coloured petals to attract insects / scented flowers/nectaries/produce nectar to attract insects / large, sticky pollen grains that stick easily to insects / a sticky stigma to collect pollen from insects *(1 mark for each correct answer)*.

3 a) Runners are rapidly growing stems that grow sideways from the plant above ground *(1 mark)*. The runners take root, producing new plants that begin to grow *(1 mark)*.

   b) Because the strawberry plant's offspring are clones of the parent plant/ genetically identical to the parent *(1 mark)*.

4 A pollen grain from one plant lands on the stigma of another plant. A **pollen tube** *(1 mark)* grows out of the pollen grain, down through the **style** *(1 mark)* to the ovary and into the ovule. A **nucleus** *(1 mark)* from the male gamete travels to the ovule to fertilise the female gamete, producing a **zygote** *(1 mark)* that divides to form an embryo. The fertilised female gamete forms a **seed** *(1 mark)* while the ovary develops into a **fruit** *(1 mark)*.

5 a) Because oxygen is needed for germination *(1 mark)* and oxygen was removed from the air in flask A by the sodium pyrogallate solution *(1 mark)*.

   b) From food reserves stored within the seeds *(1 mark)*.

c) E.g. normally, after seeds have produced green leaves, they can start to obtain energy through photosynthesis *(1 mark)*. But in flask B, sodium hydroxide has removed the carbon dioxide from the air, so photosynthesis can't occur *(1 mark)*. The seedlings have used up their food reserves, so there is no energy available for growth *(1 mark)*.

Page 109
Warm-Up Questions

1) To make sperm.

   The other function of the testes is to produce testosterone.

2) To carry the sperm from the testis towards the urethra.

3) testosterone

4) Extra hair on underarms and pubic area. Widening of hips. Development of breasts. Ovum release and start of periods.

5) To allow the blood of the embryo and mother to get very close to allow the exchange of food, oxygen and waste.

Exam Questions

1

Structure	Function
Ovary	Produces ova (eggs) / sex hormones.
Fallopian tube/ oviduct	Carries the ovum (egg) from the ovary to the uterus.
Uterus	Contains the growing embryo.

(1 mark for each correct answer)

2 a) A, because a rise in the level of oestrogen stimulates egg release *(1 mark)*.

b) The uterus lining is thickest during the second half of the cycle/after the egg is released/between days 14 and 28 *(1 mark)*. This is because the uterus is preparing to receive a fertilised egg/zygote *(1 mark)*.

c) The level of progesterone would remain high *(1 mark)* to maintain the lining of the uterus during pregnancy *(1 mark)*.

Pages 115-116
Warm-Up Questions

1) Different versions of the same gene.

2) Which alleles something has.

3) dominant alleles

4) The Y chromosome.

Exam Questions

1 a) She has brown hair *(1 mark)*.

b) heterozygous *(1 mark)*

2 a)

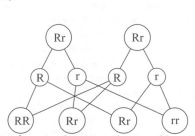

Genotypes of parents:

Genotypes of gametes:

Genotypes of offspring: RR Rr Rr rr

Phenotypes of offspring: red eyes red eyes red eyes white eyes

(1 mark for correct genotypes of the parents, 1 mark for correct genotypes of gametes, 1 mark for correct genotypes of offspring, 1 mark for correct phenotypes of offspring)

b) 1 in 4 / 25% *(1 mark)*

3 a) AA, Aa *(1 mark)*

b) (7 ÷ 12) × 100 *(1 mark)* = **58.3%** *(1 mark)*

c) i) E.g.

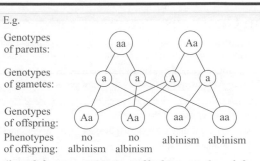

Genotypes of parents:

Genotypes of gametes:

Genotypes of offspring: Aa Aa aa aa

Phenotypes of offspring: no albinism / no albinism / albinism / albinism

(1 mark for correct genotypes of both parents, 1 mark for correct genotypes of gametes, 1 mark for correct genotypes of offspring, 1 mark for correct phenotypes of offspring)

ii) 50% *(1 mark)*

iii) Fertilisation is random/the genetic diagram only shows the probability of the outcome, so the numbers of offspring produced will not always be exactly in those proportions *(1 mark)*.

4 Dd *(1 mark)*. Polydactyly is a dominant disorder, so if she was DD all of her children would be affected *(1 mark)*.

5 a)

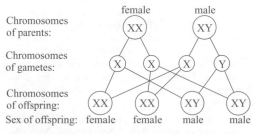

Chromosomes of parents:

Chromosomes of gametes:

Chromosomes of offspring: XX XX XY XY

Sex of offspring: female female male male

(1 mark for correct chromosomes in parents, 1 mark for correct chromosomes in gametes, 1 mark for correct chromosomes in offspring, 1 mark for correct sex of offspring)

b) Male children will not inherit the colour blindness allele because they don't inherit an X chromosome from their father *(1 mark)*.

c) 0 / 0% *(1 mark)*

A daughter of this couple would inherit the recessive colour blindness allele from her father, but also a dominant allele from her mother, so she would not be colour blind.

6 a) Codominant *(1 mark)*, because the spotted flowers display both red and white characteristics *(1 mark)*.

b)

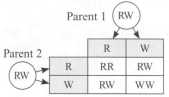

Parent 1 RW

Parent 2 RW

	R	W
R	RR	RW
W	RW	WW

(1 mark for correct genotypes of both parents, 1 mark for correct genotypes of gametes (shown in grey boxes), 1 mark for correct genotypes of offspring)

c) 1 : 2 : 1 (red : spotted : white flowers) *(1 mark)*

Pages 121-122
Warm-Up Questions

1) E.g. sunlight, moisture level, temperature, mineral content of soil.

2) Life began as simple organisms from which more complex organisms evolved (rather than just popping into existence).

3) E.g. X-rays, gamma rays, ultraviolet light. It can cause mutations.

4) E.g. tobacco.

Exam Questions

1 a) No, because hair colour is controlled by genes *(1 mark)* and identical twins have the same genes *(1 mark)*.

b) The difference in weight must be caused by the environment *(1 mark)*, because the twins have exactly the same genes *(1 mark)*.

In this case, the environment can mean the amount of food each twin eats or the amount of exercise they each do.

c) No, because if they were caused by genes both twins should have the birthmark *(1 mark)*.

2 a) A rare, random change in an organisms's DNA *(1 mark)* that can be inherited *(1 mark)*.

b) Mutations change the sequence of DNA bases *(1 mark)*, which can change the protein produced by a gene *(1 mark)* and lead to new characteristics, increasing variation *(1 mark)*.

c) i) E.g. a mutation could cause a gene to produce a different protein that is an improvement on the one it usually produces *(1 mark)*, which gives an organism a survival advantage *(1 mark)*.

ii) E.g. the mutation may cause any offspring that are produced to develop abnormally/die *(1 mark)*.

3 E.g. ancestors of the modern buff tip moth showed variation in their appearance *(1 mark)*. The moths that looked like broken twigs were less likely to be seen and eaten by predators/more likely to survive *(1 mark)* and so were more likely to reproduce *(1 mark)*. As a result, the alleles that caused the moths to look like broken twigs were more likely to be passed on to the next generation *(1 mark)*, meaning that over time these genes became increasingly widespread in the population and eventually all buff tip moths had this appearance *(1 mark)*.

4 a) E.g. gamma rays released by the explosion increased the chance of spontaneous mutations occurring in DNA *(1 mark)*. The mutations caused cells to multiply uncontrollably *(1 mark)*, resulting in thyroid cancer *(1 mark)*.

b) E.g. the X-rays caused mutations in the DNA/genes of the sex cells *(1 mark)*. The adult flies were unaffected but their offspring inherited the altered genes *(1 mark)* and developed a different characteristic *(1 mark)*.

5 a) natural selection *(1 mark)*

b) C, B, D, A *(1 mark for each correct answer)*

c) E.g. people in hospital are more likely to have weakened immune systems than people in the rest of society *(1 mark)*, and so are more likely to develop serious illness as a result of MRSA infection *(1 mark)*.

d) E.g. it can lead to infections becoming more widespread/difficult to control *(1 mark)*.

e) When antibiotics are used, resistant bacteria have an advantage over non-resistant bacteria *(1 mark)*, so they will increase in number meaning the resistance spreads *(1 mark)*. Reducing the use of antibiotics will slow/reduce the spread of antibiotic resistance *(1 mark)*.

Revision Summary for Section 7 (page 123)

19) E.g.

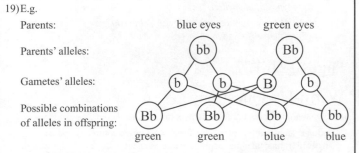

Parents: blue eyes   green eyes

Parents' alleles: bb   Bb

Gametes' alleles: b b B b

Possible combinations of alleles in offspring: Bb Bb bb bb

green   green   blue   blue

Probability of the couple having a blue-eyed child is 50%/1 in 2. Phenotypic ratio is blue:green, 1:1.

Pages 128-129

Warm-Up Questions

1) a) a community

b) an ecosystem

2) A producer is an organism that makes its own food using energy from the Sun. A consumer is an organism that eats other organisms.

3) A stage/feeding level in a food chain.

Exam Questions

1 a) E.g. He could have placed quadrats at regular intervals *(1 mark)* in a straight line from the wood to the opposite side of the field *(1 mark)*, and counted the dandelions in each quadrat *(1 mark)*.

b) The number of dandelions increases with distance from the wood *(1 mark)*.

2 a) mussel *(1 mark)*

b) The first trophic level/plankton *(1 mark)*

3 a) C *(1 mark)*, because the total mass of organisms decreases at each trophic level, which is what is shown in pyramid C *(1 mark)*.

b) The Sun *(1 mark)*.

4 a) $2070 \div 10 = 207$ kJ available to the second trophic level *(1 mark)* $207 - (90 + 100) = $ **17 kJ** available to Animal A *(1 mark)*

b) Any two from, e.g.: respiration / heat loss / loss in waste/faeces *(1 mark for each correct answer)*

c) Because energy is lost at each trophic level *(1 mark)* so there's not enough energy to support more levels *(1 mark)*.

5 E.g. the weevils eat platte thistles so could decrease this population, reducing the food available for honeybees *(1 mark)*. If the honeybee population decreases, the amount of wild honey produced will decrease *(1 mark)*.

Pages 138-140

Warm-Up Questions

1) Sources of 'man-made' methane are on the increase, for example rice-growing and cattle rearing.

2) E.g. aerosols and fridges

3) Trees stop rainwater reaching rivers too quickly. When they're cut down, rainwater can run straight into rivers, which can cause flooding.

Exam Questions

1 a) i) photosynthesis *(1 mark)*

ii) carbon dioxide *(1 mark)*

b) respiration *(1 mark)*

c) Microorganisms break down/decompose material from dead organisms *(1 mark)* and return carbon to the air as carbon dioxide through respiration *(1 mark)*.

d) i) Fossil fuels are formed from dead animals and/or plants which contain carbon *(1 mark)*.

ii) Carbon is released into the atmosphere as carbon dioxide when fossil fuels are burnt *(1 mark)*.

2 E.g. carbon stored in the small branches will be returned to the atmosphere as carbon dioxide during combustion *(1 mark)*. The green plants could be eaten by animals *(1 mark)* which will release some carbon as carbon dioxide during respiration *(1 mark)*. The green plants could be broken down by microorganisms/decomposers *(1 mark)* which will release carbon as carbon dioxide during respiration *(1 mark)*. The wood that is taken away to be made into furniture will eventually return the carbon to the atmosphere through decomposition/combustion when its life span as furniture is over *(1 mark)*. *(Maximum of 5 marks available)*

3 a) $(9.8 + 9.4 + 7.1) \div 3 = $ **8.8 micrograms/m³** *(2 marks for correct answer, otherwise 1 mark for adding the individual site results together and dividing by 3)*

b) Sulfur dioxide mixes with water vapour in the atmosphere/clouds to form sulfuric acid that falls as acid rain *(1 mark)*. Acid rain can kill organisms living in lakes/aquatic ecosystems because it makes the water more acidic *(1 mark)*. Acid rain can kill trees because the acid damages the leaves/releases toxic substances from the soil that make it hard for trees to take up nutrients *(1 mark)*.

4 a) Greenhouse gases absorb heat that is radiated away from the Earth *(1 mark)* and re-radiate it in all directions, including back to Earth *(1 mark)*.

b) E.g. it would be very cold at night *(1 mark)*.

c) Increasing levels of greenhouse gases in the atmosphere *(1 mark)* have enhanced the greenhouse effect *(1 mark)* causing the Earth to warm up, which is global warming *(1 mark)*.

d) E.g. melting ice caps/glaciers *(1 mark)* could lead to flooding of human towns/settlements *(1 mark)*. / Changing rainfall patterns *(1 mark)* could lead to changing crop growth patterns/less food being grown *(1 mark)*.

5 a) transpiration *(1 mark)*

b) Any two from: rain / snow / hail *(1 mark for each correct answer)*

c) Heat from the Sun evaporates water from the ocean *(1 mark)*, so the water molecule enters the atmosphere as water vapour *(1 mark)*. The warm water vapour rises, then cools and condenses into clouds *(1 mark)*. The water molecule then falls from the clouds as precipitation/rain/snow/hail into a garden pond *(1 mark)*.

6 a) Denitrifying bacteria convert nitrates into nitrogen gas *(1 mark)*, so *P. denitrificans* would reduce the level of nitrates in the lake, which would cause eutrophication to slow down/stop *(1 mark)*. *P. denitrificans* can live in anaerobic conditions, so would be able to work in the oxygen-depleted water *(1 mark)*.

b) *P. denitrificans* would break down the nitrates into nitrogen gas, so the nutrients would not be available to the rice crop *(1 mark)* meaning the crop yield would increase by less than if *P. denitrificans* were not present *(1 mark)*.

7 a) As the concentration of nitrates increased, the number of fish per cubic metre decreased *(1 mark)*.

b) E.g. increased use of fertilisers. / Increased runoff/leaching of fertilisers due to higher rainfall *(1 mark)*.

c) Eutrophication *(1 mark)*.

8 The number of microorganisms increases downstream of the sewage pipe *(1 mark)*. The sewage provides extra nutrients causing rapid algal growth *(1 mark)*. The algae block out light from plants causing them to die *(1 mark)*. The dead plants provide food for microorganisms, causing the number of microorganisms to increase *(1 mark)*.

9 a) When forests are cut down, less carbon dioxide is removed from the atmosphere by photosynthesising trees *(1 mark)*. The trees that are cut down are often burnt to clear the land, which releases carbon dioxide into the atmosphere *(1 mark)*. Trees that aren't burned may be decomposed by microorganisms, which release carbon dioxide through respiration *(1 mark)*. All of these processes increase the level of carbon dioxide (a greenhouse gas) in the atmosphere, which contributes to global warming *(1 mark)*.

b) Tree roots hold the soil together *(1 mark)*. When trees are removed soil can be eroded/washed away by rain *(1 mark)*.

c) Trees take up nutrients from the soil and return them when fallen leaves decay/the trees die *(1 mark)*. When trees are removed, the nutrients are washed out of/leached from the soil by rain and are not replaced, leaving infertile soil *(1 mark)*.

Pages 148-149
Warm-Up Questions

1) To reduce the number of plants being damaged or destroyed by pests, increasing crop yield.

2) *Lactobacillus* bacteria

3) Any two from, e.g. temperature / pH / oxygen level

4) Because only anaerobic respiration produces alcohol.

Exam Questions

1 a) carbon dioxide *(1 mark)*

b) E.g. by counting the bubbles of carbon dioxide produced over a certain amount of time *(1 mark)*.

c) i) E.g. she could stand the test tube containing the yeast suspension in a water bath *(1 mark)*.

ii) It would increase the rate of respiration *(1 mark)*.

2 a) E.g. more frogs could be introduced (to eat the cockroaches) *(1 mark)*.

b) E.g. an advantage of biological control is that it's not poisonous to humans, unlike some chemical pesticides *(1 mark)*. Also biological control can have a longer-lasting effect than spraying chemical pesticides *(1 mark)* and it can be less harmful to wildlife than chemical pesticides *(1 mark)*. A disadvantage of using biological control is that some organisms introduced as a biological control may become pests themselves *(1 mark)*.

3 a) To increase her crop yield *(1 mark)* as she can create the ideal conditions for photosynthesis inside a polythene tunnel *(1 mark)* and it's easier to keep her plants free from diseases/pests *(1 mark)*.

b) i) Fertiliser C *(1 mark)* because strawberry yield was highest with this fertiliser for 4 out of the 5 years/in total over the 5 years/on average over the five years *(1 mark)*.

ii) Fertilisers contain some of the elements that crops need in order to grow and to carry out life processes *(1 mark)*. These elements may be missing from the soil, so fertilisers are used to replace them *(1 mark)* or to add more to the soil *(1 mark)*.

4 Paraffin heaters increase the carbon dioxide concentration *(1 mark)* and the temperature *(1 mark)* inside a glasshouse. These can both increase the rate of photosynthesis *(1 mark)*, meaning plants will grow faster and bigger, so crop yields will be higher *(1 mark)*.

5 a) Conditions inside a fermenter are carefully monitored and controlled. For example, the **temperature** *(1 mark)* and pH are kept at **optimum** *(1 mark)* levels so that the microorganisms' enzymes can work efficiently. **Paddles/Stirrers** *(1 mark)* stir the mixture so that the microorganisms can always have access to **nutrients** *(1 mark)*, which are needed for growth.

b) Aseptic conditions increase product yield, as the microorganisms aren't competing with other organisms *(1 mark)*. They also mean that the product doesn't get contaminated (with other microbes/products from other microbes) *(1 mark)*.

c) i) To supply oxygen for aerobic respiration *(1 mark)*.

ii) Water-cooled jacket *(1 mark)*, which is used to control the temperature inside the fermenter *(1 mark)*.

Pages 155-157
Warm-Up Questions

1) Organisms with the best characteristics are selected and bred with each other. The best of their offspring are then selected and bred. This process is repeated over several generations.

2) True

3) Something that is used to transfer DNA into a cell.

4) restriction enzymes

5) E.g. insulin.

6) A clone is an organism that is genetically identical to another organism.

Exam Questions

1 The tall and dwarf wheat plants could be cross-bred *(1 mark)*. The best of the offspring/the offspring with the highest grain yield and highest bad weather resistance could then be cross-bred *(1 mark)*, and this process repeated over several generations *(1 mark)*.

2 a) i) E.g. wasted food / excrement / parasites *(1 mark)*

ii) E.g. pH / temperature / oxygen level *(1 mark)*

b) E.g. to protect the fish from predatory birds / interspecific predation *(1 mark)*.

c) Intraspecific predation is where organisms eat individuals of the same species *(1 mark)*. It can be avoided on a fish farm by keeping small fish separate from big fish / providing regular food *(1 mark)*.

212

d) selective breeding *(1 mark)*

e) E.g. rear some fish in cages in the sea and some in tanks. Use the same species and age of fish in both places. Make sure the fish in both places have the same access to and type of food and the same protection from predators. Measure the mass of the fish in each place at the start of the experiment and again after three months. Repeat the experiment at least three times and calculate the mean change in mass in each place.

(1 mark for stating that some fish will be raised in cages in the sea and some in tanks, 1 mark for stating that all the fish used will be the same age and species, 1 mark for describing a control variable that needs to be kept the same (e.g. type of food used), 1 mark for describing a second control variable (e.g. same protection from predators), 1 mark for stating how long the fish will be allowed to grow for (e.g. three months), 1 mark for stating what will be measured (e.g. the mass of the fish), 1 mark for stating that repeats should be carried out. Maximum 6 marks available.)

Have a look at the Describing Experiments section for more tips on what you need to include when you're answering this type of question.

3 a)

Step	Description	Enzymes involved
1	Human insulin gene is cut from human DNA.	restriction
2	A plasmid from a bacterial cell is cut open.	restriction
3	The human insulin gene is joined with the plasmid to produce recombinant DNA.	ligase

(1 mark for each correct answer)

b) plasmid *(1 mark)*

c) The recombinant DNA is inserted into bacterial cells *(1 mark)*. These bacteria will use the inserted DNA to produce human insulin *(1 mark)*. The bacteria are grown in huge numbers in a fermenter to produce large amounts of human insulin *(1 mark)*.

4 a) E.g. the useful genetic characteristics are always passed on, which doesn't always happen in breeding. / Farmers don't have to wait for the breeding season. / Infertile animals can be cloned *(1 mark)*.

b) E.g. cloned animals might not be as healthy as normal ones. / Embryos formed by cloning from adult cells often don't develop normally. / Cloning is a new science and might have consequences we're not yet aware of. / At the moment it's difficult/time consuming/expensive *(1 mark)*.

c) E.g. animals that have been genetically engineered to produce human antibodies in their milk could be cloned (to produce large quantities of the antibodies) *(1 mark)*.

5 a) Yes, because the average milk yield has increased over the generations *(1 mark)*.

b) 5750 − 5000 = **750 litres per year per cow**
(2 marks for 750, otherwise 1 mark for correct calculation)

6 The tomato shown will contain genes transferred from another species *(1 mark)*.

7 a) The nucleus was removed from a sheep's **egg** *(1 mark)* cell to create an enucleated cell. A diploid **nucleus** *(1 mark)* was removed from an adult cell of a different sheep and inserted into the enucleated cell.

b) i) Small pieces of a plant/explants are taken from the tips of the plant's stems and side shoots *(1 mark)*. The small pieces of plant/explants are sterilised and grown *in vitro (1 mark)* on nutrient medium *(1 mark)*. Cells in the small pieces of plant/explants divide and grow into a plant *(1 mark)*.

ii) E.g. lots of plants with desirable characteristics can be grown *(1 mark)*.

8 a) E.g. yes, because for three out of the four kinds of crop grown, more butterflies and bees were found on the normal crops compared to the GM crops *(1 mark)*.

b) Any two from: e.g. transplanted genes may pass into other organisms in the environment *(1 mark)*. / GM crops could adversely affect food chains *(1 mark)*. / GM crops could adversely affect human health *(1 mark)*. / GM crops might create unforeseen problems, which could get passed on to future generations *(1 mark)*.

c) E.g. it would mean that farmers could produce bigger crop yields, as less of their crops would be affected by pests *(1 mark)*.

Pages 163-187

Practice Paper — 1B

1 a)

Description	Mitosis	Meiosis
occurs during growth and repair	✓	✗
produces gametes	✗	✓
produces cells that are genetically identical	✓	✗
occurs during asexual reproduction	✓	✗
produces four new cells	✗	✓

(4 marks if all 8 correct, 3 marks if 6 or 7 correct, 2 marks if 4 or 5 correct, 1 mark if 2 or 3 correct, 0 marks otherwise.)

b) i) haploid *(1 mark)*

ii) 23 *(1 mark)*

iii) testes *(1 mark)*

c) At fertilisation a male gamete fuses with a female gamete *(1 mark)* to form a zygote *(1 mark)*. The zygote then undergoes cell division and develops into an embryo *(1 mark)*.

2 a) oxygen *(1 mark)*

Remember, plants give off oxygen when they photosynthesise.

b) The volume of gas collected would decrease *(1 mark)* because when the lamp is turned off the light intensity will decrease *(1 mark)*, so the rate of photosynthesis will decrease too *(1 mark)*.

c) Carbon dioxide is needed for photosynthesis *(1 mark)*, so adding it to the water ensures that the rate of photosynthesis is not limited by a lack of carbon dioxide *(1 mark)*.

d) The enzymes needed for photosynthesis work more slowly at low temperatures, so the rate of photosynthesis will be slower at low temperatures *(1 mark)*. But if the temperature is too high, the enzymes are denatured so photosynthesis won't happen *(1 mark)*. The temperature could be controlled, for example, by putting the beaker into a warm water bath to keep the temperature constant *(1 mark)*.

e) i) Dry the leaf in an oven to remove water *(1 mark)*.

ii) Yes. The pondweed has been photosynthesising, so it will have produced glucose, which is stored as starch *(1 mark)*.

3 a) They provide a large surface area so that digested food is absorbed into the blood quickly *(1 mark)*. They have a single permeable layer of surface cells to assist quick absorption *(1 mark)*. They have a very good blood supply to assist quick absorption *(1 mark)*.

b) Amino acids are absorbed into the blood by active transport *(1 mark)*. They are absorbed against the concentration gradient using energy (from respiration) *(1 mark)*.

The diagram shows more amino acids in the blood than in the gut, so they must be absorbed by active transport.

c) i) To carry oxygen from the lungs to the cells *(1 mark)*.

ii) They have a large surface area for absorbing oxygen *(1 mark)*. They don't have a nucleus, so they have more room to carry oxygen *(1 mark)*. They contain lots of haemoglobin, which combines reversibly with oxygen in the lungs to become oxyhaemoglobin *(1 mark)*.

4 a) Light coming through the hole in the box *(1 mark)* caused more auxin to accumulate on the shaded sides of the shoots *(1 mark)*. This made the cells on the shaded sides of the plants grow faster *(1 mark)*, so the shoots bent towards the light *(1 mark)*.

b) (positive) phototropism *(1 mark)*

5 a) i) E.g.

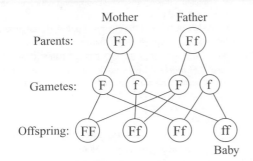

Parents: Mother Ff   Father Ff

Gametes: F f F f

Offspring: FF Ff Ff ff

Baby

(1 mark for showing that the parents both have the Ff genotype, 1 mark for showing the gametes' genotypes as F or f, 1 mark for correctly showing all three possible genotypes of the couple's offspring.)

The parents must both have one copy of the recessive allele for cystic fibrosis — so they're both Ff. In a question like this, the marks are allocated for the correct genotypes of the parents, gametes and offspring. It doesn't matter what type of genetic diagram you draw as long as it shows this information — so you could have drawn a Punnett square.

   ii) Homozygous, because he has two alleles the same/both of his alleles are recessive *(1 mark)*.

b) 1 in 4 / 25% *(1 mark)*

6 a) The dark variety is better camouflaged in soot polluted areas, so it is less likely to be eaten by predators *(1 mark)*. This means more dark moths survive to breed *(1 mark)* and pass the gene(s) for this characteristic on to the next generation *(1 mark)*. As this process continues over time, the dark variety of moth becomes more common *(1 mark)*.

It makes sense that if an organism blends in with its background it'll be harder for predators to spot it.

b) Town B is the most polluted because it contains a higher percentage of dark moths *(1 mark)*.

c) 77% − 25% = **52%**

(2 marks for correct answer, otherwise 1 mark for correctly reading 77% and 25% off the graph)

7 a) E.g. osmosis only refers to the movement of water molecules, whereas diffusion can refer to the movement of any type of molecule *(1 mark)*. Osmosis always happens across a partially permeable membrane, whereas diffusion can take place without the presence of a partially permeable membrane *(1 mark)*.

b) Mean change in mass = (−0.78 + −0.81 + −0.82) ÷ 3
= **−0.80 g**
(2 marks for correct answer, otherwise 1 mark for adding together 3 values and dividing by 3)

c)

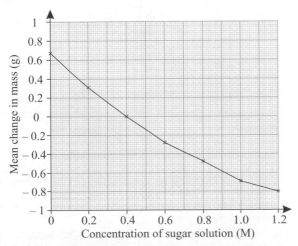

(1 mark for choosing a suitable scale, 1 mark for using straight lines to join the points, 1 mark for having axes labelled correctly (with correct units), 1 mark for having the axes the correct way round, 2 marks for correctly plotted points. Deduct up to 2 marks for incorrectly plotted points, 1 mark per incorrect point. Plotting marks may still be given if an incorrect answer to 7 b) has been plotted correctly.)

d) The concentration of sugar inside the original potatoes was approximately 0.4 M *(1 mark)*. This is the point where there was no change in weight of the potato cylinders, therefore no net movement of water, because the concentrations on both sides of the (partially permeable) membrane were the same *(1 mark)*.

e) To give more reliable results *(1 mark)*.

Repeating an experiment also means that you should be able to spot any glaring errors — like reading the balance wrongly in this experiment.

8 a) i) A producer is an organism that makes its own food using energy from the Sun *(1 mark)*.

   ii) 130 J *(1 mark)*

Tertiary consumers are the <u>third</u> consumers in a food chain — so in this case the tertiary consumers are the snakes.

b) D, because the biomass of the organisms decreases at each trophic level *(1 mark)* and the bars on this pyramid get smaller at each trophic level *(1 mark)*.

c) (130 ÷ 1100) × 100% = **11.8%**
(2 marks for correct answer, otherwise 1 mark for using 130 ÷ 1100 in working)

d) Energy is lost at each level of a food chain *(1 mark)*. After about five levels the amount of energy being passed on is not sufficient to support another level of organisms *(1 mark)*.

9 a) Gas A = oxygen *(1 mark)*, Gas B = carbon dioxide *(1 mark)*

b) They provide a large surface area for diffusion to occur across *(1 mark)*. They have a moist lining for gases to dissolve in *(1 mark)*. They have thin walls, so gases only have to diffuse a short distance *(1 mark)*. They have permeable walls so gases can diffuse across easily *(1 mark)*. They have a good blood supply to maintain a high concentration gradient *(1 mark)*. *(Maximum of 3 marks available)*

c) intercostal muscles/diaphragm *(1 mark)*, diaphragm/intercostal muscles *(1 mark)*, decrease *(1 mark)*, increases *(1 mark)*

10 E.g. plant some lettuce seeds outside and some under a polythene tunnel. Ensure that the lettuce seeds are of the same variety and plant them in compost taken from the same batch. Allow the lettuces to grow for 28 days, making sure that the lettuces in both environments receive the same amount of water and fertiliser during this time. After 28 days take three lettuces from outside and three lettuces from the polythene tunnel and measure the mass of each lettuce using a balance. Calculate the average mass of the lettuces grown outside and compare it to the average mass of those grown under the polythene tunnel.

(1 mark for stating that some lettuces will be grown in a polythene tunnel and some will be grown outside, 1 mark for stating that the lettuce seeds should be of the same variety, 1 mark for describing one control variable, 1 mark for describing a second control variable, 1 mark for stating how long the lettuces will be allowed to grow for, 1 mark for stating what will be measured (e.g. the mass of the lettuces), 1 mark for stating that repeats should be carried out (e.g. by measuring the mass of three lettuces from each environment). Maximum 6 marks available.)

You're not expected to know exactly how to do this investigation or to have done it before. This type of question is designed to test your knowledge of experimental skills, even when the scenario is unfamiliar to you.

11 a)

glomerulus

loop of Henlé

(1 mark for each correct label)

b) The blood is filtered in the Bowman's capsule and proteins are too big to pass through the membranes *(1 mark)*.

c) i) Urea is not reabsorbed into the blood, so its concentration increases through the nephron as sufficient water is reabsorbed *(1 mark)*.

ii) The concentration of sugar at point B would be high and there would be no sugar at point C *(1 mark)*, as all sugar is reabsorbed back into the blood in the proximal convoluted tubule/first part of the nephron *(1 mark)*.

d) ADH increases the permeability of the nephron *(1 mark)*, causing more water to be reabsorbed into the blood *(1 mark)*.

12 a) Beaker B was low in nitrates *(1 mark)*. Nitrates are needed for making amino acids/proteins *(1 mark)*, which are essential for growth *(1 mark)*.

b) They would have yellow leaves *(1 mark)* because without magnesium the plants can't make the chlorophyll that gives them their green colour *(1 mark)*.

c) Any two from: e.g. the amount of light shining on each beaker *(1 mark)* / the level of other substances in the mineral solution *(1 mark)* / the size of the beakers *(1 mark)* / the amount of air available *(1 mark)* / the amount of water available *(1 mark)* / the temperature of the beakers *(1 mark)*.

d) E.g. they could have measured the height of the pea plants in millimetres/to one decimal place *(1 mark)*.

e) E.g. pea plants of this species grow at a faster rate with both magnesium and nitrates *(1 mark)*.

13 a) i) E.g. the graph suggests that the more cigarettes male doctors smoke per day, the more likely they are to die from coronary heart disease *(1 mark)*. The male doctors who give up smoking are less likely to die from coronary heart disease than those who do smoke *(1 mark)*. The male doctors who have never smoked are the least likely to die from coronary heart disease *(1 mark)*.

ii) E.g. you could include women as well as men in the study. / You could use a sample of people from several different professions *(1 mark)*.

b) Any two from: e.g. smoking damages the walls inside the alveoli *(1 mark)*, reducing the surface area for gas exchange/leading to diseases like emphysema *(1 mark)*. / The tar in cigarettes damages the cilia in the lungs/trachea *(1 mark)*, leading to the build up of mucus/increasing the risk of chest infections *(1 mark)*. / Tar irritates the bronchi and bronchioles, *(1 mark)* leading to excess mucus/a smoker's cough/chronic bronchitis *(1 mark)*. / Tobacco smoke contains carcinogens *(1 mark)*, which can lead to lung cancer *(1 mark)*.

14 a) i) heart rate *(1 mark)*

ii) exercise *(1 mark)*

b) 129 beats/min (accept 128-130 beats/min) *(1 mark)*

c) 8 − 2 = **6 minutes** *(1 mark)*

d) Gary's heart rate increases during exercise *(1 mark)*. This is because when he exercises he needs more energy, so he respires more *(1 mark)*. Respiration increases the amount of carbon dioxide in his blood *(1 mark)*, which is detected by receptors (in his aorta and carotid artery) *(1 mark)*. The receptors send signals to his brain, which signals for his heart rate to increase *(1 mark)*.

e) i) glucose + oxygen → carbon dioxide + water (+ energy)

(1 mark for glucose + oxygen on the left-hand side of the equation, 1 mark for carbon dioxide + water (+ energy) on the right.)

ii) E.g. aerobic respiration releases more energy than anaerobic respiration. / Aerobic respiration doesn't cause lactic acid to build up in the muscles, but anaerobic respiration does *(1 mark)*.

Pages 188-202

Practice Paper — 2B

1 a) E.g. in developed countries people generally have a diet containing enough of the vitamins they need *(1 mark)*. / Sources of dietary vitamin A are affordable to a majority of people in developed countries *(1 mark)*. / Farming is more reliable, so the availability of foods containing vitamin A is likely to be more constant *(1 mark)*. / Healthcare is more widely available, so a lack of dietary vitamin A is more likely to be treated *(1 mark)*.

b) i) E.g. liver *(1 mark)*

ii) E.g. to improve vision / to keep skin/hair healthy / to help fight infection *(1 mark)*

c) E.g. it contains genes transferred from other species — a maize plant and a soil bacterium *(1 mark)*.

d) E.g. because it is a substance/compound which is converted into vitamin A inside the body. / Because it is substance/compound which is needed early on in the chemical pathway that produces vitamin A. / Because it is a precursor to vitamin A. *(1 mark)*

e) Any two from: e.g. bacteria can be genetically modified to produce insulin *(1 mark)*. / Crops can be genetically modified to be resistant to insect pests *(1 mark)*. / Animals can be genetically modified to produce human antibodies (in their milk) *(1 mark)*. / Animals can be genetically modified to produce organs suitable for transplantation into humans *(1 mark)*.

f) 150 ÷ 70 = 2.14 × 100 = **214 g** *(2 marks for the correct answer, otherwise 1 mark for using 2.14 in calculation)*

g) E.g. by growing Golden Rice, farmers grow their own source of vitamin A and they can earn money by selling any surplus rice *(1 mark)*, whereas regularly buying tablets is likely to be more expensive and no income can be made *(1 mark)*.

h) E.g. they don't have to buy new seed at the start of a growing season *(1 mark)* so it reduces their costs *(1 mark)*.

2 a) B — nitrifying bacteria *(1 mark)*

C — nitrogen-fixing bacteria *(1 mark)*

D — denitrifying bacteria *(1 mark)*

b) They decompose/break down dead plant and animal matter/waste, releasing carbon dioxide back into the atmosphere *(1 mark)* as they respire *(1 mark)*.

3 a) At point 9 *(1 mark)* because this is where the oxygen level is lowest *(1 mark)*.

b) The sewage provides extra nutrients, causing rapid algal growth *(1 mark)*. The algae block out the light, causing plants below to die *(1 mark)*. The dead plants provide food for microorganisms, causing the number of microorganisms to increase *(1 mark)*. The microorganisms then deplete/use up the oxygen in the water *(1 mark)*.

c) Oxygen-depletion near the source of the pollution has caused the death of fish and other animals in the water *(1 mark)*. This means there's little/nothing for the herons to feed on in this area *(1 mark)*.

4 a) E.g.

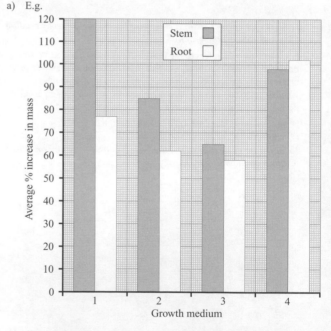

(1 mark for a bar chart covering at least half of the grid, 1 mark for correctly labelling the axes, 1 mark for including the correct units for average increase in mass, 1 mark for correctly labelling stem and root columns or including a key, 2 marks for correctly plotted points. Deduct up to 2 marks for incorrectly plotted points, 1 mark per incorrect point.)

b) The combination of stem tissue and growth medium number 1 gave the best results *(1 mark)* as this combination had the highest average percentage increase in tissue mass *(1 mark)*.

c) Any two from: e.g. the temperature in the incubator *(1 mark)* / the size of the tissue samples/blocks *(1 mark)* / the volume of growth medium used *(1 mark)*.

d) Any three from: sexual reproduction involves the fusion of male and female gametes, asexual reproduction doesn't *(1 mark)*. / Sexual reproduction involves two parents, asexual reproduction involves one parent *(1 mark)*. / There is mixing of genetic information in sexual reproduction, but not in asexual reproduction *(1 mark)*. / Asexual reproduction produces clones, sexual reproduction doesn't *(1 mark)*.

5 a) Lactobacillus *(1 mark)*

b) Lactose in the milk is broken down/fermented by the bacteria/ Lactobacillus into lactic acid *(1 mark)*. The lactic acid causes the milk to curdle into yoghurt *(1 mark)*.

c) E.g. it will increase the product yield *(1 mark)* because Lactobacillus/ the bacteria in the starter culture won't face competition from other bacteria *(1 mark)*. / It will prevent the yoghurt from being contaminated *(1 mark)* with disease-causing bacteria/(harmful) products from other bacteria *(1 mark)*.

d) 45 °C *(1 mark)*. This is the optimum temperature for the bacteria in the starter culture / this is the temperature at which the fermentation is fastest *(1 mark)*.

6 a) It is broken down into sugars/maltose *(1 mark)*.

b) To make the experiment a fair test *(1 mark)*.

c) The time taken for the reaction to complete increases dramatically (from 5 minutes to 30 minutes) *(1 mark)*. This is because the increasing temperature causes the enzyme to change shape/denature *(1 mark)*. This means that it no longer matches the shape of the starch, so cannot catalyse its breakdown, and the reaction slows down *(1 mark)*.

d) i) The result for 20 °C is anomalous *(1 mark)* because the time taken until starch is no longer present is quicker than expected/quicker than at 30 or 40 °C *(1 mark)*.

ii) E.g. the student may not have used the correct volume of starch solution. / The student may have started timing the experiment too late. / The student may have stopped the experiment too early *(1 mark)*.

7 a) Any two from: e.g. they have cell walls made of chitin *(1 mark)*. / They can't photosynthesise *(1 mark)*. / They can store carbohydrate as glycogen *(1 mark)*.

b) Yeast is added to a mixture of barley, hops and water, and ferments sugars in the mixture *(1 mark)* into alcohol/ethanol *(1 mark)*.

c) Air entering the demijohn would allow the yeast to respire aerobically *(1 mark)*. Aerobic respiration does not produce alcohol/ethanol *(1 mark)*.

Working Out Your Grade

- Do both exam papers.
- Use the answers to mark each exam paper.
- Use the tables below to record your marks.

Paper 1

Q	Mark	Q	Mark
1		8	
2		9	
3		10	
4		11	
5		12	
6		13	
7		14	
	Total		/120

Paper 2

Q	Mark	Q	Mark
1		5	
2		6	
3		7	
4			
		Total	/60

- Add together your marks for the two papers to give a total mark out of 180.

Total Mark = Paper 1 Total + Paper 2 Total

Total Mark = ☐ / 180

- Look up your total mark in this table to see what grade you got.

Total Mark	Grade
139	A*
121	A
103	B
85	C
73	D
62	E
50	F
39	G
0	U

Important!

The grade boundaries above are given as a guide only.
Exam boards tinker with their boundaries each year, so any grade you get on these practice papers is no guarantee of getting that grade in the real exams — but it should give you a pretty good idea.

Index

Index

Index

Index